St. Mary Valley from Logan Pass, Glacier National Park. *(Photograph by Hileman.)*

Editors · OTIS W. FREEMAN

HOWARD H. MARTIN

The
Pacific Northwest

AN OVERALL APPRECIATION

SECOND EDITION

NEW YORK · JOHN WILEY & SONS, INC.

LONDON · CHAPMAN & HALL, LIMITED

Library of Congress Catalog Card Number: 54–9235

To

JOHN B. APPLETON
N. F. G. DAVIS
WILLIAM L. FINLEY
C. S. KINGSTON
ALBERT L. SEEMAN
R. M. SHAW
WARREN D. SMITH

who assisted in pioneering the first edition of

THE PACIFIC NORTHWEST

List of Contributors

WALLACE T. BUCKLEY — *Associate Professor of Geography, State College of Washington, Pullman*

HARRY H. CALDWELL — *Assistant Professor of Geography, University of Idaho, Moscow*

PHIL E. CHURCH — *Professor of Meteorology and Climatology, University of Washington, Seattle*

HOWARD J. CRITCHFIELD — *Assistant Professor of Geography, Western Washington College of Education, Bellingham*

JOHN O. DART — *Assistant Professor of Geography, Portland State College, Portland, Oregon*

N. F. G. DAVIS (deceased) — *Department of Geology and Geography, University of British Columbia, Vancouver*

SAMUEL N. DICKEN — *Professor of Geography and Geology, University of Oregon, Eugene*

FRANCES M. EARLE — *Associate Professor of Geography, University of Washington, Seattle*

OTIS W. FREEMAN — *Emeritus Professor of Geography, Eastern Washington College of Education, Cheney*

CHARLES M. GATES — *Professor of History, University of Washington, Seattle*

ERNA GUNTHER — *Professor of Anthropology, University of Washington, Seattle*

A. L. HAFENRICHTER — *U. S. Soil Conservation Service, Portland*

JOSEPH T. HAZARD — *Former Director of Study Excursions, Public Schools, Seattle*

OLIVER H. HEINTZELMAN — *Associate Professor of Natural Resources, Oregon State College, Corvallis*

R. M. HIGHSMITH, JR. — *Associate Professor of Natural Resources, Oregon State College, Corvallis*

ix

List of Contributors

EDWIN T. HODGE *Professor of Geology, Oregon State College, Corvallis*

J. GRANVILLE JENSEN *Professor of Natural Resources, Oregon State College, Corvallis*

C. S. KINGSTON *Late Emeritus Professor of History, Eastern Washington College of Education, Cheney*

CARL H. MAPES *Geographer, Rand McNally & Co., Chicago*

HOWARD H. MARTIN *Professor of Geography, University of Washington, Seattle*

MARION E. MARTS *Assistant Professor of Geography, University of Washington, Seattle*

WILLIS B. MERRIAM *Assistant Professor of Geography, State College of Washington, Pullman*

W. H. PIERSON *Associate Professor of Geography, University of Florida, Gainesville*

HALLOCK F. RAUP *Professor of Geography, Kent State University, Kent, Ohio*

J. LEWIS ROBINSON *Professor of Geography, University of British Columbia, Vancouver*

W. A. ROCKIE *Formerly with U. S. Soil Conservation Service, Portland*

R. M. SHAW (deceased) *Former Associate Professor of Geography, Central Washington College of Education, Ellensburg*

JOHN C. SHERMAN *Associate Professor of Geography, University of Washington, Seattle*

JAMES STEVENS *Public Relations Council, West Coast Lumbermen's Association, Portland and Seattle*

STEPHEN N. WYCKOFF *Director, Forest and Range Experiment Station, U. S. Forest Service, Berkeley*

Preface

In the decade that has elapsed since the first publication of *The Pacific Northwest,* many changes have taken place in the region, necessitating a complete revision of the book. Six of the original thirty contributors, Warren D. Smith, W. L. Finley, N. F. G. Davis, C. S. Kingston, A. L. Seeman, and R. M. Shaw are deceased, and, in addition, John Appleton, who wrote the Foreword. Others have moved from the area. Replacing them are thirteen new authors. Certain chapters have been revised by other geographers than those responsible for them in the first edition. A new chapter has been added on the modern economic history. The material on forests has been split into two chapters prepared by different experts. On the other hand, four chapters in the first edition have been consolidated into two. Numerous new maps and photographs appear in the revised text.

The organization of the book is based on the assumption that a knowledge of the physical characteristics and natural resources is fundamental to an accurate understanding of the economic pattern and of the problems confronting the region. Throughout the book, regional relationships are stressed, and economic, social, human, and physical factors are integrated.

In addition to utilizing published and unpublished research of many individuals and agencies, the book incorporates the results of many new investigations based upon field studies necessary to fill the gaps in regional information and to bring materials up to date.

OTIS W. FREEMAN
HOWARD H. MARTIN

May, 1954

Acknowledgments

The editors wish to acknowledge assistance rendered by numerous agencies, organizations, corporations and individuals in securing data and illustrative materials. Among the individuals who helped in the gathering and analyzing of material were Woodrow R. Clevinger, John O. Dart, and Douglas B. Carter, graduate students at the University of Washington. Dr. Frances M. Earle, University of Washington, assisted in editing the manuscript. Miss Cecil Dryden, of Eastern Washington College of Education, read Dr. Kingston's chapter on early history. Dr. John C. Sherman was responsible for and supervised much of the cartographic work.

By special permission, portions of the map, "Landforms of the Northwestern States," drawn by Erwin Raisz, of Cambridge, Massachusetts, have been used as base maps for various physiographic regions. Copies of the map can be purchased from Dr. Raisz.

Contents

Contents

PART V. INDUSTRY, COMMERCE, AND URBAN DEVELOPMENT

PART

1

Changing Human Adjustments

CHAPTER

1

The Population Pattern

HOWARD H. MARTIN and CARL H. MAPES

Distant from older and more highly developed areas, hemmed in by mountain and desert barriers, and confronted with the economic and social problems characteristic of youth rather than maturity, Oregon, Washington, Idaho, and the mountain counties of western Montana have developed a significant unity, a unity symbolized by the name "The Pacific Northwest." In a larger sense, both British Columbia and Alaska can be included in this region. In spite of marked intraregional diversity, the Pacific Northwest has a regional identity differentiated from other areas of the United States.

The most potent element and probably the greatest single unifying factor is the Columbia River with its tributaries. This vast river system dominated the exploration and settlement of the region, providing the artery by which its people have been linked and its products distributed. Today a string of well-populated settlements is found along the river both east and west from Portland. East of the Cascades, economic development is dependent to a large degree upon the life-giving waters of the Columbia-Snake system. Its lower reaches provide a navigable waterway which facilitates both intraregional and external contacts. The future industrial, agricultural, and population growth of the region is inextricably bound up with the mighty Columbia.

Compared with many other parts of the United States, the Pacific Northwest is in a pioneer stage of development. Its economy is based largely upon resource exploitation, with part of the raw materials processed elsewhere. At present only 5 to 10 per cent of the area is in productive crops, with the success of agriculture resting upon careful crop specialization. Through scientific reclamation it might be possible to increase the cropped area by 50 per cent. Although the

3

region comprises one-tenth of the land area of the country, it contains only 2⅔ per cent of the people, a total considerably lower than its resources warrant.

Basic Population Pattern

The population pattern of the Northwest as shown on a dot map (see Fig. 1) presents a number of diverse features, which challenge geographical interpretation. Like other cultural aspects of human geography in the region, the distributional pattern of population is closely correlated with the major natural features. In human settlement, as in other primary distributions, the Cascade Mountains stand out as a dominant boundary zone. Over three-fifths of the people of the Northwest live in the marine section west of the Cascades, which includes less than one-fifth of the total area. Here the rural pattern represents an adjustment to surface and soil conditions in the humid lowlands, whereas the larger urban concentrations reflect the commercial importance of interconnections between major land and water transportation routes.

In the continental interior, east of the Cascades, the population pattern is one of dispersion rather than concentration. Here, two-fifths of the region's population is widely scattered over four-fifths of the total area. Three distinct rural patterns may be recognized: (1) the separated clusters in the valleys tributary to the middle Columbia and the upper Snake rivers, where a combination of water supply, gently sloping topography, and fertile soils makes irrigated farming possible; (2) a scattered distribution throughout the interior areas, where density varies with sufficiency of rainfall for dry farming or ranching; and (3) the strings of settlement in the mountain valleys, which offer access to otherwise isolated soil, forest, and mineral resources.

The empty areas on the population map are as expressive of the influence of natural conditions as the dots that show settlement. In the west, these vacant spaces represent areas where rugged relief and excessive rainfall effectively limit economic activities. The Olympic Mountains, Coast Ranges, Klamath Mountains, and Cascades have extremely sparse population. East of the Cascades, aridity as well as mountain conditions helps to account for thinness of settlement. Thus, lack of rainfall (or irrigation water) is largely responsible for the scanty population in southeastern Oregon and neighboring Idaho, and in the Columbia Basin of Washington, whereas relief is the controlling

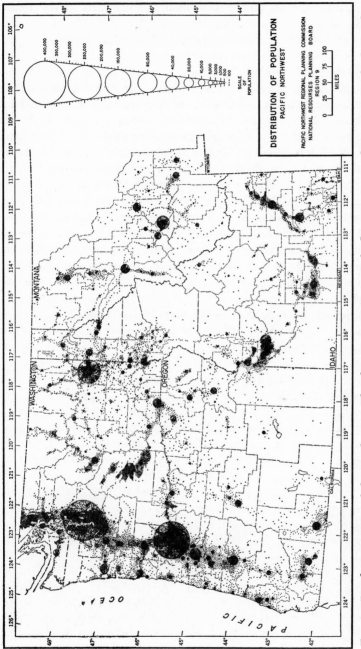

FIG. 1. Population pattern of the Northwest. The changes in 1950 were chiefly gains in population near Portland, Seattle, Tacoma, and Spokane, together with increases in the Columbia Basin of Washington, especially in the Tri-Cities area.

factor in the northern and eastern mountainous parts of the Inland Empire.

THE PUGET-WILLAMETTE LOWLANDS. The concentration of population in the 400-mile lowland lying between the Coast and Cascade ranges is the most striking demographic feature of the Pacific Northwest (Fig. 1). In the Willamette Valley of Oregon the land-seeking pioneer farmer found a combination of rainfall, temperature, and soil and surface conditions that favored subsistence agriculture. In the Puget Sound area of Washington as well as in Oregon the almost solid mantle of commercial timber that originally covered and surrounded this giant trough provided a rich and easily exploited source of wealth which attracted and gave support to semiskilled workers in logging camp and mill town. Puget Sound and the Columbia River extended an ocean highway into the heart of the interior lowland, leading to the establishment and growth of seaport cities to serve as both regional and national shipping centers. Finally, the development of great hydroelectric power resources is bringing an increasing number of new manufacturing industries to tidewater locations.

Essentially similar in their major natural advantages as centers of population, the northern and southern basins of this trough differ in certain important respects, and these differences are clearly reflected in their respective population patterns. The southward extension of Puget Sound brings the advantages of ocean transportation to a considerable inland area. In actual practice Puget Sound is one huge port, with its import trade handled largely by the shipping facilities of Seattle, but with its export business divided among the various ports along its shores. Most of the large sawmills have their own docks, where lumber and other wood products can be loaded directly from mill yard to ship with a minimum of handling. Many of the vessels entering Puget Sound call at several of the smaller sawmill ports in order to obtain a full cargo. This service favored the growth of medium-sized cities along the shores of this inland sea that serve as export centers for their timbered hinterlands, while some also developed into trading centers for small agricultural areas. In the Willamette Valley, on the other hand, both the import and the export trade are concentrated at Portland. A number of smaller export centers are found along the north-south stretch of the Columbia, between Vancouver and Longview. Salem and other cities of the northern Willamette Valley are primarily local trading centers dependent upon nearby agricultural areas and upon small-scale lumber operations. Eugene, near the south border of the valley, was a farming and trading center before large sawmills and plywood plants caused a marked increase in the population.

In comparison with the Willamette Valley, relatively small areas of land in the Puget Basin are favorable for agriculture. The cultivated land is in shoestring valleys, on the deltas and floodplains of the larger rivers, and on the drained bottoms of glacial lakes. The interstream upland soil of glacial origin is porous and has been too thoroughly leached to make good farmland. In consequence, these well-drained uplands, with an elevation of 200 to 500 feet above sea level, form an irregular pattern of sparsely populated areas, partially or entirely surrounded by delta clusters and valley strings in the alluvial bottomlands. Only where they border upon the harbors of Puget Sound and are suitable for city sites or suburban centers, are the uplands densely settled.

Population in the Puget Sound area is almost entirely confined to the lands below an elevation of 500 feet. Above this height, the glacial uplands merge rapidly into the mountain slopes. The heavy rainfall and thin rocky soils of the foothills and mountains give them value chiefly as forestgrowing lands. A sustained yield program is imperative if the mills that support a considerable part of the population are to receive a perpetual supply of timber and pulpwood.

The rural pattern of the Willamette Valley reflects more favorable topographic and soil conditions for agriculture than are found in the Puget Sound area. Population is evenly distributed throughout this lowland. Including Clark County, Washington, which is economically a part of the Willamette Valley, the twelve southern counties of the Puget-Willamette Lowland average 40 per cent of their area in farms, in contrast to the fifteen northern counties with about 15 per cent.

THE COASTAL ZONE. The narrow strip of territory between the Coast Range and the Pacific Ocean is low in population. Exposed to the saturated westerlies and backed by hill and mountain barriers, it has excessive rainfall, poor soils, and limited areas of level land. Although there is a relatively long frost-free season, temperatures are low even in summer and agriculture is limited. The long and rainy growing season is favorable for tall growth, various species of conifers reaching their maximum in size and timber yield.

The dominant population control along the coast, therefore, is climate, which finds expression in low growing temperatures, leached soils, and dense forest growth; rugged hill and mountain topography is also of major significance. Population is concentrated in a dozen

TABLE 1

POPULATION OF THREE NORTHWEST STATES, 1850–1950 *

Year	Idaho	Oregon	Washington	Total
1850		13,294		13,294
1860		52,465	11,594	64,059
1870	9,118	90,923	23,955	123,996
1880	20,789	174,768	75,116	270,673
1890	62,555	317,704	357,232	737,491
1900	92,531	413,536	518,103	1,024,170
1910	145,965	672,765	1,141,990	1,960,720
1920	194,402	783,389	1,356,621	2,334,412
1930	225,565	953,786	1,563,396	2,742,747
1940	250,742	1,089,684	1,736,191	3,076,617
1950	290,529	1,521,341	2,378,963	4,190,833

	Idaho	Oregon	Washington	
Per cent of increase, 1940–50	12.1	39.6	37.0	
Population per square mile, 1950	7.1	15.8	35.6	U. S. av. 50.7

* *Statistical Abstract of United States*, 1951, pp. 30–31.

small centers, where harbor facilities and cheap ocean transportation favor the marketing of wood products. The largest of these are at the mouth of the Columbia (Astoria), around Grays Harbor, and at Coos Bay, all with good access to the interior. The smaller coastal harbors serve only as local export centers.

Settlements based upon forest exploitation alone are semipermanent and, unless the land can be used for agriculture, tend to decline with depletion of the original resource. The 50-year population curve for Grays Harbor County in Washington shows that the declining stage has already begun in the coastal section. Between 1930 and 1950, this typical lumbering county of 60,000 inhabitants declined to 53,000, a 12 per cent loss. Less desirable woods, such as hemlock, are being substituted for Douglas fir, and new industries are developing. Since forest depletion has progressed further here than in most other coastal areas, the decline may be indicative of possible trends in other timbered sections.

MOUNTAINS OF SOUTHERN OREGON. Here in the Klamath Mountains are two clusters of population, one on the upper Rogue River Valley, the other in the Klamath Valley. Both are based on forest products and on irrigation agriculture and are well isolated from other main centers of habitation.

IRRIGATED VALLEYS OF THE EASTERN CASCADES. Along the drier eastern slopes of the Cascade Mountains in Washington, and extending from the Okanogan Valley on the Canadian border to the junction of the Snake and the Columbia, are a series of rich valleys with concentrated clusters of population. In addition to several smaller ones, the Wenatchee, the Kittitas and the Yakima valleys stand out sharply; in the Yakima, over 100,000 people constitute one-third of the entire population along the eastern Cascade flank. Water supply, sunshine, and length of growing season are favorable; on the better soils, agriculture is intensive and well developed, with high returns from small acreages of vegetables and fruits for sale fresh, canned, or quick frozen. Farm populations are dense and the towns are roughly proportional to the rural areas which they serve.

Beginning in the 1940's a large population increase occurred in the quiet rural communities near the junction of the Yakima and Columbia rivers. The Atomic Energy Commission's selection of the Hanford-Richland area for its plutonium works resulted in census figures for Benton County, 12,053 in 1940, rising to 51,370 in 1950, a 326 per cent increase.

THE WHEAT LANDS OF THE COLUMBIA BASIN. The crescent-shaped wheat belt of eastern Washington and northern Oregon extends south and west from Spokane across the Snake River and beyond Pendleton and La Grande.

Here the resource base for population is the fertile soil, which, where rainfall is sufficient, is favorable for the growing of wheat by dry farming. Much of the area, however, receives only enough precipitation for open-range grazing and therefore supports a sparse population. The rural dry-farming areas have shown a steadily declining population since around 1910, owing in part to the mechanization and consolidation of farms. The census showed a greater population for the basin in 1910 than in either 1920 or 1930. The census of 1950 shows a slight increase largely because of urban growth in the Spokane district.

The Columbia and Snake rivers flow through the plateau in canyons several hundred feet below the surface of the land, making it impracticable in the past to use their waters for large-scale irrigation. The Grand Coulee project will eventually bring water to a considerable area of the basin, causing appreciable changes in the population pattern.

THE IRRIGATED PLAIN OF SOUTHERN IDAHO. There are three district clusters in the population pattern of Idaho, all of them along the great crescent of the Snake River which crosses the state. Natural conditions are similar to those in the Cascade valleys, with the population supported largely by irrigated crops, such as alfalfa, sugar beets, and potatoes. The Boise-Payette district on the western side of the state is the oldest and best developed; the people of central Idaho are clustered around Twin Falls and Burley; the upper valley depends on the American Falls Reservoir. In the development of all three districts, water has been the limiting factor, necessitating numerous costly water-supply projects.

ROCKY MOUNTAINS OF WESTERN MONTANA. In Montana most of the population is concentrated in narrow mountain valleys where farmland or mineral deposits provide the basis for livelihood. Most strongly delineated on the population map is the long north-south Rocky Mountain Trench, which contains the larger share of the farming and grazing land and supports almost two-thirds of the western Montana population. The forests of the mountain slopes also help provide a resource base for employment, and most of the valley cities are lumber as well as trading centers. Mining operations are well scattered throughout the mountains, with the heaviest concentration near Butte and Anaconda. A similar mining district in northern Idaho, Coeur d'Alene, is within the tributary area of Spokane.

TABLE 2

POPULATION OF STANDARD METROPOLITAN AREAS, 1940 AND 1950 *

	1940	1950	Per Cent Increase
Seattle, Wash.	504,980	726,464	43.9
Portland, Ore.	501,275	701,202	39.9
Tacoma, Wash.	182,081	275,802	51.5
Spokane, Wash.	164,652	220,149	33.7

* *Statistical Abstract of the United States*, 1951.

POPULATION TRENDS IN THE PACIFIC NORTHWEST. With its basic population pattern largely fixed by physical factors at least a quarter of a century ago, the Pacific Northwest shows few subsequent changes in its map of occupance. There has been an intensification of settlement in the most favored urban areas and a decline in intensity for some of the farm areas, such as the wheat-growing Palouse of eastern Washington. Certain settlements based primarily on logging or sawmilling have become static in population or have shown slight declines.

The general trend since early days in the three northwestern states of Washington, Oregon, and Idaho has been a gradual rise each census decade. The greatest 10-year influx of new residents occurred between 1900 and 1910, followed by a more moderate migration until 1940. In 1950 the three states had 4 million people.

The war accelerated the movement, as many thousands flocked to Northwest plants or visited the region while in the armed services, later becoming permanent residents. In 1950, the combined migration and natural increase for the decade reached 1,114,000 (Table 1), breaking the old record of a 936,000 increase between 1900 and 1910. In percentage, the seaboard states showed the greatest gain over 1940.

	Per Cent Gain
Washington	37.0
Oregon	39.6
Idaho	12.1
U. S. average	14.5

Areas with the greatest influx were those where defense industry (shipbuilding, aluminum, airplane manufacture, Navy Yards, and atomic energy) were added to the previous economy. The Puget Sound-Willamette Valley has profited most from the war hegira, and its dominance in the region is more firmly established than ever. Each of the half-dozen largest cities has annexed various adjacent suburbs, and the creation of new metropolitan areas (Table 2) is further proof that the Pacific Northwest is following the national trend toward more city dwelling and less rural habitation.

CHAPTER

2

Indian Life of the
Pacific Northwest

ERNA GUNTHER

Since we live in a civilization where great adaptations to environment have been made, it is enlightening to study simple cultures where
the relationship is more direct. In the area defined here as a modern
economic unit, there were two main streams of Indian cultural development, one on the Coast and one in the Plateau region. To describe
these patterns of life, it is necessary to throw them in relief against the
picture of American Indian culture as a whole, so that their distinctive
traits may be appreciated.

The American Indian belongs to the Mongoloid race and came into
America from Asia about 15,000 years ago. In North America he developed possibly ten distinctive cultures as well as a number of diversified physical types. Archeology has shown that neither the cultures
nor the physical types were static. Changes have been more rapid
in the last three centuries, in keeping with the general acceleration
of cultural change. Some of these developments took place before
any European influence brought them about; in the area under consideration, however, it is probably safe to say that the greatest changes
have occurred since the late eighteenth century.

Culture History

When Europeans discovered America, the Indians had developed a
high type of political organization east of the Great Lakes, adobe
architecture and agriculture with irrigation in the Southwest, and a
seminomadic life in the Great Plains. Their only domesticated animal
was the dog. They used the bow and arrow intensively, and practiced the weaving of cloth and making of pottery more or less in those
areas where agriculture was also carried on. Into this picture the

Spaniards introduced the horse and Christianity, the horse being much more widely adopted. The people of the Great Plains had both an environment and a culture into which the horse could easily be adapted. They gradually became more nomadic, discarded agriculture and earth lodges to live in tipis, hunt buffalo, and spend much time decorating their clothing and their horse trappings with paint, beads, fringe, and feathers, in art styles whose beauty is heightened through motion.

It is this changed culture of the late eighteenth century that gradually moved westward and penetrated the eastern portion of the area here under discussion. When today the Yakima, Nez Perce, and Umatilla parade in their glorious regalia, they are exhibiting a very superficial and recent form of their culture. From the Flathead and Kutenai to the eastern slopes of the Cascades in Washington and Oregon, most tribes have been affected by the dramatic and colorful culture from the East. Only in southern Oregon, the Klamath, strongly influenced by California cultures, did not succumb to this invasion of spectacular ideas.

In the coastal strip of the Northwest, barred by the Cascade Range from the cultural development associated with the horse, culture also quickened its pace in the late eighteenth century. The Spaniards, the Russians, the English, and later the Americans visited these shores, asking for furs, which formerly had no great value to the Indians, and giving in return goods that greatly stimulated trade throughout the area. Life in this region was competitive, based on the acquisition of wealth. When these new sources of wealth appeared, emphasis on the possession of goods was intensified with a rapid development of a system of social ranking, as exemplified by the potlatch.

Since without these outside stimuli the Pacific Northwest Indian cultures would not have presented the picture known to students today, it seems advisable to review briefly the history of this area.

Territory and Dwellings [1]

West of the Rocky Mountains the country varies from semiarid plateaus to fiordlike inlets, giving thousands of miles of shore line.

[1] Appended to this paper is a list of the principal tribes of the area, with their location and the language family to which each belongs. In the brief space allotted it has not been possible to discuss the linguistic affiliations of all these tribes, but it should be apparent from this list that many languages are represented in the area. Each of these languages constitutes a totally different type of speech, not mutually intelligible and in many instances represented by many dialects.

The Coast Range rises directly from some of these waterways, forming an almost impenetrable barrier for the coast tribes. Their only intercourse with interior tribes was through the mountain passes, which in many instances have become the highways of today. Penetrating these mountains are also two great rivers, the Fraser and the Columbia. The coastal aspect of Thompson and Lillooet culture on the Fraser River, as compared with other tribes equally far from the coast but not on the river, shows clearly the effect of this route of travel. That the Columbia was undoubtedly a great highway is revealed by the type of archeological finds common along the river. Scattered finds indicating temporary camps and the few places where successive layers would point to continuous occupation have led to the belief that this region as well as a large part of eastern Oregon held only a shifting population. In northeastern Washington and northern Idaho the people were more stable; the Colville, Kalispel, Coeur d'Alene, and Pend d'Oreille migrated only seasonally as the search for food indicated.

Along the coast there were the following considerations in choosing a village site: protection from marauders (raiding for slaves was a widespread diversion); access to a good canoe beach; availability of fresh water; and nearness of fishing grounds. Where all these conditions could be obtained, a permanent winter village was built. This consisted of a number of large wooden plank houses, each sheltering two to ten families. Such quarters were used for winter villages, but, when the rains were over and fish runs began, these Indians left their villages and in family groups went to summer camps for fishing and berry picking. No village can in a short time assume a greater aspect of dilapidation and desertion than a coastal Indian settlement. The first traveler to note this was Captain Vancouver, who wrote in his dairy in 1792 on passing the sandspit at Dungeness, Washington, that he had seen a deserted Indian village and it looked as though some time ago an epidemic might have carried away all the inhabitants. But in reality the inhabitants were just a few miles back of the coast on the Dungeness River for a salmon run.

The summer base camp consists of a cattail mat tent, rectangular, gabled, and just large enough to accommodate one family for sleeping. Brief trips were made with just enough mats for a lean-to, or travelers depended on a windbreak of cedar boughs.

The linguistic diversity on the Pacific coast is a very striking phenomenon; frequently, tribes not more than 25 miles apart speak languages that differ as much as English and Chinese.

In the Plateau area there was greater diversity in dwellings. Village sites were only semipermanent; in winter, however, headquarters were located by preference on protected southern exposures near water and wood, and in summer sites were chosen favorable for taking salmon at the rapids of the Columbia and its tributaries. The earth lodge was probably an old form of dwelling, as was the house covered with tule mats. Intrusive from the east is the tipi, the conical tent familiar in the Great Plains; coming into the Plateau from the west is the plank house, which is known only along the two rivers mentioned earlier. On the Fraser it ascended to the Lower Lillooet and on the Columbia as far east as the Nez Perce. The earth lodges were built over a pit which might be circular or square and have a pyramidal or a flat roof. This dwelling was especially used by the southern British Columbia tribes.

The mat-covered house, rectangular with rounded ends, had a wide distribution in the eastern part of this area, although today, when these tribes move into so-called native houses instead of the frame houses in which they ordinarily live, they use the tipi, another example of the Plains penetration that just preceded the European.

This very brief survey of dwellings should not be ended without once more mentioning the plank houses of the northern coastal area. Aside from the great adobe dwellings of the Southwest, they were the most remarkable architectural feat of the Indians north of Mexico. The placement of the roof beams 60 feet long and 2 or 3 feet in diameter without any machinery was a real engineering feat. Artistically, the great killer whales and thunder birds painted in red and black across a house, perhaps 30 to 40 feet broad and 15 to 20 feet high, are a sight to be remembered. In addition to this, the Haida incorporated the totem pole into the house front by making the entrance through the pole. It is unfortunate that the weather in this region is not so kind to these materials as in the Southwest and that the glories of this unique architecture are no longer here for us to admire.

Economic Life

The Pacific Northwest is the most extensive region in North America to support a well-developed culture without agriculture. The dense forests of the coast and the semiarid plateau of the interior might be considered severe drawbacks to such a venture, but the precedent of agriculture in the semiarid Southwest shows that environmental handicaps can be overcome. No other fishing, hunting, and gathering area in North America provides its inhabitants with such a bountiful supply of easily available foods, and a study, especially of the Coast economy, shows that the people took ample advantage of their opportunities. The food problem in all primitive types of life is to find a way to preserve the oversupply of one season to use in the period of scarcity, and the obtaining and preparing of food stores dominate the annual economic cycle.

In spite of the differences of environment, the entire Northwest was bound together by the extensive use of fish. Salmon runs occur in all streams in the Pacific slope. The difference in the food habits of the coast and the interior people was the proportion of fish to meat. Both groups used salmon, hunted, and gathered vegetable foods. On the coast, the Nootka, Haida, and Makah augmented their fish with seal, whale, and porpoise. The tribes along the Columbia used sturgeon; those of the interior proper used deer, antelope, and rabbits; the people with access to the Olympics hunted elk. And everywhere there was no bag limit on birds.

To return to fishing, for that was the basic food supply, fishing grounds belonged to families or to individuals who were the heads of families. On the coast a wealthy and generous person when he was not using his fishing place often allowed poor people who had no fishing rights to use his station. Fishing was done by men and involved the damming of streams, construction of weirs and traps behind which the fish were speared, and on the great rivers like the Fraser and Columbia spearing salmon at the falls. In the gentler streams a variety of dip and drag nets were used. During the heavy runs a family would camp close to the stream and the women cleaned and dried the fish for storage. Fish was sun-dried or smoked according to weather and choice. Alder wood was preferred for smoking.

Hunting, of course, was also done by men, the women sometimes going to a base camp to butcher and dry the meat. Frequently hunting trips were combined with berry picking. Huckleberries were the favorite dried fruit in this whole area. Indian families looked forward to a berry-picking trip with the same expectation that we anticipate a vacation jaunt. In August the Yakima can still be found in tipi camps on the slopes of Mount Adams. Although an occasional automobile reminds us that we are in the 1950's, the horse and the spring wagon are also very prominent.

Sprouts in the early spring, bulbs such as camas, among the Klamath, water-lily seeds, and in eastern Washington and Idaho the bitterroot make up the vegetable foods in common use. To this the coastal tribes added the use of shellfish, especially clams in Puget Sound and the inland passage northward.

On the coast the greatest economic activity took place from April to November, and this concentration of effort allowed a winter season of leisure, with assurance that there was sufficient food stored for a comfortable existence. A surplus supply of food was a great social asset and, before the expansion of wealth through trade goods, the surplus was used in potlatches or ceremonial feasts.

Political and Social Life

To a discussion of tribal territories on the Pacific slope we too frequently bring our own ideas of primitive political organization and distort the true pattern. The atomistic nature of political organization is brought out in this statement of Kroeber's: "From Alaska to California there does not appear to have been a group that could be designated as a political unit, other than what it is usual to call the village; that is, the settlement on one spot." [2] Then how can the areas outlined on the map with tribal names be explained?

In an analysis of Plateau culture Ray answers the question as follows:

The answer is partly historical, partly theoretical. Early settlers, traders, missionaries, and government officials carried with them from the east the notion that all Indian groups were of necessity organized along tribal lines. Upon learning a village name from a native the whites immediately and indiscriminately applied it to all Indians of the vicinity. The term Sanpoil, for example, is a French corruption of the native name (snpui ·lux^n) of the people who lived in a single village (npui ·lux^n) located at the mouth of the Sanpoil river. . . . In other cases, a name of English or French derivation was applied arbitrarily, such as Colville, Columbia, and Thompson.[3]

Often the Indians themselves do not recognize the tribal names in use by the whites. Furthermore, by reviewing again the type of economy prevalent throughout the area this lack of political unity can be understood. A hunting, fishing, and gathering people need a

[2] A. L. Kroeber, "Tribes of the Pacific Coast of North America," *Proceedings of the Nineteenth International Congress of Americanists,* p. 396, 1917.

[3] Verne F. Ray, "Cultural Relations in the Plateau of Northwestern America," *Publications of the Frederick Webb Hodge Anniversary Publication Fund,* Vol. III, p. 9, 1939.

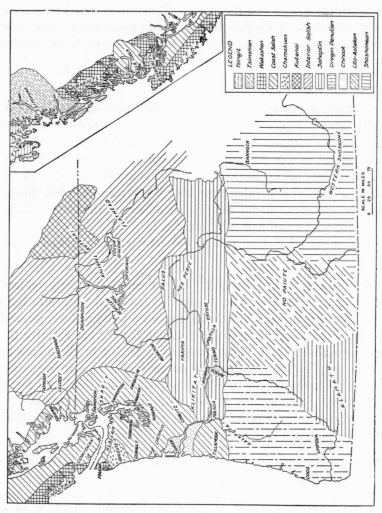

Fig. 2.   Tribes of the Pacific Northwest divided into language families.

greater area for their subsistence than an agricultural group. Also, they do not use most of their country the greater part of each year; but every part of it has some place in their annual subsistence cycle: one place for fishing, another for hunting deer, a long sandspit for ducks, a mountain trail to berry fields. With a large part of the so-called tribal territory used so seldom it is not surprising that the ethnographer frequently gets some slight overlapping in the statements of two adjoining tribes. This might in the old days have given rise to disputes, but usually they had more important issues at stake.

The unit of political organization therefore is the village, a statement that applies equally in the entire area. A number of villages occupying contiguous territory share many culture traits, including the language they speak. They trade together, intermarry, come to each other's ceremonies, in case of stress possibly even unite against a common enemy, but they are just as likely to turn on each other. Their relationship is in a constant state of flux. Consequently a more accurate way of recording the location of Pacific Northwest tribes would be to mark each village. New villages were often settled by people who left an old village because of quarrels.

The leader in a Coast village was usually the wealthiest man in the group who also had some qualities of leadership. His son did not necessarily become the leader after his father's death unless he also possessed the wealth and the ability, but, since he was definitely trained for his position, that succession was usual.   •

Individuals on being asked their affiliations customarily name the village in which they were reared. This generally means in many Coastal tribes that this person's father was also born in that village or, anthropologically speaking, the custom of patrilocal residence prevails. Marriages were arranged by families, and alliances were sought where political and social advantage could be gained. Among the northern Coastal tribes, the clan, a kinship group where descent was reckoned through the mother, controlled also inheritance and marriage.

The detailed structure of society cannot be given in this brief space, but a short discussion of social ideals may clarify the picture. Among Coastal tribes was a strong sense of caste, strongly developed in the north and gradually diminishing southward. In each group there was an upper class, common people, and slaves. The upper class was finely graded within itself so that in reality each person was in a rank of his own. This grading was largely based on wealth, not actually possessed but accumulated and given away to the glory of the family name. Part of this property consisted of slaves, either poor people within the tribe or captives taken in raids. The Plateau people were very unsympathetic to this class system, and also frowned on slavery, stress on wealth, and war. Among the Sahaptin-speaking Plateau groups some of the Plains system of war honors gained footing in the nineteenth century, but with this exception all men were regarded free and equal. Where the social ideas of the Coast ascended the Columbia and Fraser, slaves were found among the Wishram and Lillooet and Thompson.

The social system of the Coast was based on the possession and distribution of surplus goods or wealth in the form of an investment. The potlatch system developed here, in fact, is one of the best-paying investment systems ever devised. The basis of it is the desire to elevate the family in the social scale of the tribe, and although one individual gives the potlatch the whole family profits by reflected glory. A potlatch is a great feast to which guests are invited from many tribes and during which the host gives all the leading guests such presents as canoes, slaves, food, and in more recent years commercial blankets. Each guest in receiving these gifts obligates himself to give the donor a gift that is larger by 50 to 100 per cent. The relative status of host and guest is reflected in the size of the gift, the host giving only to such guests as are certain to fulfill their obligations; in other words, a guest's credit must be good. If contact with white peoples had not disrupted this system, it would have been interesting to see how long it could have withstood the lack of balance created through the accumulation of wealth in the hands of a few families.

This system prevailed especially in the northern part of the Coastal area and to a lesser degree south to the mouth of the Columbia. In the interior, it was not observed and in consequence the social system was less complicated or definitive.

Ceremonial and Religious Life

On the Coast, as in the interior, the quest for an individual guardian spirit was the basis of religious life. But in that area on the Coast where the secret society and the attendant ceremonials of the potlatch dominated, the guardian-spirit concept was less prominent. Throughout the region, except among the Plains-influenced Kutenai, Flathead, Bannock, and western Shoshone, ceremonial life was at its height in the winter with the winter festival of the Coast and the spirit dances of the Plateau as the leading features. These ceremonials involved dancing, gambling, and much intertribal visiting.

The secret society previously mentioned was a dominant factor in the ceremonial life on the Coast, centering among the Kwakiutl. This society was often called the false power because it did not derive its supernatural strength from a legitimate spirit quest. In its initiation ritual, the novice was supposedly killed and restored to life; in order to maintain this illusion the uninitiated were kept at a proper distance, and the rites were carried on largely under the cover of darkness. Membership was again tied up with the establishment of social prestige; the younger a child was inducted, the greater the credit to its family.

In conclusion the following major points should be reiterated.

1. The area defined here includes two main streams of Indian cultures, the Coast and the Plateau.

2. Although the environment differs considerably, both cultures are a hunting and fishing type with fishing predominating except in the easternmost part, beyond the watershed of the Columbia.

3. The social life of the Coast is dominated by social class and wealth; the Plateau is essentially democratic with a slight infiltration of the war complex of the Plains.

4. The basic religious concept is the guardian-spirit quest, overlaid on the Coast by the secret society.

5. Even before white civilization disrupted Indian life, these cultures were not static but underwent appreciable changes through contacts with one another.

TABLE 1

Gazetteer of Principal Tribes of the Pacific Northwest

Tribe	Location	Language
Bannock	Southern Idaho	Shoshone
Bella Coola	Dean Channel, British Columbia	Coast Salish
Cayuse	Northeastern Oregon	Sahaptin
Chehalis	Grays Harbor	Coast Salish
Chinook	Pacific coast of Washington, mouth of the Columbia	Chinook
Coeur d'Alene	Border of Idaho and Washington	Interior Salish
Comox	Northeastern Vancouver Island	Coast Salish
Coos	Southwestern Oregon	Oregon Penutian
Cowichan	Southern Vancouver Island	Coast Salish
Duwamish	Puget Sound	Coast Salish
Flathead	Western Montana	Interior Salish
Haida	Queen Charlotte Island	Haida
Kalapuya	Northwest Oregon	Oregon Penutian
Kalipsel	Northeastern Washington	Interior Salish
Klallam	North shore, Olympic Peninsula	Coast Salish
Klamath	Southeastern Oregon	Sahaptin
Klickitat	South-central Washington	Sahaptin
Kutenai	Western Montana	Kutenai
Kwakiutl	North Vancouver Island	Wakashan
Lillooet	Fraser River	Interior Salish
Lower Chinook	Pacific coast of Washington, mouth of the Columbia	Chinook
Lower Cowlitz	Lower Valley, Cowlitz River	Lower Salish Upper Sahaptin
Lummi	Northwestern Washington	Coast Salish
Makah	Northwestern Washington	Wakashan
Molala	North-central Oregon	Sahaptin
Nespelem	Big Bend of the Columbia River	Interior Salish
Nez Perce	Border of Idaho, Oregon, and Washington	Interior Salish
Nisqually	Southern Puget Sound	Coast Salish
Nootka	West coast of Vancouver Island	Coast Salish
Northern Paiute	Southeastern Oregon	Ute-Aztekan
Okanagon	North-central Washington and south-central British Columbia	Interior Salish
Palus	Eastern Oregon	Sahaptin
Pend d'Oreille	Border of Idaho and Washington	Interior Salish
Puyallup	Southern Puget Sound	Coast Salish
Quileute	Northwestern Washington	Chemakuan
Quinault	Pacific coast, Washington	Coast Salish
Sanpoil	Big Bend of Columbia River, Washington	Interior Salish
Shuswap	Fraser River	Interior Salish
Skagit	Skagit River, Washington	Coast Salish

TABLE 1 (*Continued*)

GAZETTEER OF PRINCIPAL TRIBES OF THE PACIFIC NORTHWEST

Tribe	Location	Language
Snohomish	Puget Sound	Coast Salish
Snuqualmi	Puget Sound	Coast Salish
Spokan	Eastern Washington	Interior Salish
Squamish	Southwestern British Columbia	Coast Salish
Swinomish	Puget Sound	Coast Salish
Tenino	North-central Oregon	Sahaptin
Tillamook	Northwestern Oregon	Coast Salish
Tlingit	Southeastern Alaska	Tlingit
Tsimshian	Northwestern British Columbia	Tsimshian
Umatilla	Northeastern Oregon	Sahaptin
Umpqwa	Lower, southwest coast of Oregon	Oregon Penutian
	Upper, Umpqwa River	Athapascan
Upper Cowlitz	Upper Valley, Cowlitz River	Sahaptin
Wasco	North-central Oregon	Chinook
Wenatchi	North-central Washington	Interior Salish
Western Shoshone	Southern Idaho	Shoshone
Wishram	South-central Washington	Chinook
Yakima	Central Washington	Sahaptin

CHAPTER

3

Explorations, Political Adjustments, and Settlement

C. S. KINGSTON

The early history of the Pacific Northwest is closely related to the histories of other countries and other peoples. Isolated by distance, this great habitable area remained unknown until after the middle of the eighteenth century. Then from various nations came explorers and adventurers, following the lure of far places, fame, or fortune. To these shores came the trading ships of Spain, Russia, England, and the United States. In due time, British and American men of action surmounted the obstacles of the interior of the continent and blazed trails from coast to coast. Settlements were made. As a result of all these activities, conflicting territorial claims were laid which were eventually adjusted by diplomacy, sometimes combined with the threat of war.

The First Explorers

Spain was the pioneer in New World exploration. Within 50 years after the discovery of America in 1492, her intrepid *conquistadores*, driven by the incentives of "gospel, gold, and glory," had carved out an empire that made her the most powerful of modern nations.

In 1513, Balboa discovered the Pacific Ocean, giving Spain a claim to this "Spanish lake" and all the lands washed by its vast waters. A few years later, Magellan found the Philippine Islands, and the lucrative trade which centered in this area gave impetus to further West Coast exploration. Cortez conquered the Aztecs, and soon thereafter the viceroyalty of New Spain was created in Mexico.

Thus, in the fore part of the sixteenth century, Spain was well entrenched in the Pacific and in an advantageous position for exploration northward by both land and sea, and she lost no time in getting

24

started. The Coronado expedition reached the canyons of the Colorado and crossed the wide plains east of the mountains. Between 1533 and 1534, Jimenez discovered the peninsula of Lower California, and Ulloa explored the Gulf and the greater part of the west coast of the peninsula.

In 1542, Cabrillo and Ferrelo set out with even bolder plans. They discovered the bay of San Diego. Cabrillo died as the result of an accident, but he instructed his pilot to "sail north at all hazards." Ferrelo did so, picking his uncertain way along the extensive coast line as far as southern Oregon. In the incredibly short space of 50 years, Spain had set up a colonial empire and was knocking at the gates of Northwest America. This was more than 60 years before England had made her first settlement at Jamestown, Virginia.

Spain's interest waned, however, after these first glorious efforts. No port of California was established for the Philippine trade, and the colonial administration seemed virtually to have forgotten the upper California region for nearly 200 years. Then Spanish concern was aroused by accounts of the settlements of Russian hunters and traders along the islands of the Bering Sea and on the American mainland in the wake of the voyages of Bering and Tchirikov. It was now feared that the Russians intended to extend their sphere of influence southward along the western coast of the continent, and thus into an area claimed by Spain.

Spurred by these apprehensions, Spain immediately resumed her activities. Ships were dispatched to the north for the double purpose of exploring the coast and discovering evidences of Russian advance. In 1774, Juan Perez discovered Nootka Sound on Vancouver Island and reached latitude 55 degrees, but he found no trace of Russian settlements.

In 1775, Heceta and Quadra continued the work of Perez, and in that memorable year Europeans set foot on the soil of the Northwest. On July 14, 1775, Naval Lieutenant Don Bruno Heceta, commander of the *Santiago*, landed at Point Grenville, 30 miles north of Grays Harbor, and in an appropriate ceremony, took possession in the name of Spain. This was the year of the battles of Lexington and Bunker Hill. English settlements had been in existence along the Atlantic coast for 168 years, and during that time had grown into thirteen colonies containing 2½ million people.

During the next 25 years, the entire Pacific coast was explored and mapped. Traders came with European goods to barter for furs. A settlement was made by the Spaniards at Nootka in 1789–90, and a temporary settlement in 1792 at Neah Bay on the south side of the Juan de Fuca Strait. In one sharp clash of international interests a quarrel arose which nearly dragged England and Spain into war. This was the Nootka Sound controversy. After the difficulty was settled, Spain gradually withdrew from the Northwest coast. The excellent work of the Spaniards in exploring the Vancouver Island region should be recognized.

The Maritime Fur Trade

The first of the English expeditions was that of Captain Cook, whose third official voyage to the Pacific brought him to the Northwest coast in 1778. While he refitted his ships at Nootka, his men purchased sea-otter skins from the natives at trifling cost. From Nootka, Cook skirted the outer coast to the Arctic. After his death, the expedition made further explorations in the north, then sailed to Canton, China, where the skins were sold for high prices. The news spread. By 1785, the maritime fur trade had begun in earnest.

A few French traders and one official expedition commanded by La Perouse came to the coast during this period. The best-known American traders were Captains John Kendrick and Robert Gray. Captain Gray is to be remembered as the discoverer of the Columbia River, which he entered May 11, 1792.

The most outstanding exploratory work was done by George Vancouver, commander of a British governmental expedition, 1792–94. He made a careful survey and maps of the Northwest coast, leaving such familiar names as Mt. Rainier, Bellingham Bay, Puget Sound, and Hood Canal.

As time went by, English trade declined, partly at least because of the monopolistic practices of the East India and South Sea companies against British subjects. Being unhampered, the Americans did most of the fur-trading business along the Northwest coast. Between 1790 and 1814, 82 American ships are known to have engaged in the trade. During the same period, only 26 British ships made their appearance.

The fur most sought after and most in demand in the Canton market was the sea otter's. However, there were losses as well as profits in the trade. When the markets were glutted, the prices fell disastrously; when the prices were high, skins were often scarce because the hunting of the otter was overdone. Aside from financial risks, the business was hazardous in other ways: stormy seas, uncharted coasts, and danger of Indian attacks. Many voyages yielded little; others were remarkably profitable. Captain Sturgis, himself a trader, cites one case when an investment of $50,000 resulted in a gross return of $285,000.

Ships carrying furs from the Northwest coast would often sail to the Hawaiian Islands to pick up such additional products as sandalwood, tortoise shells, and shark fins to sell to Chinese merchants. In Canton, the cargo would be exchanged for tea, silk, and porcelain goods.

Across the Continent to the Northwest

By the close of the seventeenth century the French had explored the region around the Great Lakes. In the interests of the fur trade, Pierre Gaultier de La Vérendrye and his sons followed the waterways westward from Lake Superior and succeeded in exploring a considerable area in the very central part of the North American continent. This was between the years 1731 and 1743.

After the French and Indian War, Scottish, English, and American traders made their way from the Great Lakes to Lake Winnipeg, and then by the intricate watercourses on toward the North and West. A few years later, these stout-hearted fur hunters merged their interests in an organization known as the North West Company of Canada and continued energetically exploring the unknown western regions and developing the fur trade.

Alexander Mackenzie descended the Mackenzie River and reached the Arctic in 1789. Four years later he crossed the Rocky Mountains and the Coast Range, reaching the Pacific July 22, 1793. He was the first European to cross the continent north of Mexico. In 1808, Simon Fraser explored the lower reaches of the Fraser River. David Thompson of the North West Company crossed the Rocky Mountains to the headwaters of the Columbia River, where in 1807 he built a trading post at Lake Windermere. During the next four years he carefully explored the upper Columbia drainage basin, together with the Kootenai and Clark Fork rivers. Thompson was an excellent mathematician and cartographer, and his maps and journals are of great importance both to the history and the geography of the Northwest. Among the trading posts that were built under his direction were Kootenai House, Kullyspell, Saleesh, and Spokane.

The Lewis and Clark Expedition, sent out by Thomas Jefferson, was the most important single achievement in the annals of the exploration of the American West. The party ascended the Missouri River in 1804 as far as the Mandan villages near the Montana line.

They wintered here, and, in the spring of 1805, continued up the Missouri River (Plate 1A) almost to its source. Crossing the continental divide, they made their way down the Bitterroot Valley, then followed an Indian trail over the Bitterroot Range to the Clearwater River. By canoe, they descended this river, the Snake, and the Columbia to the Pacific. Here they built Fort Clatsop and spent the winter of 1805–06. In 1806 the party returned to St. Louis. The Lewis and Clark Expedition demonstrated the practicability of an overland route to the Pacific and the wealth of furs available in the Northwest.

The Astorians

John Jacob Astor was a prominent merchant of New York. He had become wealthy in the fur business, and the American Fur Company which he had founded was one of the great enterprises of that day. He decided to start another fur company to trade on the northwestern coast and in the Columbia River interior. His plan was to maintain a central establishment near the mouth of the Columbia, with smaller posts in the upper country; these were to be supplied with goods carried by sea from New York. Trade with Russian Alaska and China was to be a part of his comprehensive plan.

Composing this Pacific Fur Company were several partners, young men who had already gained fur-trading experience, and who were willing to join Astor's enterprise for a share in the profits. Two parties were organized, one to go with the *Tonquin* by sea, and the other, the overland Astorians, to cross the continent by the Missouri River route.

In 1811 the *Tonquin* arrived at the mouth of the Columbia, where the partners soon constructed a post called Astoria. After unspeakable hardships crossing the Snake River Plains the overlanders reached their destination in the spring of 1812. The Astorians started one trading post at the mouth of the Okanogan River and another at Spokane close to the North West Company's post. For a time they were very active in pushing their trade.

In spite of difficulties and loss of life at the beginning of the enterprise, it is probable that the Astor company would have been successful if the War of 1812 had not broken out. The Astorians found themselves in a predicament and decided to sell the property to the North West Company. The sale was made in 1813, and during the next decade the North West Company of Canada represented British interests in the Pacific Northwest. The failure of Astor's enterprise was a blow to the Americans.

The Fur Economy Period

The first resource of the Northwest to be exploited was fur; ships came and explored the coast in search of fur; the fur trade led men into the interior to explore the river systems and mountain ranges. Operating in the northern areas were the two great British companies, the North West Company of Canada and the Hudson's Bay Company of England. On the American side of the border were the Missouri Fur Company, American Fur Company, and the Rocky Mountain Fur Company. Travelers, missionaries, and some settlers crossed the plains under the protection of the fur traders. When the business of trapping was over, some of the employees of the companies settled in the fertile lands of the Willamette Valley.

To put an end to the bitter rivalry between the Hudson's Bay and the North West companies, Parliament in 1821 forced a merger of the two. The new organization bore the old name, the Hudson's Bay Company, but the North West partners were allotted the same amount of stock as their opponents. The consolidation was followed by a general reorganization of the business throughout the trapping and trading areas of British North America.

The first result in the Northwest was the building of a new and larger post known as Fort Vancouver, where the present city of Vancouver, Washington, now stands. Under the able direction of Dr. John McLoughlin, this post for many years was the center of European enterprise in the Northwest. Here was a small, almost self-sufficient community. There were storehouses for furs, trading goods, and grain, and workshops where blacksmithing, carpentry, barrelmaking, etc., were carried on. There was a village of some fifty small houses where the employees lived with their Indian wives. There was a farm of several hundred acres. Here, crops were planted and herds of cattle and other domestic animals were kept. There were a gristmill, a sawmill, and a large dairy. Wheat and meat were raised to supply the inland posts, and also to export to the Russians in Alaska. From Vancouver as a supply point, some twenty secondary posts up the coast and in the interior were furnished with goods required in the Indian trade.

Among the secondary posts established were Fort Langley on the Fraser River and Nisqually on Puget Sound. In the Columbia Valley were Fort Walla Walla, Fort Colville, and Fort Okanogan (Plate 1B).

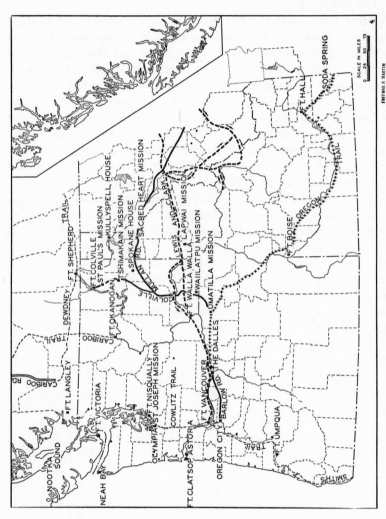

FREEMAN & MARTIN

FIG. 3. Historic routes and early posts and missions in the Pacific Northwest.

In Idaho, there were Fort Boise and also Fort Hall near Pocatello, originally founded by Nathaniel Wyeth (Fig. 3). Only a few of the old fur-trading posts had locations favorable for modern railroad and highway transportation and became cities. For the most part, the sites were abandoned with the close of the fur epoch.

For more than 20 years Dr. John McLoughlin was head of the Hudson's Bay Company in Oregon, and all persons who came in contact with him were impressed by his noble appearance, fine character, generosity, and kindness.

The Missionaries

Certain events stand out in strong relief, marking the history of the Pacific Northwest in the different decades of the nineteenth century. Lewis and Clark came in the first decade; the Astorians and Northwesters in the second; in the third, the Hudson's Bay consolidation took over the entire fur business, and only an occasional American came into the Pacific Northwest; and in the fourth decade, 1831–40, the missionaries of different denominations appeared.

Jason Lee, the first missionary to Oregon, began his work in the Willamette Valley in 1834. The Methodists supported their missions generously, sending as reinforcements a total of more than sixty persons. Many of these lived out their lives in the Willamette Valley and strongly influenced its educational and religious life.

The American Board of Commissioners for Foreign Missions, a cooperative organization of the Presbyterian, Congregational, and Dutch Reformed churches, sent Dr. Marcus Whitman and the Reverend H. H. Spalding to Oregon in 1836. Their wives were the first women to cross the American continent. Dr. Whitman located at Waiilatpu, near Walla Walla, and Spalding set up his mission at Lapwai, near Lewiston, Idaho. In 1838, Cushing Eells and Elkanah Walker and their families located at Tshimakain, near Spokane. The missionary work continued until 1847, when the massacre at Waiilatpu put an end to the efforts of the American Board for many years.

Fathers Blanchet and Demers came in 1838 to serve the employees of Hudson's Bay Company and to missionize the Indians. In the Willamette, they opened St. Joseph's School for boys and St. Mary's School for girls. Priests and sisters of Notre Dame de Namur came to assist the early missionaries. The Jesuits, led by Father De Smet, established many missions in the Inland Empire. The missionary work of the Catholics was carried on effectively by the aid of a thorough organization, a distinctive garb, celibacy, and the absence of personal secular interests. When the large immigration began in 1843, Catholic influence in the Willamette diminished because the majority of the settlers were Protestants.

Coming of the Pioneers. Provisional Government

If the decade of the 1830's was the period of missionary endeavor, that of the 1840's marked the arrival of American pioneers. They were permanent settlers with families, who came to Oregon because they believed it was a good country in which to live. In 1840 there were said to be 137 men, women, and children in Oregon. Some of these were attached to the missions; a few, like Joseph Meek, were "mountain men" who had finished their trapping careers; others had come with Nathaniel Wyeth or Ewing Young in 1832–34 or with the Peoria Party in 1839. The British element in the valley was composed of Canadians, former employees of Hudson's Bay Company, who were settled here with their Indian wives and children. Such was the situation in Oregon before the large pioneer movement began.

Hudson's Bay Company looked after the interests of the Canadians, and the Americans early began to petition Congress for protection by their own country. To meet their temporary needs the residents of the Willamette organized a provisional government in the spring of 1843, which continued with some modifications until 1849. The Hudson's Bay Company gave its adherence to this government in 1845. The provisional government of Oregon is an example of the ability of people of American and British traditions to govern themselves peaceably during a period of transition.

The interest of the outside world in the Northwest at this time is shown in the number of notable visitors and expeditions. The expedition of Lieutenant Charles Wilkes was sent out by the United States in 1841; Sir Edward Belcher was on the lower Columbia in 1839, John C. Fremont in 1843, and Sir George Simpson in 1841.

There was marked interest in the Northwest among Americans living in the eastern states. This was displayed in the newspapers and in the discussions of the Oregon Question in Congress. Emigration societies were organized to encourage and assist people who were willing to go to faraway Oregon. An Oregon convention was held in Cincinnati in July, 1843, which was attended by delegates from many states. The widespread sentiment in favor of the Oregon country is shown in the Democratic platform of 1844.

Why did people want to leave the Mississippi Valley to go to Oregon? The principal reasons were these: the depression that followed the panic of 1837 had involved individuals as well as states in financial difficulties; there was overproduction of agricultural products, as well as inadequate transportation; Oregon was believed to be a more healthful country; the Orient would furnish a large market for Oregon products; and there was hope of securing land without paying the usual governmental price. To all these reasons were added the restlessness and mobility of a frontier population with a tradition of moving ever westward from the settled to the new lands of America. The emigration to Oregon from 1840 to 1850 was a significant incident in the occupation of the continent by the American people.

The emigration parties would gather in the spring at Independence and Westport in western Missouri, where they organized by choosing leaders to direct the march. Starting about the first of May, and averaging 12 to 15 miles a day, they would arrive in western Oregon in the fall if there were no accidents or unusual delays. The route became known as the Oregon Trail and was approximately 2000 miles in length. It led from Independence, Missouri, to the Platte River, and then to Fort Laramie; it crossed the Rocky Mountains at South Pass, and went to Fort Hall, near the present city of Pocatello, Idaho. Next it followed the Snake River across the Blue Mountains to the Columbia River and down that stream to the mouth of the Willamette. The last stage was sometimes made by raft or boat.

Nearly 15,000 people are estimated to have crossed the plains and mountains to Oregon during the period 1840–50. Some returned, and some went on to California, but the census of 1850 shows that there were 13,294 white people in the Oregon country. Most of this population lived in the Willamette Valley, as only 1201 had settled north of the Columbia River.

The Oregon settlers lived the simple, frugal life of all pioneers. They took what nature offered in the form of fish, game, fuel, and pasturage, and produced the rest: food, clothing, and implements. Goods were for sale at Fort Vancouver, but lack of means forced all to practice the strictest economy. There was very little money, and for a time wheat was used as a medium of exchange.

Pioneer Roads

In the days of early settlement people made their own roads, in many cases by simply traveling along the most convenient routes. The most important of all pioneer highways, the Oregon Trail, is an example. But when major difficulties lay in the way, it was necessary to adopt a different kind of roadmaking. The Cascade Mountains and the rapids on the Columbia River were such formidable obstacles that in 1846 Samuel Barlow constructed a toll road south of Mt. Hood which was used thereafter by most of the immigrants coming with wagons and teams (Fig. 3).

The road to California gradually emerged from earlier Indian, miners', and cattle-driving trails, and by 1860 had been sufficiently improved to make regular stage and mail communication practicable. The distance from Portland to Sacramento was estimated at 710 miles, and the scheduled time of stages was 6 days and 7 hours. The road ran through Oregon City, Salem, Corvallis, Roseburg, Canyonville, Jacksonville, Yreka, and on to Sacramento.

The modern road through the Snoqualmie Pass, lowest of the Cascade Mountain passes and the most-traveled highway route between eastern and western Washington, was originally an Indian trail. Its history is like that of the California road. At first it was followed by traders, trappers, and miners. Later, herds of cattle were driven by this route to Puget Sound markets from the grasslands east of the Cascades. Its development into a wagon road went on gradually as the population east and west of the mountains increased.

Military roads were built at the expense of the Federal Government to add to the effectiveness of the army forces, but these roads were also used by civilians and were an important factor in the development of the country. To connect the navigation systems of the Columbia and Missouri rivers, the United States Government built the Mullan Road (1850–62) at a cost of $230,000. It was 624 miles from Fort Benton to Wallula. Although constructed primarily to control the Indian tribes, it was also used by many travelers. The Cariboo Trail connected the mouth of the Fraser River with the gold diggings in the interior; a branch of this route extended to Fort Okanogan on the Columbia River, and the Dewdney Trail in the Columbia Valley of Canada connected eastward to the Great Plains.

The Cowlitz Road was the communication link between the Columbia River and Puget Sound. At first, canoes were used on the Cowlitz as far as Cowlitz Landing (Toledo) where the road to Tumwater, Olympia, and Steilacoom began. In the years from 1856 to 1861, the military authorities expended $50,000 to convert what was little more than a trail into a wagon road and to extend the road along the Cowlitz to its mouth.

Territorial roads were authorized by the territorial assembly of Washington, but no money was granted for their construction. The counties were expected not only to build the roads but also to keep them in repair. The county officials could assess work requirements upon men living in the area, and the men so assessed would either have to work out the number of days designated or pay for men to work in their place. This method was popular, and during the period 1857–61 some 22 of these territorial roads were authorized by the assembly—all west of the Cascades.

This was a system of public ownership and maintenance, but there were also some toll roads authorized by the assembly which were built and kept up by private parties as business enterprises. River ferries, like toll roads, required governmental authorization and were subject to rate regulation. Some well-traveled roads came into existence because freighters and packers selected the easiest routes to and from the ferries. The Texas Road and the Kentuck Trail in eastern Washington are examples.

The Settlement of the Boundary Question

The Oregon Country was a loosely defined region lying between 54–40 on the north, and the forty-second parallel of latitude on the south. Its eastern boundary was roughly the Rocky Mountain watershed. Russia, Spain, England, and the United States asserted claims to all or part of this area, and in due time these overlapping claims came up for adjustment. In 1819, the United States bought Florida from Spain, and at the same time Spain gave the United States a quitclaim deed to all the territory north of the forty-second parallel. In 1821 an imperial Russian ukase declared that Russian rights on the coast extended south to the fifty-first parallel. This extension of Russian claims was opposed by both England and the United States, and their opposition was one of the causes of the formation of the Monroe Doctrine. However, Russia was not inclined toward belligerency. In 1824, the United States made a treaty with the Czar's government in which both countries agreed that the boundary line should be 54 degrees and 40 minutes north latitude. The following year Great Britain accepted the same parallel as the boundary. This left only two claimants, England and the United States.

Not being able to settle their dispute over the boundary, England and the United States drew up a temporary agreement in 1818. This provided that, during the next 10 years, the country might be jointly occupied by the citizens of both nations. In 1827 it was decided that the joint occupation of Oregon would be indefinitely extended, with the proviso that either country might terminate the arrangement on 12 months' notice. In the years that followed, the Oregon question was frequently before Congress and the executive department. During this period the United States government refused to yield its claims to the forty-ninth parallel as the boundary, and Great Britain insisted on the Columbia River. When American settlers began to go to Oregon in large numbers, the British government became less insistent upon its earlier demands, an attitude which may also have been influenced by the "54–40 or fight" slogan in the Democratic campaign of 1844. In 1846, the British government accepted the forty-ninth parallel, with the United States conceding British ownership of all Vancouver Island. Looked at after the lapse of more than a century it seems to have been a fair and reasonable settlement, because the claims of both nations overlapped each other about equally.

Indian Wars

The period of pioneer settlement which began about 1845 was followed by a series of Indian wars. The Waiilatpu massacre of November, 1847, in which fourteen people, including Dr. and Mrs. Whitman, lost their lives, brought on the Cayuse War. It ended with the surrender of five members of the tribe accused of participating in the massacre, their trial and execution.

The Indian policy of the American government was to place the Indians on reservations. The United States agreed to guarantee the fishing and hunting privileges of the Indians, establish schools, build mills, shops, and hospitals, and pay instructors to teach the tribesmen how to operate them. In addition, the head chief was to be granted a salary. Liquor was to be excluded from the reservation, and the tribes were to remain at peace with their neighbors.

A number of treaties were made with the Indians living west of the Cascades, and, in the spring of 1855, Governor Stevens and General Palmer opened negotiations at Walla Walla with the Umatilla, Yakima, Cayuse, Walla Walla, and Nez Perce tribes. The chiefs finally consented to the reservation plan, but, with the exception of the Nez Perces, their consent was given with manifest reluctance.

The Indians generally were not satisfied with the reservation policy. A grave situation developed, and 1855–56 became a period of widespread unrest and hostility among the northwestern Indians. The Indian population of Oregon and Washington territories at this time has been estimated at less than 25,000, whereas, the white population was probably over 30,000.

The fighting took place in several areas: in the Yakima Valley; at the Cascades on the Columbia; and in the Puget Sound country. Many communities west of the Cascade Mountains built blockhouses as places of refuge. At one time the Indians boldly attacked the little settlement of Seattle, but without success, and gradually the hostile tribesmen were brought under control.

In 1858 the Spokane, Coeur d'Alene, and Palouse Indians, who had not been actively engaged in the war, defeated the Steptoe expedition, but they were thoroughly subdued later in the same year by a larger and better-organized force under the command of Colonel George Wright.

In 1877 the nontreaty Nez Perce Indians, under Chief Joseph, went on the warpath, and, after worsting the troops in several encounters, nearly succeeded in escaping into British territory. Joseph retreated into Montana, where he was intercepted and captured by General Miles. In the following year, 1878, the Bannocks, a branch of the Shoshones, joined the Paiutes and carried on hostilities in southern Idaho and eastern Oregon.

Among the costs of these wars must be reckoned the effects produced on the people who were living in or near the Indian country. They had good reason for their fears. Frances Fuller Victor, author of *The Early Indian Wars of Oregon*, estimates that the average number of white people killed annually between 1850 and 1862 was 160. The majority of the victims were not soldiers but isolated settlers, men working alone, small parties of immigrants, and travelers or prospectors in the Indian country.

Gold Mining in the Northwest

Gold was discovered in California in 1848, and, in the years following, prospectors worked through all the western territories examining the stream gravels and sands. Placer deposits were found in the Colville country in 1855, and the influx of miners was one of the causes of the Indian wars from 1855 to 1858. The Fraser River and Cariboo discoveries took thousands of American miners into British Columbia. The first discovery in Idaho was made in 1860 by Captain E. D. Pierce at Oro Fino. Gold deposits were discovered in 1861 in the Salmon River valley and the next year at Warrens in the Boise Basin. At about the same time prospectors in western Montana found gold on Grasshopper Creek; in 1863 they discovered Alder Gulch, the greatest of the Montana placers; and in 1864 Last Chance Gulch, where Helena now stands. It is estimated that the Pacific Northwest, excluding British Columbia, produced about $142,000,000 in placer gold in the early years.

The effect of gold mining was felt in many ways. Gold was a boon to the country during Civil War days, when the currency was greatly depreciated. It provided the Federal Government with foreign exchange necessary to buy materials that could not be produced in this country. Towns grew up as a result of the demands of the mines for supplies of every kind. Lewiston, Boise, Portland, and Walla Walla are examples. Later, Seattle and Spokane benefited by the development of mines within their regional trade areas. The wealth produced in the mines added to the capital resources, and this to the development of the Northwest. Disappointed prospectors and miners became homesteaders and contributed to agricultural production. Mines were a stimulus to transportation. Pack trains and freight wagons carried goods from river towns like Lewiston, Umatilla, and Wallula to the mines; the agricultural and grazing regions produced food and sent herds of cattle to the mining camps. It was a colorful and exciting period, invested with a romantic atmosphere that has given it an enduring interest to the present time.

Territories and States

Oregon Territory, as the American portion of the old Oregon Country was called, included all the area of the present states of Washington, Oregon, and Idaho, besides considerable portions of western Wyoming and Montana. In 1848 Congress passed the necessary legislation for setting up territorial government. Joseph Lane was appointed the first territorial governor, and with his arrival the provisional government which had functioned since 1843 went out of existence.

No changes in political geography were made until 1853, when the settlers living north of the Columbia secured a territorial organization of their own. They had come to the conclusion that their interests would be better cared for if they were separated from the people living south of the Columbia. No serious objections being offered by the Willamette population, Washington Territory was created. Now there were two territories in the American Northwest, divided by the Columbia River and the forty-sixth parallel of latitude (Fig. 4).

In 1859 Oregon was admitted to the Union with its present boundaries. The remainder of the vast area that had formerly been a part of Oregon Territory was now attached to Washington Territory. Washington thus became a huge, unwieldy region extending a thousand miles from Puget Sound to the South Pass in Wyoming. This was not for long, however. Because of gold-mining operations, the populations of Idaho and Montana increased at a rapid rate. Congress created Idaho Territory in 1863, and the following year Montana was given a separate territorial organization. Between 1879 and

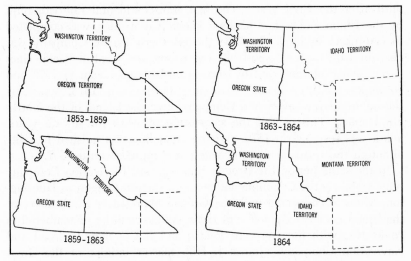

Fig. 4. Territorial and state boundary changes in the Northwest.

1886 several futile attempts were made to annex the Panhandle counties of Idaho to Washington. Washington and Montana attained statehood in 1889, and Idaho in 1890.

The Railroad Era. The Great Migration

When the possibility of railroad extension to the Pacific Northwest was first considered, Puget Sound and the Lower Columbia seemed to be the natural outlets and terminal points. These areas also had the largest populations and were eager for rail connections with the outside world. However, the first lines to make use of steam power were built in 1861 and 1862 at the portages of the Columbia River by the Oregon Steam Navigation Company, the principal carrier of passengers and freight on the river. Other railroad projects of a local character were planned, but lack of capital generally caused their suspension or failure. One well-paying enterprise was the narrow-gauge railroad from Walla Walla to Wallula, promoted by Dr. Dorsey S. Baker in 1875. It was later sold to the Oregon Railroad and Navigation Company.

The people in the Northwest were demanding railroads, and Congress was interested in finding ways and means of supplying them. In 1853 it authorized the War Department to make surveys to the Pacific Coast to determine the best route for a transcontinental railroad, but nothing much was accomplished, aside from the surveys, until after the Civil War. The first transcontinental railroad, built by the Union Pacific and Ceneral Pacific Companies, was completed to California in 1869. In 1864 the Northern Pacific Company was chartered by Congress, and like the Union and Central Pacific lines it received a liberal grant of land. Construction began in 1870 and continued for three years. Then came the panic of 1873, caused by the failure of Jay Cooke and Company, financial agents of the Northern Pacific. This caused the suspension of work for several years. Work was resumed in 1879, and the main line was finished in 1883, although the Cascade division was not completed until 1887.

In the same period the Oregon Railroad and Navigation Company built a line up the Columbia and through eastern Oregon to Huntington, where it connected with the Oregon Short Line, a subsidiary of the Union Pacific. The name of Henry Villard will be remembered in connection with the Northern Pacific and the Oregon Railroad and Navigation Company. James J. Hill, master builder of the Great Northern, completed that line to the coast in 1893. Oregon and California were connected by rail in 1887. The last great railroad to cross the Northwest to salt water was the Chicago, Milwaukee, St. Paul, and Pacific, which was finished in 1909. During the period after the building of the main lines, numerous feeder lines were constructed to serve the outlying productive areas.

In 1880, when the period of railroad building was beginning, the combined population of Washington, Oregon, and Idaho was 282,494. In 1910, when it was virtually completed, the population for the same three states had grown to 2,140,349. In 30 years, the number of inhabitants had increased 7½ times. The railroads were mainly responsible for this great migration of people from every state in the Union and from many foreign countries.

When railroad building ceased, the Northwest was ready to enter a new era. With the new era was to come a slower growth, the conservation and more intensive use of natural resources; great expansion in the utilization of power; new forms of transportation; the development of manufacturing opportunities; a higher degree of technical skill in many fields of production; and an ever-increasing interest in the cultural elements of life.

SELECTED BIBLIOGRAPHY

GENERAL REFERENCES. GEOGRAPHIC NAMES

Bancroft, Hubert Howe, *History of the Northwest Coast*, The Bancroft Co., San Francisco, 1884, 2 vols.

Carey, Charles Henry, *History of Oregon*, Pioneer Publishing Co., Portland, 1922.

Clark, Robert Carlton, *History of the Willamette Valley*, S. J. Clarke Publishing Co., Chicago, 1927.

Fuller, George W., *A History of the Pacific Northwest*, Alfred A. Knopf, New York, 1931.

McArthur, Lewis A., *Oregon, Geographic Names*, Koke-Chapman Co., Eugene, Oregon, 1928.

Meany, Edmond S., *History of the State of Washington*, The Macmillan Co., New York, 1924.

Meany, Edmond S., *Origin of Washington Geographic Names*, University of Washington Press, Seattle, 1923.

Rees, John E., *Idaho—Chronology, Nomenclature, Bibliography*, W. B. Conkey Co., Chicago, 1918.

Schafer, Joseph, *History of the Pacific Northwest*, The Macmillan Co., New York, 1930.

Scholefield, E. O. S., *British Columbia from Earliest Times to the Present*, S. J. Clarke Publishing Co., Vancouver, 1914, 2 vols.

Walbran, John T., *British Columbia Coast Names*, Ottawa Government Printing Bureau, Ottawa, 1909.

EXPLORATION. THE FUR TRADE

Chittenden, N. M., *The American Fur Trade of the Far West*, Francis P. Harper, New York, 1902, 3 vols.

Cochrane, C. N., *David Thompson, Explorer* (Canadian Men of Action), Macmillan and Co., Toronto, 1924.

Godwin, George, *Vancouver, A Life, 1757–1798*, Philip Allan, London. 1930.

Hosmer, James K., *History of the Expedition of Captains Lewis and Clark, 1804-5-6*, A. C. McClurg & Co., Chicago, 1905, 2 vols.

Irving, Washington, *Astoria*, Putnam, New York, 1868.

Meany, Edmond S., *Vancouver's Discovery of Puget Sound*, The Macmillan Co., New York, 1907.

Thwaites, Reuben Gold, *A Brief History of Rocky Mountain Exploration, with Special Reference to the Expedition of Lewis and Clark*, D. Appleton and Co., New York, 1914.

Wrong, Hume, *Sir Alexander Mackenzie, Explorer and Fur Trader* (Canadian Men of Action), Macmillan and Co., Toronto, 1927.

SETTLEMENTS, INDIAN WARS, MINING, RAILROADS

Bell, James Christy, *Opening a Highway to the Pacific (1838–1846)*, Columbia University Press, New York, 1921.

Brosnan, Cornelius J., *Jason Lee, Prophet of the New Oregon*, The Macmillan Co., New York, 1932.

Drury, Clifford Merrill, *Marcus Whitman, M.D., Pioneer and Martyr*, Caxton Printers, Caldwell, Idaho, 1937.

Hedges, James Blaine, *Henry Villard and the Railroads of the Northwest*, Yale University Press, New Haven, 1930.

Holman, F. V., *Dr. John McLoughlin, The Father of Oregon*, Arthur H. Clark Co., Cleveland, Ohio, 1907.

Jacobs, Melvin Clay, *Winning Oregon, A Study of an Expansionist Movement*, Caxton Printers, Caldwell, Idaho, 1938.

Langford, N. P., *Vigilante Days and Ways*, A. C. McClurg & Co., Chicago, 1912.

O'Hara, E. V., *Catholic History of Oregon*, Catholic Book Co., Portland, Oregon, 1916.

Pyle, Joseph Gilpin, *The Life of James J. Hill*, Doubleday, Page & Co., New York, 1917, 2 vols.

Stevens, Hazard, *Life of Isaac Ingalls Stevens*, Houghton Mifflin Co., Boston, 1900, 2 vols.

Trimble, W. J., *Mining Advance into the Inland Empire*, University of Wisconsin Press, Madison, Wisconsin, 1914.

Victor, Frances Fuller, *The Early Indian Wars of Oregon*, Frank C. Baker, Salem, Oregon, 1894.

CHAPTER

4

Modern Economic History

CHARLES M. GATES

Preceding chapters have described something of the background of Indian occupancy and early frontier history, against which a study of the modern geography of the Pacific Northwest should be viewed. Before considering the many and varied aspects of the economy of the region, it will be desirable to point out in general terms the nature of the far-reaching changes that have taken place here since the 1870's as the frontier gave way to conditions of modern exploitation and development.

The completion of the main line of the Northern Pacific Railroad marked the beginning of this new era in Northwest history. Improved transportation has hastened economic growth on many other American frontiers. In this region changes came with unusually dramatic suddenness, because the first trains from St. Paul arrived at a time when industrialism and urbanization were transforming the entire western world. In few parts of the United States did a local economy advance so rapidly from primitive conditions toward a full realization of modern regionalism.

Progress was spelled out in many ways. Big business came to the Northwest, seeking out its products and exploiting its resources on a large scale, applying all the agencies of industrial capitalism to the task. People came to Puget Sound and the valley of the Columbia by the tens of thousands, emigrants from places of lesser opportunity who were attracted by the unusual promise of this fast-moving area of farms and mills, of mines and shipping. Cities arose at the water's edge or among the wheat fields, their warehouses, wharves, stores, and office buildings serving the needs of the greatly expanding population while their colleges, libraries, and museums brought a measure of cultural refinement to an area that previously had been isolated

43

and largely out of touch with intellectual and artistic endeavor. Politics and the activities of public life, reflecting the progress of the people from territorial vassalage to statehood and full self-government, assumed the forms and followed the trends of the nation at large.

The economic history of the Pacific Northwest since 1883 may be reviewed in three broad periods, each of which was marked by some years of rapid advance, and each (save the current one) by succeeding stages of hesitation and stagnation. The first of these intervals extended from the first railroad boom to the outbreak of war in 1914. The second included the years of World War I, the consolidation of the postwar decade of the 1920's, and the panic and depression years that continued with only slight improvement to 1941. The third stage is the period of wartime expansion and reconversion that has elapsed since the attack on Pearl Harbor. Although all three stages repeated something of the same rhythm, each was marked by its own conditions which served to promote or retard the development of the region, and each witnessed the attainment of a new and higher level of economic activity, than the preceding one.

Economic Development.

EARLY 1880's TO 1914. The first great period was the time of most marked formative change. Begun by the railroad builders and carried forward in the excitement of the Yukon gold rush of 1897, the transformation was indeed far-reaching. More people came to Puget Sound in the 2 years 1887–89 than in 25 years of prerailroad emigration. When Washington inaugurated her first state governor in 1889, the officials made a special place in the parade for the "ever-to-be-remembered" pioneers, "who in early days crossed a continent by long and weary marches." The journey "by the cars" involved no such hardships, and when one made his home in the Far West he no longer felt that he was leaving civilization behind him.

This was the time when the urban pattern was first established, with its new balance of cities and rural areas. No longer primarily a matter of finding new agricultural areas, westward expansion was now related even more closely to the urbanization movement that carried people from the country to the city in every part of the United States. New cities shared the attractions of the older ones, drawing population to the Pacific Northwest in such numbers that in 1910 the Federal census disclosed the fact that the population of Washington was 53 per cent urban and that of Oregon 45.6 per cent urban. There, as throughout the trans-Mississippi West, several metropolitan

centers emerged, each of which served and at the same time drew
its support from a large surrounding rural area. Seattle, Tacoma, and
Spokane challenged the primacy of Portland, and for some years the
four cities together accounted for about 40 per cent of the increase
in population of the states of Washington and Oregon. Thus, the
Sound, the lower Columbia, and the Inland Empire each came to
have its own metropolitan center. A number of lesser communities
dreamed for a time of attaining a similar status but never became
anything more than secondary trading centers.

The growth of these urban communities took much the same form
as in other western cities. The drab wooden structures that characterized the frontier town were pulled down (if they did not burn
down in one of the big fires that broke out in almost every community), and in their places there appeared large new buildings of
brick and stone. Whole blocks of new office buildings, banks, and
stores were put up, many of which are still in service. As the business
community grew larger it became more highly specialized. Real-
estate subdivisions were opened up one after another to become residential districts in the outlying sections of town. Church properties
were sold for the profits they would bring, and new buildings were
erected either on the fringes of the downtown sections or out in the
developing neighborhoods where the people lived. Large and costly
regrade and land-filling projects were undertaken to level down hills
and make room on the flats for railroad yards and industrial sites.
Bridges, canals, and waterfront improvements were built; streets were
paved; sewage and water systems were completed; and gas and electricity were distributed throughout the cities either as private or public utilities. Professional fire and police organizations took the place
of the volunteer forces of earlier days. Institutions and organizations
of art, music, and higher learning served the intellectual and cultural
interests of the people. It was an age in which a complex environment of steel, stone, and machines became the habitat of men in the
Far Western cities as elsewhere. Improvements and new construction have likewise marked succeeding periods, but they have never
involved the same abrupt and sweeping changes that occurred during
these first years at the turn of the century.

It was also at this time that the exploitation of natural resources
was first put on a truly large-scale basis. Vast acreages of timberlands
were bought up in a wave of speculative trading that involved a number of large lumber interests of the Middle West and thousands of

small purchasers as well. The Federal Bureau of Corporations made a study of the concentration of the lumber industry which was thus affected. At the same time conditions of competition in the mills brought about the formation of a strong trade association the purpose of which was to achieve uniformity in standards and stability in prices. In 1905 Washington became the top-ranking state in the production of lumber. Forest industries and mills were soon supporting, either directly or indirectly, more than half the wage earners in Washington and were accounting for a high proportion of freight by land and sea alike. But although the lumber industry stimulated pay rolls and freight receipts, the dependence of the economy upon it was the cause of some apprehension.

Fisheries and mines were subjected in similar fashion to intensive exploitation. Capital in considerable amounts went into the halibut boats and the gear which took salmon with such efficiency that Washington reported a peak catch in 1915. Canneries became the chief economic enterprise in several places on the lower Columbia and Puget Sound. Experience in mining ventures was more spotty. Much was said about the great untapped mineral resources of the region. Mining companies were organized to develop deposits both in the Cascades and the Rockies, and some of them attracted investments from the largest capitalists of the East. Although some of the ore deposits proved to be much smaller than the early estimates indicated and others yielded only low-grade ores, the silver and lead mines of Idaho and the copper deposits at Butte, Montana, were developed by highly mechanized and expensive operations which proved what big business could do with the resources of the Northwest under favorable conditions.

Northwest farmers achieved a productivity comparable to that of the loggers and fishermen. Plows and harvesters invaded the grasslands of the Palouse country to such good effect that Whitman county alone raised a $10 million crop in 1910. Wheat from the Inland Empire moved in huge quantities to Portland and Tacoma and thence to markets situated in some instances halfway around the world. The rise of fruit growing evidenced in the crops, which in 1917 put Washington first among the states in apple production, marked the growing importance of reclamation. Irrigation ditches worked indeed a transformation as first private enterprise and later the Federal projects created rich garden and orchard lands in arid valleys including the Yakima, Wenatchee, and Okanogan. These years before 1914 were years of demonstration, when the Reclamation Bureau first launched its building program of canals and reservoirs. This was the time when the people in the dry interior threw in their lot with Uncle Sam, convinced that only with Federal projects would the water resources of their valleys be fully utilized.

The dominant note in all this energetic activity was a confident belief that after its long years as an undeveloped frontier the region was at last coming into its own. It was the heyday of the boosters and promoters whose exertions reached a dramatic climax at the Lewis and Clark Exposition at Portland in 1905 and the Alaska-Yukon Exposition at Seattle four years later. Very little economic analysis went into such exhibitions as these. They were intended to advertise the region, not to appraise it.

Behind the advertising and display, however, considerable hardheaded calculation went on as the Northwest gauged its gains and considered its disadvantages. Lumbermen fought for better freight rates to Chicago. Fruit growers experimented with different varieties of apples to discover those that could be delivered most successfully in distant markets. The Coeur d'Alene miners discovered very quickly that their returns depended upon an intricate balance of costs and prices that had little to do with promotion. The region might be plentifully supplied with resources, but the problem of competition and integration with other areas was difficult.

PERIOD 1914–1941. The second period opened with a new kind of expansion, a production boom born of wartime conditions. The stimulus of special demand and government distribution of war orders throughout the nation created in the Pacific Northwest a flourishing economy that was no longer severely limited by competitive production and marketing. Shipyards attracted thousands of workers, who prided themselves in winning pennants for the number of ships and the speed with which they were built. Mills grew larger and more numerous. The new population spurred a general expansion of many lines of manufacturing. The coast cities hummed with feverish activity and wrestled with pressing new problems of congestion. Manufacturing in Oregon and Washington increased in value by 230 per cent between 1914 and 1919. The farmer too had never been so prosperous.

War production lifted the economy of the region to a new high level. At first it seemed as if little of the advance could be maintained; shipyards disappeared quickly, the general level of manufacturing declined abruptly, and a sharp drop in agricultural prices caused great distress. Postwar depression and dislocation were nationwide, yet, because the war boom had brought a relatively greater expansion in the Northwest, the return to prewar conditions was the more disheartening.

The setback was only temporary, however. The decade of the 1920's was significant in the Northwest chiefly for the fact that production climbed up in peace time very close to the wartime level. This was achieved through diversification and the development of a number of new specialities.

Agriculture and lumbering continued to be the backbone of the economy, but the pattern was changing. Special marketing and promotional agencies increased their efforts to sell Northwest products in distant markets. Producer cooperatives proved their worth, especially among the fruit growers and dairy farmers. As egg and poultry businesses grew in number and size, outside markets were developed. A dozen items on the Census Bureau's list of manufactures expanded significantly to offset the collapse of ship building.

In this process of putting the region on a broader economic foundation, government agencies, both state and Federal, played a part, notwithstanding the laissez-faire trend of postwar "normalcy." In Washington the state attempted, though not too successfully, to give its support both to the banks that were hard pressed and to the irrigation districts whose bonds were at a discount. State money was also put into a study of the practicability of irrigation works for the Columbia Basin. Meanwhile the Federal Bureau of Reclamation pushed its projects in Idaho, Oregon, and Washington; the United States Forest Service carried forward its policies of regulated cutting, and a joint Canadian-American commission was created by treaty in 1924 to study depletion on the North Pacific halibut grounds (see chapter 10).

In the depression decade of the 1930's, conservation began to be emphasized. The general drop in production figures brought about a serious consideration of Northwest problems. Some currency was given to the idea that the West was prevented from realizing its full potentialities because of economic colonialism which kept it under eastern capitalist controls. Without raising the issue of absenteeism, both state and Federal planning agencies stressed the importance of preserving and utilizing the resources on a sustained basis, thus building a diversified economy.

Since diversification involved the creation of new industries, which required heavy capital investment, progress was slow during the depression years. However, the foundations were laid in public policies and programs for resource development. The sustained yield program gained ground in forestry, both private and public. The effort to preserve the halibut fisheries moved from the stage of scientific inquiry into the stage of administrative regulation, while steps were taken in a treaty of 1937 to rehabilitate the salmon runs on the Fraser River (see chapter 10). Grand Coulee Dam, authorized as a public-works project, was completed in 1941, though neither agriculture nor industry was directly benefited by it before Pearl Harbor. Thus the region was building for the future by protecting its essential products and by increasing very significantly its hydroelectric power potential.

WORLD WAR II TO PRESENT. The outbreak of World War II marked the beginning of the third period, which is currently in progress. The battle of production worked its miracles again in the Northwest, in an even more dramatic fashion than before. Manufacturing employment increased 2½ times as the war contracts mounted into billions of dollars. Shipyards on the Willamette River and around Puget Sound attracted thousands of migrants and set new records, while the manufacture of aircraft alone added 25,000 new workers. Twelve new electro-process plants were built at a capital cost of $160 million. Building and construction needs for the added population and a system of subcontracting served to distribute the wartime stimulus among many workers who did not find employment at the war plants. The regional index of business activity climbed 63 points between 1940 and 1944. In 1946 the farmers' cash receipts were 244 per cent above the 1935–39 level.

These developments came so fast, however, that they seemed artificial and temporary. Many observers believed that the end of the war would see the big payrolls vanish, forcing the new population to return home. Business research agencies tried to forecast the probable peacetime employment by sending out questionnaires to pre-war industries, asking them how many jobs they expected to have. Chambers of Commerce developed plans for attracting new industries to the region. The Bonneville Power Administration made studies of particular areas to propose possible lines of expansion.

Happily the region made a considerably better showing in this second attempt at postwar reconversion. Populations were maintained and even increased, as people who had come to know and like the Northwest during the war established permanent homes there. Construction expanded to meet the needs of the larger population. Aluminum plants were taken over by private enterprise, and other industries found a strong attraction in favorable power rates. Natural resources continued to be the foundation of the economy, but as a wider diversification was achieved, and more fabricating and processing industries developed, the farms, forests, and fisheries gave direct employment to a significantly smaller proportion of the laboring population. Agriculture not only conserved its gains but added a fast-growing canning and quick-freezing industry.

The Pacific Northwest thus entered upon its second century of development under conditions the most favorable in its history. The region was being integrated into the national economy more completely and more satisfactorily than ever before. Isolation was largely broken down as airlines and fast trains made possible an easy mobility between East and West. Industries came in until they absorbed the full capacity of regional resources and of hydroelectric power installations. Individuals from the Northwest left the region to take places of responsibility in other sections, while the influx of new population from all states in the Union diminished the regional self-consciousness that had marked the earlier years. Less was said of colonialism and of discrimination against the Northwest. Instead there was a new sense of maturity and confidence born of the realization that the "far corner" was now an integral part of the nation.

PART

2

The Physical Environment

Regional Framework
of the Northwest

INTRODUCTION

The foundations on which the Pacific Northwest is built consist of its natural resources and other environmental factors. For example, the Cascade Mountains divide the region into two realms: a humid west side and a dry east side, the latter being bounded on the north and east by the Rocky Mountains. In the United States the Northwest includes three major geographic provinces: western Oregon and Washington, Columbia Intermontane, and the Rocky Mountains. Only the northern margin of the Basin and Range Province lies within the area. Southern British Columbia is another and large unit. Division into provinces is based on location and relief features. The provinces are further divided into sections or other smaller units. Some factors of environment, for example, the character of mountains and lowlands, the occurrence of minerals, the climate, soils, and plant life, are often related to certain provinces. The regional framework, discussed in this chapter, is closely associated with the patterns of location of natural resources, the human use or industries, and the distribution of population. Succeeding chapters will include many correlations between Northwest resources and industries and the environmental features of the geographic regions.

SECTION 1. WESTERN OREGON AND WASHINGTON

SAMUEL N. DICKEN

An irregular north-south line, immediately east of the Cascade Mountains, divides the states of Oregon and Washington into two broad, contrasting regions. The contrast is based primarily on variation in the underlying rocks and on climate, but is more evident in the land forms, natural vegetation, population patterns, types of production, and way of life. The west is underlain largely by sedimentary rocks and by older igneous rocks; only the crest of the Cascades reveals large areas of recent lavas. Elongated north-south ranges and lowlands, moderate to heavy rainfall, mild temperatures, and a dense forest cover are characteristic of the west, as are the large proportion of urban population and the dependence on forest production and humid agriculture.

To the east the broad basins, narrow ranges, and dissected plateaus are underlain largely by young lavas. The climate is semiarid to subhumid, with forests only in favored areas. Dry farming, irrigation agriculture, and grazing are widespread, whereas forest products are limited to comparatively small areas. There are few large cities; the population is sparse, except in the districts of intensive irrigation. Although the eastern region has over twice the area of the western, it supports less than one-third of the population of the two states.

The western region, with which this section is concerned, consists of three elongated parallel belts. The first belt, the coastal mountains, includes the Olympic Mountains, the Coast Range proper, and the Klamath Mountains of southwestern Oregon. This belt continues to the north as the mountains of Vancouver Island and Queen Charlotte Island, and to the south as the Klamath Mountains of California. The second belt is represented by a series of lowlands: notably the Willamette Lowland and the Puget Lowland, which, together with a few smaller basins such as the Rogue Valley of Oregon, provide a north-south corridor from Vancouver, British Columbia, to California. The third belt is the Cascade Range itself, which runs the entire

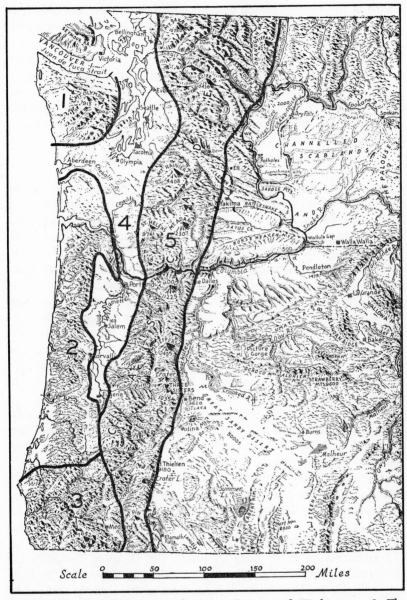

FIG. 5. The physical provinces of western Oregon and Washington. 1. The Olympic Mountains. 2. The Coast Range. 3. The Klamath Mountains. 4. The Willamette-Puget lowland. 5. The Cascade Mountains. (*Base map from Erwin Raisz.*)

length of the western region without interruption save for the narrow gorge of the Columbia River. These three belts exhibit such a variety of surface features, climate, soils, and human activities that it is advisable to describe them under the heading of 5 provinces (Fig. 5): Olympic Mountains, Coast Range, Klamath Mountains, Willamette-Puget Lowland, and Cascade Mountains. Each of these provinces is interpreted to include associated features, such as small lowlands adjacent to the mountains and hill land lying within the lowlands.

1. THE OLYMPIC MOUNTAINS

Bounded by the Puget Lowland, the Strait of Juan de Fuca, and the Pacific Ocean, the Olympic Mountain Province is a compact massif approximately 60 miles in diameter. In the interior, many ridges, arranged in a radial pattern, rise to 5000 feet, and the highest peak, Mt. Olympus, is 7915 feet above sea level (Plate 2A). From the central area the general level declines to about 2000 feet, at which point there is a sharp break to the bordering lowlands. The rocks of the Olympics are mostly sedimentary, with some metamorphics near the center and a rim of igneous flow rocks. The Olympic Mountains have been severely glaciated and remnants of the former glaciers still exist. Deep cirques have been carved in the upper slopes and U-shaped valleys radiate from the center to the edge of the bordering lowlands. These valleys have a moderate grade except in the upper reaches.

A lowland of varying width surrounds the mountains on all sides with an elevation up to 400 feet. This lowland does not in most cases represent a coastal plain but rather a belt of low hills through which the main streams from the Olympics have carved broad valleys. The lower margin of the lowland, particularly to the north and west, is being attacked by the sea, and steep sea cliffs up to 300 feet high are common. At the foot of the cliffs and extending out to sea for a mile or more is a series of wave-cut platforms, the highest of which is partially exposed at low tide.

Surrounded on three sides by water, the Olympic Peninsula has moderate temperatures which vary according to altitude. The highest peaks are too cool in summer for trees and are partly covered by snow even in summer. The west slope of the mountains receives very heavy precipitation, probably the highest in the United States. In a few places on the west side at intermediate elevation the average annual precipitation probably exceeds 150 inches, much of it coming in the winter season in the form of snow. On the other hand, the eastern slope, in the rain shadow, receives moderate to light precipitation. Port Angeles receives less than 27 inches, annual average, Port Townsend less than 20. But the areas of light rainfall have nevertheless a high proportion of cloudy weather.

Climatic variations based mainly on altitude and exposure to wind and sun are associated with a diverse pattern of natural vegetation. On the west and southwest of the Olympic Mountains forests of cedar, spruce, and hemlock are common. To the southeast and to the north large stands of Douglas fir are found on the valley floors and on the adjacent slopes. The higher elevations have large areas of subalpine vegetation, and the highest peaks are devoid of trees.

The lowland border of the Olympic Mountains shows declining yields of lumber and other forest products. Fires and logging have depleted large tracts of timber on the south, east, and north, some of which are now undergoing satisfactory regrowth. The west and northwest, the more humid portion of the province, has suffered less from fires, and because of its comparative remoteness has been logged less severely.

The Olympic National Park, 1300 square miles in area, was established in 1938 to preserve the primeval wilderness for recreational purposes. The valleys and lower slopes are densely forested but the upper slopes are too high, cool, and bare of soil to support much vegetation. Numerous glaciers and glacial lakes, like Lake Crescent, contribute to the variety of landscape. During glacial times the valley glaciers from the Olympic center pushed far out into Puget Sound and were met by the continental ice sheet coming down from the north. Complex structure, glaciation, and heavy precipitation have combined to make the park one of the most variegated and fascinating provinces in North America.

2. THE COAST RANGE

The Coast Range Province of Washington and Oregon extends from the Chehalis River in the vicinity of Aberdeen, Washington, to the Coquille River of Oregon, and inland from the sea to the Willamette-Puget Lowland. The province is approximately 250 miles long and has an average width of over 50 miles. It is not a lofty range, reaching only 4097 feet at Marys Peak near Corvallis, Oregon. The Washington portion is a dome-shaped uplift called the Willapa Hills (Plate 2A). The Coast Range is made up largely of sedimentary rocks, such as sandstone, shales, and small amounts of limestone, together with lava flows and some intrusive igneous rocks. Resistant to erosion, the igneous rocks usually form the highest and most rugged portions of the range and the most striking headlands. The most persistent feature, in contrast with the Olympic Mountains and the Klamath Mountains, is the series of long, narrow, parallel ridges resulting from the structure of the rocks. The rocks of the Coast Range are gently folded, the axis of the folds generally paralleling the coast.

The land forms of the Coast Range are varied. Along the coast are bold headlands with nearly vertical slopes in which the sea has carved numerous caves, alternating with smooth beaches suitable for clam digging, surf fishing, agate hunting, and other recreational activities. Back of the beaches are numerous dune areas and many lakes, the latter formed by the blocking of streams by sand. These offer a strong contrast to the more rugged coastal features. Each of the numerous tidal estuaries of the larger streams such as the Chehalis, Willapa, Columbia, Nehalem, Yaquina, Siuslaw, Umpqua, and Coos has its individual characteristics, but all are "drowned" either by the latest rise in sea level or by downwarping. The eastern side of the range consists of foothills, which descend gradually to the floor of the Willamette-Puget Lowland. The interior of the Coast Range is made up of numerous ridges and valleys, with a general north-south alignment. A few large rivers, such as the Columbia and the Umpqua, flow entirely across the Coast Range.

Adjacent to the ocean and under its immediate influence, the Coast Range has a mild climate with cool, rainy winters and comparatively dry summers. The coastal margin of the province, together with the western fringes of the Olympic Mountains, has the highest average winter temperatures in the Pacific Northwest and shares with the west slopes of the Olypmics a high annual rainfall. Precipitation diminishes in the southern portion of the province, with a minimum of about 40 inches in the rain shadow of the eastern side. Near the coast, forests of hemlock, spruce, and cedar are interspersed with smaller tracts of grassland, brush and cleared land. Inland, the Douglas fir forest predominates, often with an understory of hardwoods, although fires and logging operations have greatly altered its character. Large "burns" such as near Tillamook, are especially noticeable in the northern part of the province.

In Washington the more important clusters along the coast include Aberdeen-Hoquiam on Grays Harbor and Raymond-South Bend on Willapa Bay. Both these clusters depend mainly on wood products and fisheries for their support. In Oregon, the Astoria district profits from shipping as well as from fishing and wood products. The Tillamook area is noted for dairying, especially cheesemaking. Coos Bay (Plate 2B), the largest ocean port in Oregon south of the Columbia, exports lumber and provides anchorage for commercial fishing boats. Beaches and other shore attractions give rise to resort areas, for example, Seaside, Oregon, and Long Beach, Washington. On the inner margin of the province the agricultural economy of the lowlands is being extended farther into the foothills as more land is cleared. This is a favored site for sawmills and other wood-processing plants, using timber from the Coast Range and having access to the roads and railroads of the lowland.

3. KLAMATH MOUNTAINS

South of the Coquille River of Oregon and west of the Cascade Mountains are the Klamath Mountains Provinces, a rugged area almost equally divided between the states of Oregon and California. The Oregon portion, to which this description is limited, is underlain by older and in many cases more resistant rocks than is the Coast Range. Sandstone, limestone, shale, granodiorite, basalt, serpentine, and marble are common. Each of the major rock types tends to give distinctive qualities of soil and land forms to its portion of the province. The general structural orientation of the province is northeast-southwest and most of the faults and folds follow this trend, but the erosion history is so complicated that the effects of the structure are not always apparent in the landscape. The most characteristic upland forms are the narrow, elongated ridges with steep slopes, above which rise rounded peaks. The coastal terraces and alluvial basins of the Rogue River and its tributaries account for most of the level land. Briefly, the province may be described in terms of the coastal margins, the interior portions of high relief, and the alluvial basins.

The coastal margin of the Klamath Province is either bold and rugged with steep cliffs rising several hundred feet from the sea, or the cliffs rise from marine terraces which begin a hundred feet or more above present sea level and may extend up to 1500 feet. In many places the coastline is so rugged that access to the sea is difficult even on foot, and the coastal highway turns inland to find easier terrain. In areas of steep slopes landslides are a problem. A large terrace north of Port Orford is 5 miles wide and several miles long, varying in elevation from sea level to more than 200 feet. A similar terrace is found near the Oregon-California line in the vicinity of Brookings. The lower terraces are used for agriculture and grazing, affording also excellent sites for roads.

The interior of the Klamath Mountains has a relief ranging from 2000 to 4000 feet or more. The various peneplains first described by the geologist Diller show many departures from a uniform surface. Although from an airplane there appears to be concordance of summits, yet from the floor of one of the basins the country appears rugged indeed (Plate 2B). It is evident from the nature of the slope that the rate of erosion has varied from time to time. The higher elevations tend to be rounded, as a result of uplift following peneplanation. This is true in spite of some glaciation in the higher parts of the Klamath Mountains. In many places the lower slopes are oversteepened, and the streams such as the Rogue and its tributaries often flow in narrow gorges. This contrast of the upper slopes and the lower steeper slopes produces a valley-in-valley effect, with the profile of a large broad letter "V" in the bottom of which a small "v" has been cut.

The alluvial basins, although small in area, are the most favored spots for human occupation. These basins are wide portions in the valleys of the Rogue and its tributaries, partially filled with aluvium. Most of the aluvium contains some gold, and the first settlers were attracted by placer mining. Later, mining was replaced by agriculture and now fruit growing and general farming are common.

Most of the province is drained by the Rogue, Umpqua, and Chetco rivers. The Rogue and the Umpqua have their headwaters in the Cascade Range and supply water for irrigation, for power, most of which is undeveloped, and for recreation.

The climate of the Klamath Mountains is similar to that of the Coast Range but with more variety because of the greater elevation and greater width of the province. The rainfall ranges from less than 16 inches in the vicinity of Medford to nearly 100 inches on the west slope of the higher ridges near the sea. In the interior the summers are dry and warm. Medford is also the warmest point west of the Cascades, averaging 72° for July.

The Douglas fir forest is dominant as in the Coast Range, but the large areas of hardwood, such as oak and madrone, reflect the drier summers. Chaparral is common. Most of the region now lies in the national forests, but on the privately owned land the logging rate is very rapid. Some land cleared for agriculture or grazing has reverted to chaparral or scrub forest.

In and near the alluvial basins, and along certain parts of the river valleys, conditions for road and railroad building are easy. But in some portions the alternating ridges and canyons present such obstacles that certain districts are many miles from a surfaced road. Furthermore, the first railroad connecting the Willamette Lowland with California had so many curves and grades that it is now used for freight only, and passenger trains follow a newer route across the Cascades to Klamath Falls, which avoids the Klamath Mountains entirely. Another drawback to road building has been the small population.

4. THE WILLAMETTE-PUGET LOWLAND

This broad lowland, sometimes described as a valley or trough, stands out in strong contrast to the Coast Ranges on the west and the Cascades on the east. It is essentially an alluvial plain, 350 miles long and 50 miles wide, produced by the covering of a former more rugged surface by quantities of sediments from the Coast Range and the Cascades. In the northern part the lowland is partially drowned and is penetrated by various arms of the sea such as Puget Sound, the Straits of Juan de Fuca, and the Straits of Georgia.

The northern part of the lowland, the Puget Sound portion, differs from the southern part in that it has been glaciated and much of it is covered by the sea. The continental glacier covered the Puget Lowland south of Olympia, Washington, leaving moraine and outwash gravels, so that the underlying bedrock is rarely exposed. In many places streams have cut channels in the outwash plains, leaving the interfluves as low, nearly level platforms. The valley floors provide the best land for agriculture. Glaciation produced numerous lakes along the margins of the valley, such as Lake Washington, Sammanish, and Whatcom, and overdeepened old river valleys which are now occupied by the ramifying waters of Puget Sound. In other areas, especially on the eastern margin of the Puget Lowland, the ice secured the land, leaving low hills with much bare rock exposed. Puget Sound, which provides numerous harbors for the lowland, was flooded by water at the close of the Ice Age, and the ancient stream valleys that converged and flowed into the Pacific at the Strait of Juan de Fuca have been superseded by numerous bays and channels, with the higher land forming islands and peninsulas in the Sound. From about 10 miles south of Olympia the Puget-Willamette Lowland was not affected directly by continental glaciation, but there were some indirect effects. With continental ice to the north and valley glaciers in the Cascades to the east, the lowland received large quantities of water and debris, which covered the lowland with the exception of a few hills.

The Willamette Lowland is, in part, an alluvial plain produced by the partial filling of a broad trough with sediments from the nearby mountains, the longer slope extending westward from the Cascades. The lowland extends from the Cowlitz Valley in the vicinity of Kelso and Longview, Washington, to Eugene, Oregon, a distance of approximately 160 miles. In several places, low hills rise a few hundred feet above the alluvial floor, for example, the Salem, Waldo, Eola and Amity hills. These hills are composed of resistant bedrock, mostly sandstone or basalt. Some of the hill land is still wooded, although other portions are cultivated; orchards are common.

5. THE CASCADE MOUNTAINS

The Washington and Oregon portion of the Cascade Province is 500 miles long and varies in width from more than 100 miles at the Canadian boundary to less than 50 miles at the California line. The province has the highest relief in the Pacific Northwest, varying from near sea level at the Columbia River to 14,407 feet at Mt. Rainier. This is a mountain range of many peaks, most of them volcanic cones more or less dissected by glaciation and steam action. Below the peaks at an elevation of 5000 to 6000 feet, the summit of the Cascades in both Washington and Oregon has the appearance of a plateau or peneplain. This is now generally considered to be of structural origin and not an erosional peneplain. On the margins this plateau is strongly dissected, with deep, narrow valleys and sharp ridges.

The Cascade Province is usually divided into two parts. The northern portion, north of a line drawn from the vicinity of Seattle to Ellensburg, Washington, consists of old sediments which have been intruded by granitic batholiths. Here many of the peaks, for example Mt. Stuart, and ridges have been produced by erosion rather than by accumulation of lava. The summit of the ridges is about the same elevation, but the relief is extremely rugged. The ridges in the middle of the range are between 6000 and 8000 feet, above which rise many higher peaks. This portion of the Cascades can be described as a broad upland which has been so dissected that little of the original surface remains. The main divide between the waters of the middle Columbia and those of Puget Sound is very irregular, followed on the map by county boundaries, in contrast with the crestline of the Cascades in southern Washington and Oregon, which is a much smoother line.

Alpine glaciation has played an important role in carving the detail of the northern Washington Cascades, especially above the 5000-foot level. The upper slopes of the peaks and higher ridges are marked with hundreds of cirques and some of the peaks are surrounded by cirques, thus forming distinct glacial "horns" similar to the Matterhorn. The remnants of many of the glaciers still remain, most of them on the west side, where precipitation is heavier. This is especially true of Glacier Peak and Mt. Baker, both of which have radiating glaciers.

In comparison with Rainier and Adams, the peaks of the northern Washington Cascades are lower. Glacier Peak (10,436) and Mt. Baker (10,750) are volcanic cones, but most of the others are granitic. It appears that the latter are mostly remnants of erosion, Mt. Stuart (9420), for example.

The valleys of the northern Cascades are in the form of deep, steep-sided troughs, varying in depth to 5000 feet in the case of Lake Chelan on the eastern slope. Lake Chelan (Plate 3A) is 50 miles long, the biggest of many glacial lakes, and has a depth of nearly 1500 feet.

The gradients of these valleys are remarkably flat, so that within a few miles of the water divide the streams have few rapids. This makes valleys such as the Green River Valley on the west and the Yakima Valley on the east excellent pass routes, except for a short portion near the divide. This short distance is linked by railroad tunnels.

South of the Seattle-Ellensburg line, the surface of the Cascades Range is made up almost entirely of extrusive igneous materials. Numerous volcanic cones such as Rainier, St. Helens, Adams, Hood, and Jefferson, rise from a plateau (Plate 3B), the crest of which is little dissected, with the single exception of the Columbia Gorge. Glaciation was limited largely to the slopes of the higher peaks, and the flows of lava and accumulation of tuff have been too recent to permit deep dissection. Many of the young lava flows are almost entirely devoid of vegetation and show little or no effects of erosion. The most spectacular lake is Crater Lake, which occupies the caldera of an old volcanic cone that lost its top by explosion or subsidence, or a combination of the two. This nearly circular lake lies at an elevation of 6177 feet, has a diameter of about 6 miles and a maximum depth of nearly 2000 feet.

The western portion of the Cascades is much older and rougher than the high eastern portion, although lower in elevation. The western belt can be described as a thoroughly dissected region with little of the old plateaulike surface remaining. Local relief is greater than in the higher eastern portion of the province. At Belknap Springs, Oregon, the McKenzie River is nearly 1700 feet above the sea, and the nearby ridges rise to 5500 feet. This is, indeed, mountainous country.

The pattern of natural vegetation of the Cascade Range reflects variations in rainfall. The western slope is the more humid, especially in the north. Average annual precipitation reaches more than 100 inches in places. The eastern slope is dry by comparison, so that the lower dry timberline is found at about 5000 feet in southern Oregon. On the western slope and lower elevations the outstanding formation is the Douglas fir forest, which furnishes most of the timber cut from the region. In Oregon this forest originally was a nearly continuous belt varying in altitude from less than 1000 feet to more than 4000 feet. In the northern Cascades the Douglas fir was limited to the floors and lower slopes of the valleys and did not reach the higher ridges. On the higher elevations are forests of pine, spruce, and hemlock, and at the crest is a belt, narrow in the south, wide in the north, that lies above the cold timberline. Here subalpine forms are common, and some of the higher peaks, because of steep slope and the porosity of the lava, are almost entirely devoid of vegetation. The east slope of the Cascades is dominated by the ponderosa pine, with a mixture of Douglas fir in the valleys of the northern portion.

SECTION 2. COLUMBIA INTERMONTANE PROVINCE

OTIS W. FREEMAN

One of the largest areas of volcanic rock on the earth's surface, covering more than 200,000 square miles, is located in the Pacific Northwest. Since much of this area is drained by the Columbia River and its tributaries, it has been generally spoken of as the "Columbia Plateau," although it is really not a plateau, but rather an intermountain region between the Cascades and northern Rocky Mountains. Most of the so-called Columbia Plateau is upland, with elevations of 1000 to 5000 or more feet above sea level. Some of the surface, however, consists of basins only a few hundred feet in elevation, and there are mountains that are nearly 10,000 feet high. The region is far from having the uniform surface generally considered a requirement for a plateau, but instead possesses a highly varied surface of small plateaus, both level and tilted, of hills, eroded slopes, high rugged mountains, broad valleys and basins, upfolded ridges, and flat plains. Moreover, instead of rising abruptly on at least one side as plateaus are said to do, the area is enclosed by mountains on the west, north, and east, and grades almost imperceptibly into the Basin and Range Province to the south.

The name Columbia Intermontane Province has been chosen for this region that is dominantly underlain by basalt lava flows.[1]

After an earlier period of eruption characterized by light-colored (acid) lava, mainly andesite and rhyolite, there were numerous extensive flows of dark-colored basalt.

[1] Fenneman in *Physiography of the Western United States* divided the Columbia Plateau into five sections: Walla Walla, Blue Mountain, Snake River Plain, Payette, and Harney. His Walla Walla Plateau, which included southeastern Washington and north-central Oregon, was said to have a rolling surface with young incised valleys. This region varies so greatly in its relief features that the term plateau has been found inept and inapplicable; separation into several sections has been found desirable. The other sections are retained only in part, and changes in their boundaries and rank have been made and a new division, the Owyhee, is recognized.

Especially in the northern half, volcanic vents are nearly absent, and apparently the lava emerged from enormous cracks in the earth's surface. That many years may have elapsed between successive lava flows is proved by the eroded tops of some of the flows, the presence of soil later baked to bricklike material, and large quantities of charred and petrified wood. In the Snake River Canyon nearly fifty lava flows are exposed that aggregate more than a mile in thickness. Towards the edge of the lava-covered region the flows become thinner as they encroach on the slopes of the surrounding hills and mountains. The drainage was naturally interfered with by the lava, and many temporary lakes, some of considerable size, were formed in which silts collected which later might be buried under other flows. The Spokane and Columbia rivers probably once flowed in quite different courses across the region and were pushed by the lava north and west from their former locations to the foot of the mountains there, where they eroded new valleys, almost at the contact between the lava and the exposures of much older rock. The surface over which the lava flowed differed; some areas had low relief and others had great variations in relief, especially near the margin of the Rocky Mountains. Here fair-sized mountains were wholly or partly buried by the flows in Oregon and neighboring parts of Idaho and Washington. In same places the higher hills, called "steptoes" after the classic example of Steptoe Butte in eastern Washington, rise above the plateau surface and are entirely surrounded by lava, but they were never covered by it. Following and perhaps accompanying the outpourings of thousands of cubic miles of basalt, the surface of the Columbia Plateau was warped and disturbed by upfolds, downfolds, and faults. Much of its relief results directly from these earth movements. In a minor way, erosion and deposition of sediments have modified the original surface features.

The Columbia Intermontane Province has been divided into four units: Columbia Basin, Central Highlands, High Lava Plains, and Owyhee Upland. These four units are of large size and are physiographically so distinct and different from each other that they should be recognized as subprovinces. In turn, the subprovinces are divided into sections based on less marked differences than those that characterize the four large units [2] (Fig. 6).

[2] Otis W. Freeman, J. D. Forrester, and R. L. Lupher, "Physiographic Divisions of the Columbia Intermontane Province," *Annals Assoc. Amer. Geogrs.*, Vol. 35, pp. 53–75, June, 1945.

The northern part of the province, called the Columbia Basin, is divided into minor basins, plateaus, hills, and structural uplifts. The Central Highlands bound the Columbia Basin on the south and consist of the Blue-Wallowa-Seven Devils mountains and other complex uplifts rising to an elevation of over 9000 feet above the floor of the

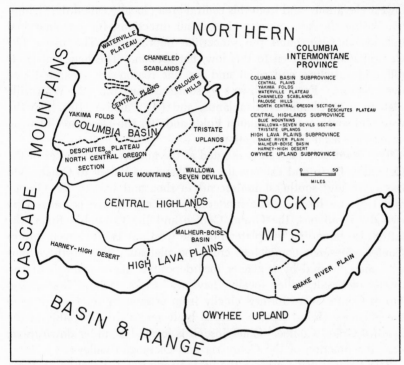

Fig. 6.   Physiographic subdivisions of the Columbia Intermontane Province.

Basin and extending between the Rocky Mountains and the Cascades. South of the Central Highlands are broad plains, called the High Lava Plains, extending from the Cascade Highlands across Oregon and southern Idaho to Yellowstone Park. These plains are covered by young lava flows and detrital material and average about 4000 feet in elevation. The High Lava Plains are modified on the south by fault-block topography of the Basin and Range Province; but between the plains and faulted ranges lies the Owyhee Upland, situated in southeast Oregon, southwest Idaho, and northern Nevada. This consist of deeply eroded plateaus and a maturely dissected mountain mass that rises above the adjacent plains.

COLUMBIA BASIN

In east-central Washington, detritus-covered plains occur at the lowest elevations, and from this central area (locally called the Columbia Basin) the lava country rises in all directions, forming marginal uplands that surround the saucerlike depression. The name (1) Central Plains is given to this low, flat section. The marginal lands differ in structure and relief and for this reason are separated into five sections. From northwest to southeast are the (2) Waterville Plateau, (3) Channeled Scablands, and (4) Palouse Hills. To the west and south are (5) Yakima Folds and (6) the Deschutes Plateau, or north-central Oregon section.

The *Waterville Plateau* is situated at the northwestern corner of the Columbia Basin and extends up the Okanogan Valley to Omak. On the south and southeast it descends a thousand feet to the Quincy and Hartline basins. The moderately rolling surface is crossed by two deep canyons, the Grand Coulee and the Columbia River, the latter also bounding the plateau on the west. A third canyon, Moses Coulee, does not completely cross the plateau. The northern part was once covered by a glacier that deposited huge erratic boulders, mostly of basalt, called locally "haystack" rocks. Grand Coulee and Moses Coulee were formed chiefly from erosion by melt water from the glacier. Grand Coulee Dam is built across the Columbia at the head of Grand Coulee. Chief Joseph is located 51 miles downstream near the junction of the Columbia and Okanogan valleys.

The *Palouse Hills* occupy the eastern edge of the Columbia Basin from near Spokane south to the Blue Mountains. Although underlain by basalt flows and older rock, the hills are not made of residual material from these rocks, but instead are covered with loess mixed with volcanic ash. Wind has heaped the loess into hills, elongated from the southwest to northeast and steepest in the latter direction (Plate 3B). Wind, nivation, and reshaping by running water have united to form the hilly, mature topography of the Palouse. Hills of old crystalline rock, like Steptoe Butte, project above the general level of the country and increase in numbers towards the mountains of Idaho. In altitude the Palouse drops from 2500 feet at the Idaho line to 1000–1500 feet southwestward, where the hill slopes become longer and less steep.

The term *Channeled Scablands* was invented by J Harlen Bretz [3] to describe a region of unique topography that had been incised into the surface of the western part of the Palouse Hills and certain other sections adjoining the central plains in eastern Washington. In reality, this area is a zone of "islandlike" hills covered with Palouse soil or other loessial soils that rise above the interlacing channels of bare lava rock, called "scabrock" by the early pioneers (Plate 4A). The term Channeled Scablands is directly applicable only to those parts from which the soil has been removed, so that, strictly speaking, the area should be described as Palouse Hills mixed with Scablands.

The Scablands were formed in the Glacial Period from erosion by glacial meltwater. Huge temporary rivers washed away the surface soil from nearly 2000 square miles of land, and many of the streams deeply incised themselves into bedrock. Before the Glacial Period the country was covered mostly with Palouse soil and had a hilly topography. The floods of melt water eroded an amazing system of interlacing channels into the solid lava bedrock amid the remnants of the old mature relief, thereby producing a topography that resembles, on a huge scale, sheet flood erosion on an ordinary hill slope. In many scabland channels, deep, rockbound lakes occur in places where the floors were most deeply excavated by the torrents of swift water. Potholes, steep cliffs, ponds and swampy meadows, rocky buttes, water-eroded pinnacles and turrets of black basalt, flat-topped mesas, dry falls, abandoned cascades, and dusty or rock-bound former water courses, now deserted, characterize the Scablands. Debris from the scabland channels deposited at the canyon mouths or other favorable locations formed extensive gravel bars and other deposits, some of which extend into the central plains of Washington.

The *Central Plains* are detritus-covered flats and gentle slopes, and, being surrounded by higher land, these plains have a climate that is desert or semidesert. The plains include the Columbia Basin in Washington, which is divided by the Saddle Mountains and Frenchman Hills into two parts, the Quincy Basin on the north and the Pasco Basin to the south. In southeastern Washington the drainage flows in all directions towards the central plains, and leaves the area through the Wallula Gateway, where the Columbia River breaks through the end of the Horse Heaven uplift that extends east from the Cascades. Deposits of the finer sand, clay, and silt helped form the level plains

[3] J Harlen Bretz, "The Channeled Scablands of Eastern Washington," *Geographical Review*, Vol. 18, pp. 446–477, 1928.

of the Quincy region that are irrigated from the Grand Coulee Dam. Locally, as near Moses Lake, are found sand dunes, practically useless to man (Plate 4A). The plains include the Walla Walla Valley and extend into northern Oregon to include the Umatilla Basin (Plate 4B). Most of the land included in the Central Plains requires irrigation for successful farming. The Columbia Basin project is the largest of the irrigation developments in this area.

The term *Yakima Folds* is applied to a series of upfolded hills and ridges alternating with downfolded valleys that extend eastward from the southern half of the Cascade Mountains in Washington, between the Columbia River on the south and the Wenatchee Valley on the north. The Horse Heaven, the longest of the uplifts, lies in the extreme south of Washington and is cut through by the Columbia River at the Wallula Gateway, a mighty water gap nearly 2000 feet deep. McNary Dam is built near the south end of the Wallula Gap. North of the Horse Heaven is the fertile, irrigated Yakima Valley. From near the city of Yakima, several associated tributary valleys extend east and west on both sides of the main valley. Beginning a few miles north of Yakima, the Yakima River has cut a series of stupendous entrenched meanders through several upfolds of basaltic lava. North of these ridges is the Kittitas Valley, which is bounded on the east by the Saddle Mountains and on the north by the old rocks of the Wenatchee Range. South of the Horse Heaven Hills a small folded area extends across the Columbia River into Oregon near Hood River.

The *Deschutes Plateau* or *north central Oregon section* is often called the Columbia Plateau in Oregon. It lies south of the Columbia River and north of the Central Highlands subprovince, and extends from the Cascade Mountains east to about where Pendleton nestles at the foot of the Blue Mountains. The surface rises from an elevation of a few hundred feet along the bluffs overlooking the Columbia River to 2500–3000 feet on the south. The sloping plateau is deeply dissected by the canyon of the Deschutes and John Day rivers and other streams. The gently rolling surfaces between the canyons are covered with light but fertile soil and, given sufficient rain, the land is divided into huge fields, alternately planted to wheat and left in summer fallow.

CENTRAL HIGHLANDS

Extending from the Cascade Mountains eastward across Oregon into Idaho and southeastern Washington is a complex group of mountain ranges and dissected plateaus. Basalt predominates in these uplands, being found to elevations in excess of 9000 feet above sea level. Several large exposures of granite, metamorphic, and deformed sedimentary rocks also outcrop in the uplifted belt. This subprovince, called the Central Highlands, includes the Blue, Wallowa, and Seven Devils mountains and Tristate Uplands, and separates the Columbia Basin on the north from the High Lava Plains on the south. The eastern boundary of the subprovince is drawn at the contact of the basalt lava with the mature topography and old rocks of the Northern Rocky Mountains, close to a major fault that determines the deep valley of the Little Salmon River. The boundary with the High Lava Plains is well defined on the southwest, where tilted and dissected mountain slopes rise steeply from flat lava plains, but toward the southeast the country is broken and the boundary is more arbitrary. On the west the Mutton Mountains, a deeply eroded uplift, abut against the Cascade Range, which is built of recent lava flows little affected by erosion. The boundary with the Columbia Basin is not clearly defined but in general is drawn at around the 2500- to 3000-foot contour. Canyons occupy over half the surface above this elevation, and below 3000 feet lie most of the areas where recent sediments cover the lavas.

The Central Highlands supply irrigation water to the lower and drier lands about and among the mountains. Important stands of timber are utilized as is also the abundant grazing, used mostly in the summer season. Recreation and hunting are other uses of the mountains. There are mines of gold, mercury, chrome, and other metals.

BLUE MOUNTAINS. The name "Blue Mountains" is applied to up-lifted and eroded plateaus and ranges that extend for about 250 miles from southeastern Washington first southward and then westward to the Cascade Mountains. Local names are applied to portions of the mountains. The northern part of the Blue Mountains consists mainly of warped and sometimes tilted plateaus, all deeply eroded. The Aldrich, Strawberry, and Ironside mountains occupy the central area and rise to 9600 feet above sea level at Strawberry Butte. South of this high ridge the Silvies Plateau descends gradually to the plains near Burns. Westward are the Ochoco and Mutton mountains. Faults are common in the Blue Mountains and account for steep scarps on the south and east. Upheavals account for the occurrences of basalt flows at elevations of over 9000 feet above sea level, but in general the higher peaks are composed of ancient crystalline rocks. Considerable mining, mainly for gold, has been done in the areas of old rocks and the associated placers deposited downstream.

Basins and broad valleys are characteristic of the Blue Mountains, both within and along the margins of the uplifted blocks. On the east the Grande Ronde Valley and the Baker Valley separate the Blue Mountains from the Wallowa Mountains in northeastern Oregon. North of the mountains is the John Day Basin, a structural and erosional depression containing great thicknesses of deformed and dissected sedimentary rocks. The John Day Uplands extend north from the John Day Basin and culminate in the Umatilla Mountains and Umatilla Plateau.

The *Wallowa-Seven Devils* section consists of two mountainous uplifts separated by a lower strip of basalt plain and the mighty canyon of Snake River.

The Wallowa Mountains are about 30 miles wide and contain the highest peaks (nearly 10,000 feet high) in northeastern Oregon. Near the center the mountains are a mass of old crystalline and sedimentary rocks, away from which dip the lava flows that originally formed a flat plain before the uplift of the range. In the Glacial Period the Wallowas were strongly eroded by ice; small remnant glaciers still exist, and the mountains contain the most alpine scenery of northeastern Oregon. Faults are common, and help to account for some precipitous slopes, for example on the north where the Wallowas descend to the Wallowa Valley. Gold has been mined in the southern Wallowas, for example at Cornucopia. There are occurrences of metals, especially copper, in the Snake River Canyon.

Across the Snake River in Idaho, west of the Salmon and Little Salmon rivers, are mountains of a character similar to that of the Wallowas. Between the Seven Devils and the Wallowas, the entire region was once buried by thousands of feet of lava. Then both the basalt and the two mountain areas were uplifted. This high, upwarped plateau attained elevations of 8000 feet or more, and has been severed by the great Snake River Canyon which for one stretch of nearly 30 miles, called Hells Canyon, averages nearly 6000 feet in depth (Plate 5A). This is the site of the projected Hells Canyon dam and power plant. Both the Wallowa and Seven Devils mountains are nearly untouched by highways, and few people live within these areas.

The *Tristate Uplands,* near the junctions of Idaho, Oregon, and Washington, are lower than the Blue, Seven Devils, and Wallowa mountains and higher than the Columbia Basin, but often a clear boundary is lacking. The Uplands are crossed by the 3000- to 4000-

feet-deep canyons of the Clearwater, Snake, Salmon, and Grande Ronde rivers and their tributaries. In general the uplands slope north and west toward the Columbia Basin, and the more gentle surfaces with good soil are devoted to wheat (Plate 4B). Sheep and cattle graze in the rugged portions.

HIGH LAVA PLAINS

The subprovince called the High Lava Plains is south of the Blue Mountains and Northern Rocky Mountains, and north of the Owyhee Upland and the Basin and Range Province. It extends as a curving zone, convex to the south, from Yellowstone Park across southern Idaho and much of Oregon to the Cascade Mountains. Throughout, the surface dominantly consists of young, flat-lying basalts, recent cinder cones, or intervolcanic sediments. The volcanic materials are much younger and generally less eroded than the lavas exposed elsewhere in the Columbia Intermontane Province. Furthermore, the area has been little deformed compared with the other subprovinces. The High Lava Plains can be conveniently divided into three parts from east to west: the Snake River Plain, Malheur-Boise, and Harney-High Desert sections. Where water is available and suitable soil has formed, irrigation has reclaimed large parts of the Snake River Plain and the Malheur-Boise sections. Much power is developed at sites along the Snake River.

The *Snake River Plain* is characterized by horizontal-lying, black basalt flows of recent (Quaternary) age that form a flat plain, marked in a few places by young cinder cones and mounds of scoriaceous basalt, as at the "Craters of the Moon." The basalt fills the trough of the Snake River downwarp. The plain is little dissected, and streams are scarce except for the Snake River that flows westerly near the southern border of the section. Erosion is generally in an initial phase, and subsurface seepage through the pervious basaltic rocks is a pronounced feature. That the Snake River is youthful is evidenced by the waterfalls, rapids, and steep canyon walls of its channel. The Snake River Plain slopes from about 6000 feet above the sea level on the east to about 3500 feet on the west. The northern and eastern boundaries are the Northern and Middle Rocky Mountains, respectively, against which the once-liquid lava rests. The southern boundary is determined by the presence of fault-block ranges that characterize the Basin and Range Province. The western boundary lies between Gooding and Glens Ferry. West from this line the country is lower, thick lake beds and other sediments are extensively interbedded with basalt flows, and the stage of erosion is mostly early maturity instead of early youth as on the Snake River Plain (Plate 5A).

MALHEUR-BOISE. This section includes adjacent areas in western Idaho and eastern Oregon. A considerable number of the underlying rocks are weakly resistant to erosion, and the section is generally maturely dissected except for some plainslike expanses protected by resistant basalt caprock. It is decidedly lower than surrounding regions. In altitude the section lies between about 2500 and 3500 feet. The western boundary is placed near the 119° meridian east of Malheur Lake because of the occurrence westward of the fresh lava and pumice that are characteristic of the Harney-High Desert.

The Harney-High Desert resembles the Snake River Plain in flatness, immaturity of erosion, desert climate, sparseness of vegetation, inadequacy of surface drainage, and recency of much of the lava flows, ash deposits, and numerous cinder cones. Except for the northwest corner near Bend, which is incised and drained by the Deschutes River, the region has few streams. Ephemeral lakes develop in season, and localized interior drainage is a feature, being directed mainly either into the Harney Basin south of Burns, Oregon, or into the Basin and Range Province. Malheur Lake in the Harney Basin is a playa that varies greatly in area, depending on the rainfall and runoff. Only small faults disturb the surface of the plain at a few localities. The elevation of the section is about 4500 feet above sea level. Southward the region grades into the Basin and Range Province, the boundary selected being that where individual ranges, separated by intermontane basins, become dominant features of the landscape. Grazing is the principal industry. The trading centers are few and are located near the edge of the section which throughout most of its extent supports only a few cattle and sheep ranches.

Along the western margin rainfall is adequate for ponderosa pine, and much timber is cut for the mills at Bend and other centers. Near Bend are numerous recent cinder cones and lava flows, among which are pockets of soil that, when irrigated, are suitable for potatoes and hay crops.

OWYHEE UPLAND

The Owyhee Upland is located in southeastern Oregon and southwestern Idaho and a little of northern Nevada. It consists of a high, warped plateau that stands well above adjoining areas and is characterized by older lavas and a greater degree of dissection than are present on the High Lava Plains. Rising above the plateau surface in Idaho are the Owyhee Mountains and South Mountain, about 20 miles apart. The Owyhee Mountains attain elevations of over 8000 feet above sea level and rise 4000 to 5000 feet above the bordering plains. Erosion has stripped away the lavas and exposed ancient mineral-bearing crystalline rock, which is surrounded by high cuestas of uneroded lava. The Owyhee River and its tributaries have cut deep canyons in their course across the high plateaus, and in Oregon this area is locally called the "Rimrock Country." Most of the Upland, which covers about 8000 square miles, drains into the Pacific Ocean.

HUMAN USE

The diversity of relief features, climate, and soils that exist in the Columbia Intermontane Province has naturally resulted in diverse industries and irregularities in distribution of population.

Mining within the area for metals is restricted to localities where old crystalline rocks have been exposed at the surface by erosion of the overlying basaltic flows or where the outcrops of the old rocks towered so high that the outpourings of lava never covered the exposures. Some gold placers have developed by erosion of gold-bearing quartz veins. Some pumice, crushed stone, gravel, and sand are used for construction. Diatomaceous earth is produced at several points, and a few opals of fair quality have been found deposited in holes of porous lava.

Timber is restricted to the higher plateaus and mountains and to the rainier part of the scablands in the northeastern section of the plateau near Spokane. The forests are utilized extensively in Oregon. The wooded mountains are also used for summer grazing, for fishing and hunting, and for resort purposes.

Soil has developed only on the old flows. The pumice and new rough lava have almost no soil and but little vegetation; they are useless for farming and of little value for grazing. The trees, if any, are likely to be juniper and of small value. Large areas where recent volcanic activity occurred in Idaho and Oregon are government owned.

Two types of agriculture are predominant in the Columbia Basin: (1) cash grain farming and (2) intensive irrigation agriculture. Dairying is important in some localities, and the drier and rough sections are some use for stock raising.

The principal cash grain areas, mainly wheat, are the Palouse Hills, Waterville Plateau, Tristate Uplands, and Deschutes Plateau, with minor areas of production elsewhere. The trading centers and farming population are rather evenly distributed over the wheat-growing sections, since the productivity of the land and its occupancy are fairly uniform.

The chief sections developed by irrigation are the flat desert plains and dry valleys that are favored by an adequate supply of water and a relatively long growing season. Major areas are the Snake River Plain in Idaho and the Yakima, Kittitas, and Wenatchee valleys within the zone of the Yakima Folds in Washington. Minor areas are the Umatilla district, around Walla Walla, Milton-Freewater, Kennewick, near Bend, Oregon, and the Spokane Valley. In the future, nearly a million acres in the Columbia Basin will be irrigated by the Grand Coulee Project. Orchard fruits, especially pears and apples, root crops, like potatoes and sugar beets, alfalfa, and small fruits and vegetables are the leading crops of the irrigated districts, although some wheat is raised, especially in southern Idaho.

Dairying is important in many of the irrigated areas and also on the fairly well-watered northern portion of the scablands near Spokane. The drier part of the scablands is the site of stock ranches for both sheep and cattle. The Harney-High Desert in Oregon and the drier parts of the Snake River Plain in Idaho support a scanty population of sheepmen and cattlemen where irrigation water is not available in quantities sufficient to attract intensive settlement and the rainfall is too small for dry farming. The Owyhee Uplands are almost wholly devoted to stock raising. In the dry parts of the province, the densely populated irrigated sections with their numerous trading centers and intensively cultivated small farms present a striking contrast to adjoining dry-farming and stock-raising country where the population may be less than one person per square mile.

THE BASIN AND RANGE PROVINCE

The Basin and Range Province extends into south Idaho and southern Oregon and is characterized by mountains formed by a series of faults extending generally in a north-south direction. The fault blocks have been uplifted to form asymmetric mountains with one face much steeper than the other. Lavas are characteristic of the higher elevations, whereas flat lake basins occupy the lower places. The steep faces of the fault blocks have been only partly dissected by erosion, showing the comparative recency of the earth movements. The depressed blocks between the uplifts are usually filled with debris washed from the adjoining mountains and mostly have interior drainage because they occur in a dry region. Towards the center of the basin shallow lakes occur, most of which are temporary playas. Goose Lake, Warner Lake, Summer Lake, and Abert Lake are among the larger and better known. During the rainier periods in the past all these lakes were much larger and deeper.

Among the fault-block mountains are Winter Ridge west of Summer Lake, Hart Mountain east of Warner Lake, Abert Rim east of Abert Lake, and, highest of all, Steens Mountain (Plate 5B). The chief exception to the dominance of interior drainage is the Klamath Lake region, which receives drainage from the Cascades and overflows to the Pacific, but the area has similar uplifted fault blocks and depressed basins and is therefore included with the Basin and Range Province.

The Basin and Range Province in Oregon has an elevation of 3000 to 5000 feet, with mountains rising to still greater heights. For example, Steens Mountain attains an elevation of nearly 10,000 feet. The lower country is treeless, and the ground is covered only with scattered sagebrush and clumps of bunchgrass, but scattered juniper appears at the 4000-foot elevation and open groves of ponderosa pine begin at about 5000 feet. Cycles of wet and dry years cause the increase and disappearance of lakes.[4]

In the extreme south-central part of Idaho, between the Rocky Mountains and the Owyhee Upland, are several fault-block mountains and associated basins which form a part of the Basin and Range Province and in the Albion Range reach an elevation of 10,450 feet.

In general both the Oregon and Idaho areas included within the Province are used for grazing rather than agriculture. Irrigation is necessary for farming, and in most of the country the supply of water is inadequate for extensive projects. Furthermore, part of the land in Oregon lies at such a high elevation that summer frosts preclude the successful growing of most crops except hay. The population is scanty, and little development can be expected in the future.

Southeastern Oregon has never been crossed by projected railroads because of its paucity of resources. Only branch lines touch the edge of this high desert area from the east at Burns; on the west, at Bend;

[4] For an excellent discussion of this subject, see *Rainfall and Tree Growth in the Great Basin*, by Ernst Antevs, American Geographic Society, New York, 1938. For the Harney Basin, see "Geology and Ground Water Resources of the Harney Basin, Oregon," A. M. Piper, T. W. Robinson and C. F. Park, Jr., *Water Supply Paper* 841, U. S. Geologic Survey, 1939.

on the south, at Lakeview and Winnemucca, Nevada. This was a frontier region when crossed by minor trails of the Oregon pioneers. It still has frontier conditions with few trading centers, schools, or churches. Harney County in southeastern Oregon is larger than Massachusetts. It has a population of one-half person per square mile, and sometimes it is hard to find the person.

SECTION 3. ROCKY MOUNTAIN PROVINCE

HARRY H. CALDWELL

The Rocky Mountain province functions as the Continental Divide separating the waters that flow to the Pacific from those that flow into the Atlantic Ocean. It also provides a major physical break between the landforms and climates on either side of it. Within its physical framework is a panorama of widely divergent geomorphic patterns. Some of the more spectacular features are located on its eastern peripheral zone in Yellowstone, Glacier, and Grand Teton national parks. Geologically, its nucleus consists of several batholiths, as immense masses of igneous rock are called, and a sizable extent of pre-Cambrian (very ancient) sediments and volcanic rocks that have been metamorphosed, folded, and faulted. The Idaho Batholith covers 16,000 square miles and is the largest known batholith in the United States. It provides much of the character that has been ascribed to the province. The mountain-forming forces that uplifted this area were associated with numerous concentrations of mineralization, largely on the margins of the batholith, though not necessarily at the same time as its intrusion. In the various periods of uplift the land level was raised sufficiently to produce a zone of high precipitation and forest vegetation in the Rocky Mountains, resulting in a landscape unlike the lower areas immediately east or west of the province.

Into this setting moved the hunter, trapper, miner, missionary, and trader, gradually replacing and displacing the Indian, and thereby paving the way for later development of the region. Mining, logging, grazing, agriculture, recreation, and water-power developments have dominated the major land-use patterns. Within each of these categories, many changes have occurred. The early gold and silver mining has been largely replaced by copper, lead, and zinc developments and more recently tungsten, antimony, magnesium, and even cobalt ores have been mined. In lumbering there have been comparable changes in the types of operation, species of trees cut, and kinds of fabrication. These changes have been brought about by population shifts, regional industrialization, and changes in logging technology and markets. The agricultural valleys include diverse types of farming, with irrigation increasing in most areas. There is also an extensive grazing economy on the drier slopes and in the open forest areas. The bases of forestry and agricultural land-use immediately reflect the climate and soil conditions; in turn, these are closely related to the configuration and elevation of the Rocky Mountains. The forces that produced mineralization are likewise related to the total orogenic picture.

Location and Extent

The northern Rocky Mountains are classed as an entity largely through the fact that they are separated from the southern Rockies and the Basin and Range Province of Utah and Nevada in their southern and eastern extent by wide, open plains or basin areas. The western edge of the province has a more complex relationship with neighboring areas and, with few exceptions, is not so clearly delineated. The southwestern edge of the huge intrusion of granite called the Idaho Batholith approximates a fairly evident province boundary, but the northwestern boundary is drawn along a physiographic break in the Okanogan Highlands that does not show a corresponding structural break. The eastern limit of the province includes those portions of Montana west of the Lewis Overthrust and extending southeast to include the fragmented areas underlain by very old and hard rocks (pre-Cambrian Age), the Boulder Batholith, and portions of the Yellowstone National Park volcanic area.

This broad province extends over 375 miles from east to west and as much as 600 miles south of the Canadian border. Its ranges are not as high as those in the Colorado Rockies though several peaks exceed 12,000 feet above sea level. In general the ranges rise from 2000 to 8000 feet above the surrounding land and differ from the other Rocky Mountain systems by being less extensively linear and by showing less marked structural control. In the middle or southern Rocky Mountains strong linear trends are apparent, and the main crests are "on structural uplifts generally flanked by outward-dipping strata making hogback foothills." [1] Fenneman regarded the northern Rockies "more like extensive plateaus, deeply and ruggedly carved by erosion" [2] (Plate 6B).

This description is particularly applicable to the central portion of Idaho, where the major streams provide a convenient means for de-

[1] N. M. Fenneman, *Physiography of Western United States*, McGraw-Hill Book Co., New York, 1931, p. 92.
[2] *Ibid.*, p. 93.

lineating the various divisions of the province. In this light, the maze of mountains immediately south of the Salmon River have been termed the Salmon River Mountains, and those north of that stream and south of the Clearwater River have been termed the Clearwater Mountains.

Numerous mountains illustrate lineation. To the north, the alignment is apparent in a series of roughly north-to-south depressions called "trenches," which separate the various ranges. Most of these illustrate both structural and glacial influence. The trenches are elongated downfaulted blocks (rift valleys) that have been modified by glacial erosion and deposition.

There are at least six well-defined long trenches in this area. Of these, the most pronounced is the Rocky Mountain Trench, which extends 1200 miles from northern British Columbia through the Flathead and Bitterroot valleys of Montana and possibly along the Lemhi valley of Idaho. It might be noted that portions of the Mackenzie, Fraser, Columbia, Flathead, and Bitterroot rivers occupy sections of this trench. Further westward are other trenches, such as the Kootenai, Purcell (Plate 6A), Pend Oreille, Colville, and Okanogan, wherein have developed the main arteries of north-south transportation, important agricultural valleys, and most of the trade centers. Where this area is traversed by the major east-west railroads there is a tendency for the railroads not only to cross from trench to trench but even to diverge from the most direct routes in order to connect these more fertile agricultural units. The trenches have been most influential in the occupance pattern of the province.

Geologic History

The Rocky Mountains are relatively young [3] compared to the older Appalachian Mountains in the eastern part of the United States and as such have existed for a relatively short period of geologic time.

Throughout much of its known geologic history the region was a trough, wherein thousands of feet of shallow-water sediments were washed in from the sides and deposited in the sea water that flooded into this depressed area.

The picture of lengthy, quiet deposition in the trough was finally upset when a series of rapid and intense periods of uplift began and the total breakup of the trough was initiated. In a sense, this might be termed the birth of the Rocky Mountains. It resulted in a great

---

[3] The term "young" is used in the geologic sense. The first appearance may be said to have occurred approximately 60 million years ago.

warping and breaking of the previously deposited sediments and the metamorphosis of many of the sediments.

After these initial disturbances, the area was uplifted several additional times, essentially vertically, with the uplift in the western portion of the province probably occurring before the major uplift in the eastern portion. Immediately at the close of the uplift periods and perhaps accompanying them, intrusions of molten material probably occurred. These now form the Idaho, Boulder, and other batholiths.

Associated with the various intrusions, emanations of mineral-bearing vapors and liquids were given off. These were concentrated along fault zones or bedding planes, resulting in some of the more important areas of metallic mineralization.

On the surface, the streams and drainage systems that developed were probably quite similar to the pre-existing patterns, for as the new land surface was formed the granitic core was progressively exposed by erosion. This condition pertained particularly to the central Idaho and southwestern Montana mountain areas that were the sites of the Idaho and Boulder batholiths. Stream patterns also followed along exposures of weak sediments. Such master streams as the Snake and Salmon rivers and their chief tributaries, which flow with little regard to older structures, were probably established and flowed much in the same direction as today though the location of the Snake River is partly related to a structural downwarp.

Uplift of the general region again occurred; in fact, some authors suggest several periods of re-uplift associated with warping, breaking, and tilting of the older erosion surfaces. Near-level surfaces, which some call "relict peneplains," can still be identified, particularly in the higher mountain areas of central and northern Idaho, where a concordance or matching of summit levels is often very impressive.

Some of the master streams were large enough to maintain their courses and cut down as rapidly as the land was raised, but many smaller streams were not able to keep pace with the uplift and became ineffective as new rivers were formed. A sizable number of the newer streams suggest joint guidance. As with the Salmon River, some of the master rivers "entrenched" themselves directly across the mountain mass, whereas others flowed in the differentially downwarped or trenchlike regions that have been previously mentioned and which were so magnificently developed in northern and eastern Idaho and western Montana. The old central erosion surface was dissected and carved up, and a very rugged and rough topography has thereby resulted.

Still later, volcanic activity again began in certain parts of the province, particularly in the southern and eastern areas. Volcanic fragmental material and great quantities of lava covered the land surface, filling and obscuring many of the valleys in their path and lapping up onto the flanks of the higher mountain sectors. Today the remnants of this activity are some 300 shield volcanic cones in Idaho that stand out mainly as butte and crater areas.

Alpine glaciers formed in the summit regions of the mountains and lobes of ice pushed their way down over part of the northern Rocky Mountain province, upsetting drainage patterns and scouring the landscape in one area while depositing its debris elsewhere. These ice masses, upon melting, have left many lakes and other evidences of their former existence (Plate 5B). In central Idaho, all the glaciers were of the valley type. They rarely moved more than 10 to 15 miles from their source areas.

Even during and since the periods of volcanic activity and glaciation some earth movements and readjustments have been taking place in the Rocky Mountains. All the complicated geologic history has united to give the complex result visible today. Every development has left its mark, and each has had a role in producing the contemporary scene.

Regional Subdivisions

The northern Rocky Mountains have contrasting relief features; some sections lack continuity of definite ranges, whereas in others there is a marked development of linear alignment and orientation of valley and highland systems.

CENTRAL IDAHO. This unit is dominated by the Idaho Batholith, which extends south to lava flows along the Snake River Valley. The batholith is composed mainly of quartz monzonite and granodiorite (granitic rocks) and is a composite structure consisting of numerous rock bodies of various ages. On the periphery of the batholith are numerous folds, and compressed, overturned, and broken rocks that show evidences of mineralization, although some of the mineral deposits may have been formed at a later period.

The little apparent lineation within the batholith is probably due to the large expanse of the granitic mass and the relative absence of sedimentary structures. Southeast of the main mass, the Lemhi and Lost River ranges have a very evident northwest-southeast alignment as a result of faulting, and these mountains rise high above the surrounding alluvial deposits.

To the west of the main mass are numerous granitic outliers that stand out above the surrounding lava. Some of these are quite extensive, such as the Palouse Range northeast of Moscow, Idaho, whereas others appear as small, isolated "steptoes" rising above the Palouse hills and described in the preceding section.

Central Idaho is traversed by dominantly westward flowing streams with pronounced V-shaped valleys. The Payette and Boise rivers drain the western and southwestern portions, while the Salmon River tributaries flow north and then west. To the north are the Clearwater River and its Selway and Lochsa tributaries. Drainage to the southeast consists of a series of streams such as the Lost and Little Lost rivers that flow over alluvial deposits only to disappear into porous Snake River lavas.

WESTERN WYOMING. Along the eastern border of Idaho and extending into adjacent western Wyoming are several noteworthy physiographic phenomena that include Yellowstone and Grand Teton national parks as well as a series of overthrust mountains further south. In this structural complex are fertile intermontane valley lands and rugged, glaciated mountain peaks.

In 1872 Yellowstone National Park was created in western Wyoming and adjacent portions of Idaho and Montana to preserve for the public the spectacular 3000 geysers and hot springs. The park is characterized by an extensive lava plateau, several volcanic peaks, numerous hot-spring terraces, and many geysers. In the central portion of the park is Yellowstone Lake, a fresh-water body drained by the Yellowstone River that cuts into the multicolored volcanic debris and plunges into a canyon about 1200 feet deep, forming the Grand Canyon of the Yellowstone River.

To the south is Grand Teton National Park, wholly within Wyoming, which contains some of the most "alpine-appearing" scenery in the country (Plate 7A). Rugged, more or less north-south trending ranges, made up of contorted, broken, and highly thrusted strata, extend northward to the volcanic, plateaulike basin area of Yellowstone National Park.

SOUTHWESTERN MONTANA. East of the Bitterroot Mountains, the mountains of Montana are relatively small masses separated by basins filled with sediments. Some of the ranges are composed of very old metamorphosed and uplifted sediments. In the highly mineralized Butte-Helena district the major feature is the Boulder Batholith, a huge intrusion of granular igneous rock. This intrusive mass is generally considered a probable source of the metal deposits that made Butte into one of the greatest copper camps in the world.

The Butte area proper is located in a basin enclosed on three sides by the sinuous line of the Continental Divide. South of the Butte district and west of the Yellowstone River are the basins of the Jefferson, Madison, and Gallatin rivers that join near Three Forks, Montana, to form the Missouri River. The intervening divides are known respectively as the Jefferson, Madison, and Gallatin ranges; each range bearing the name of the river on its west side. The fertile river valleys in this district are used for agriculture, and the terraces are used for grazing. Alder Gulch in the Jefferson Range was once a thriving gold camp, giving rise to Virginia City, the capital of Montana until 1874. Today, Virginia City, rebuilt along its former lines, thrives as a major summer tourist attraction in southwestern Montana.

NORTHERN IDAHO AND NORTHWESTERN MONTANA. The bedrock of northern Idaho and northwestern Montana is dominantly of sedimentary origin. Although granitic rocks are exposed in some isolated areas and probably underlie the sediments in much of the region, the relief features in this section are those characteristically developed in stratified materials.

The original sediments seem to have been more resistant to warping and folding by thrusting stresses than in other areas of the province. Rather, they tended to break and rupture and great blocks of the earth's crust were pushed over one another during the application of intense compressional force. The great Lewis Overthrust along the east front of Glacier Park and other extensive, north-south trending faults were formed as major structural features in the eastern part of this region. On the other hand, there are also numerous faults in the area east of Coeur d'Alene, Idaho, with almost an east-west orientation.

The Lewis Overthrust resulted in old rocks' being pushed up and forced to the east over younger rocks for a distance of approximately 25 miles. An exceptional example of this development is revealed by Chief Mountain (Plate 6A). The upper portion of the mountain is composed of ancient limestone, which rests on much younger shale formations. The lateral movement pushed more resistant rocks over softer materials which has resulted in precipitous eastern walls and no foothills along the Glacier National Park-Great Plains line of contact.

Another interesting structural feature is the Osburn Fault district in northern Idaho about 30 miles north of the exposed north end of the Idaho Batholith This is a zone of large faults which trend east to west. The largest and best known of these is the Osburn Fault, though most of them dominate zones of fractured rock and are the chief localizers of ore in north Idaho. The Osburn Fault has been mapped for 90 miles east-southeast of Coeur d'Alene Lake but it is probably much longer, for its course approximately coincides with an old valley extending from Spokane, Washington, to Deer Lodge, Montana, a distance of 300 miles.[4] Igneous intrusion and mineralization have been largely localized along the course of the Osburn Fault; for example, the silver-lead-zinc Coeur d'Alene mining district around the towns of Kellogg and Wallace, Idaho, is closely associated with it.

In addition to the structural features already noted, the landforms of this area have been greatly modified through glaciation. Great glaciers, both as ice sheets from the north and as mountain types descending from the high divide area, extensively changed pre-existing land forms. Mountain masses were scoured and cut, valleys were choked with debris, and old drainage systems were readjusted. The jagged peaks, wide U-shaped valleys, and numerous lakes, large and small, serve as evidence of this glacial activity. Of such lakes, four at least deserve special mention. They are the Coeur d'Alene, Pend Oreille, and Priest lakes of far northern Idaho, and Flathead Lake in Montana, some of which occupy sections of the previously discussed trenches. A large glacial outwash plain occupies the area immediately northwest of Lake Coeur d'Alene and the northern rim of the Spokane Valley. In the outwash area stone fences and house foundations have been built with water-worn glacial boulders, producing a landscape appearance not unlike certain portions of glaciated New England.

OKANOGAN HIGHLANDS. . The term Okanogan Highlands is applied to the Rocky Mountains in northeastern Washington, north of the Spokane-Columbia rivers and between the Cascades and the Pend Oreille Valley. Like the rest of the Rockies, this region also contains an old, uplifted erosion surface considerably dissected by streams and glaciers. The summit levels of the Okanogans have an altitude of 4000 or 5000 feet, above which rise rounded summits to elevations of over 7000 feet. These higher summits suggest possible monadnocks on an old peneplain and include such mountains as Calispel Peak, Moses Peak, Mt. Spokane, and Old Dominion Mountain. The bedrock consists of some lava and large areas of granite, much metamorphic rock, and important exposures of sediments, including slates

---

[4] F. C. Calkins and E. L. Jones, Jr., "Economic Geology of the Region around Mullen, Idaho, and Saltese, Montana," *U. S. Geological Survey Bull.* 540 (1913), pp. 9, 16.

and limestone. Mineral deposits, especially of lead, zinc, silver, and gold, are widely distributed. Limestone is quarried for cement rock at Metaline and for lime products near Marcus, and important deposits of clay are utilized at Clayton. The world's largest known deposit of magnesite occurs in the mountains a few miles west of Chewelah, where a calcining plant is located.

The most notable features of the Okanogan Highlands are the prominent north-south running trenches previously mentioned. Starting from the west, the larger depressions are (1) Okanogan; (2) San Poil-Upper Kettle Valley; (3) Columbia-Lower Kettle River Valley; (4) Colville Valley, with its extension north to the Columbia through Echo Valley; and (5) the Pend Oreille Valley. East of the Pend Oreille Valley is a southward extension of the Selkirk Range of Canada. All the important towns and most of the farms and ranches are located in the trenches. Here are the areas of level land, good soils, and longer growing seasons. In the trenches, farming is far more favorable than on the uplands. Towns are generally situated in a main valley where side valleys converge, thereby favoring the development of extensive trading areas. Omak, Okanogan, and Tonasket in the Okanogan Valley, Chewelah and Colville in the Colville Valley, and Newport and Ione in the Pend Oreille Valley are examples.

REFERENCES

Anderson, A. L., "Role of the Idaho Batholith during the Laramide Orogeny," *Economic Geology*, Vol. 43 (1948), pp. 84–99.

Calkins, F. C., and Jones, E. F., Jr., "Economic Geology of the Region around Mullen, Idaho and Saltese, Montana," *U. S. Geological Survey Bull.* 540 (1913).

Campbell, M. R., "The Glacier National Park, A Popular Guide to Its Geology and Scenery," *U. S. Geological Survey Bull.* 600 (1914).

Eardley, A. J., *Structural Geology of North America*, Harper & Bros., New York, 1951.

Eldridge, G. H., "A Geologic Reconnaissance across Idaho," *U. S. Geological Survey, 16th Ann. Report*, Part II (1895).

Fenneman, N. M., *Physiography of Western United States*, McGraw-Hill Book Co., New York, 1931.

Rhodenbaugh, E. F., *Sketches of Idaho Geology*, Boise, Idaho, 1953.

SECTION 4. SOUTHERN BRITISH COLUMBIA

N. F. G. DAVIS
REVISED BY J. LEWIS ROBINSON

Southern British Columbia has a diverse topography, characterized by high mountains, deep valleys, and gently undulating country. Rugged mountains rise on either side of a high central plateau, which narrows toward the international boundary. East of the plateau are the Columbia and Rocky systems, separated by the Rocky Mountain Trench. On the west are the Coast Mountains and the partly submerged Vancouver Island Mountains.

The Cascades extend into southern British Columbia for about 100 miles, where they comprise the deeply dissected Skagit, Hozomeen, and other ranges that lie between the lower part of the Fraser River Valley and the Interior Plateau. The Coast Mountains of British Columbia are orographically the continuation of the Cascades northward from the lower Fraser Valley. This deep valley, one of a number which cut right across the Coast Mountains, is a convenient line of division; for although the ranges north of the Fraser River Valley have a structure and history similar to the Northern Cascades, they differ in that they are bounded on the west by the Pacific Ocean. The Puget Sound lowland between the Cascades and the Olympics in Washington becomes the Inside Passage between the Coast Mountains and Insular Mountains of British Columbia. The Coast Mountains are deeply dissected and glaciated. In southern British Columbia elevations rarely exceed 9000 feet; but Mt. Waddington, the highest peak, rises to 13,260 feet.

Pacific Coast Mountains of Canada

West slopes of the Coast Mountains descend steeply into the Pacific. The coast line has a drowned appearance, and is deeply indented by arms of the sea in a reticulating (netlike) pattern of northwest- and northeast-trending stretches of fiord which meet at abrupt angles. The beauty of this fiord coast rivals that of Norway. Thick stands of almost impenetrable timber cover the slopes to over 4000 feet elevation. Excessive rainfall on the west side and great ice-field reservoirs inland feed rivers capable of great hydroelectric-power development. Valleys are deep and U-shaped in transverse profile. In longitudinal profile the valleys are steep at their heads and gentle or even reversed over the rest of their lengths. Some have been overdeepened by glacial action near their mouths, and have floors as much as 1000 feet below sea level. The Fraser and a few other valleys had established their courses before the last uplift of the land and now maintain routes across the ranges.

The mountains of the Vancouver and Queen Charlotte islands have a topography like that of the Coast Mountains, but they are not as high. Elevations of 4000 to 5000 feet are usual, and only a few mountains exceed 6000 feet. These mountains are really a northward extension of the Coast Range of Oregon and Washington. Narrow coastal plains lie on the east and southeast sides of Vancouver Island. Here there is agricultural development, especially around Courtney, Duncan, and on the Saanich peninsula north of Victoria.

The floodplain of the Fraser River from Hope, 90 miles inland, to its mouth including the delta, makes an area of about 1000 square miles of rich, flat land. Systems of dykes and drainage canals are an important factor in the development.

Interior Plateau

East of the Cascade and Coast Mountains lies the Interior Plateau region of British Columbia. For the most part the transition from the coastal mountains to the plateau is abrupt, but in places there is a zone 10 to 15 miles wide of gradually falling ridges. In the southern part, where it is called the Fraser Plateau, the elevation is 4000 to 5000 feet. The surface is flat or gently undulating, higher near the bordering mountains and sloping inward. Isolated mountain masses, either erosional remnants or volcanic accumulations, rise 2000 to 3000 feet above the plateau. Much of the flat surface is made by volcanic flows and in this respect resembles the Columbia Basin south of the border. This surface is cut by trenchlike valleys (for example, the Fraser, Thompson, and Okanagan) which lie 2000 feet or more below the plateau uplands. Normal alluvial terraces occur in these valleys; but many terraces are remnants of glacial deposition, both on a large scale in lakes formed by ice damming and on a small scale by tributary deposition when large glaciers filled the main valleys. Many of the deep valleys are still occupied by lakes, for example, Kamloops and Okanagan lakes. Flat lands suitable for agriculture or grazing are found on the valley floors, on the terraces, and on the upland between the valleys. The southern part of the plateau region has large tracts covered by sagebrush and bunchgrass, but irrigation can be prac-

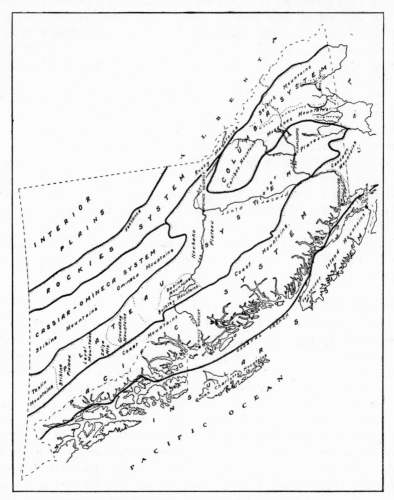

Fig. 7. Physiographic divisions of British Columbia.

ticed in some of the valleys. For the most part transportation routes follow the valleys, and thus travelers get the impression that the region is one of considerable relief. At the international boundary, mountain ranges narrow this plateau to the width of the Okanagan Valley.

Columbia System

Between the Interior Plateau of British Columbia and the Rocky Mountains lies a rugged mass of mountainous country called the Columbia System. Deep longitudinal valleys divide this system into four mountain groups. The Cariboo Mountains on the northwest are separated from the Monashee Mountains to the east and south by the deep valley of the North Thompson River and its tributary, Albreda River. The Monashee Mountains are separated from the Selkirk Mountains to the east by the south-flowing part of the Columbia River, which along its course forms the Arrow Lakes. Southeast of the Selkirk Mountains, and east of the trough occupied by the Kootenay Lake, are the rugged, jagged peaks of the Purcell Range. All four groups are bounded on the northeast by the Rocky Mountain Trench. These mountain groups are older than the Rockies, and, although their ranges do not show as distinct a parallelism as the Rockies, they present a formidable barrier to penetration, and their crests are fretted and serrated by glacial action. Some of the peaks reach elevations of over 11,000 feet, and extensive areas over 8000 feet have alpine characteristics. Most of the surface, however, consists of heavily wooded slopes between 2000 and 7000 feet in elevation, mantled in many places by thick deposits of drift. In general, the ranges maintain a northwest trend and present steep slopes both eastward and westward. The forest cover almost duplicates the thick growth of the Coast Mountains and helps make these mountains more inaccessible than the Rockies. The deep longitudinal valleys show the results of both glacial erosion and deposition, and many are occupied by long, narrow lakes such as the Kootenay and the Slocan. At the international boundary the Monashee Mountains can be divided into a number of units, the Midway, Christina, and Rossland ranges, which are members of the Okanogan highlands to the south in Washington. The Selkirk Mountains extend into Washington, Idaho, and Montana. Flat land suitable for agriculture is scarce in this region and is confined to deltas and lake shores, terraces, and floodplains of the large valleys.

The Canadian Rockies

The Rocky Mountain Trench is one of the most outstanding and persistent relief features of British Columbia. It extends in a northwesterly direction from the international boundary for over 1000 miles, being traced into Yukon Territory, and it varies from 2 or 3

miles to as much as 10 miles in width. The bottom of this great
valley has a maximum elevation of 2700 feet and is occupied by the
headwaters of the Kootenay River, flowing south, the Columbia River,
flowing north, and the Fraser River, flowing north. All these rivers
finally reach the Pacific Ocean. The Trench has a complicated structural history, which in many parts is obscured by heavy glacial
deposition. In some places, particularly from Windermere and
Columbia lakes south, the flat valley floor and wide bench lands along
the sides serve as agricultural and range country.

The Rocky Mountains are a series of parallel, northwest-trending
ranges with elevations of 7000 to 13,000 feet. Mt. Robson, the highest peak, has an elevation of 12,972 feet. Rising gradually from trough-
like valleys in the west and falling off abruptly in the east, the ranges
resemble gigantic breakers. Glaciation has serrated the crests; and
the ice, which has remained on the higher peaks, culminates in the
Columbia ice field between the Canadian Pacific and Canadian National railways. This large area of partly ice-covered alpine scenery
is one of the most popular tourist-visited areas in Canada (Plate 7A).
The jagged peaks, beautiful waterfalls, and colorful valleys of Banff
and Jasper national parks are alpine scenery at its best.

Transverse valleys, inherited from a premountain-building cycle of
erosion, penetrate the ranges. Three such valleys serve as passes for
the transcontinental railways: the Yellow Head, between the Fraser
and Athabasca rivers, at an elevation of 3720 feet; the Kicking Horse,
between the Kicking Horse and Bow rivers, at an elevation of 5372
feet; and the Crowsnest, between the Old Man River and Kootenay
drainage, at an elevation of 4459 feet.

The main features of the southern part of the Canadian Rockies
are due to crustal movements and stream erosion. Valley glaciers
have greatly modified the details of the higher uplands, and most
lakes are due to damming by glacial deposition. Numerous drainage
changes have resulted from movement of the earth, stream erosion,
and glacial deposits. The west sides of the ranges carry thick forest,
but the steep east slopes are not as thickly timbered and grasslands
extend into the mountain valleys on the east.

Glaciation

The geological story of southern British Columbia resembles that
of the United States south of the forty-ninth parallel in its sediments,

intrusive and volcanic rock, the periods of uplift and erosion, and in the recent glaciation that has affected the region.

Glaciers have affected the whole of southern British Columbia up to elevations of at least 6500 feet. Thus only ridges and peaks above that level protruded above the ice. The ice extended from the mountain regions on both sides of the Interior Plateau and completely covered that area. Stratified glaciofluvial deposits were laid down in the valley bottoms and unassorted drift mantles the slopes. On the coast near Vancouver at least 1000 feet of Pleistocene deposits were laid down. They consist of two glacial-drift deposits separated by stratified sands and clays. Interglacial beds are also found in the interior. Postglacial uplift of as much as 1000 feet is shown by elevated beaches along the coast, by the deep erosion of the glaciofluvial deposits, leaving them as hanging terraces in the Interior Plateau valleys, and by the cutting of canyons by rivers circumventing glacial plugging of their valleys.

In the Coast Mountains north of Vancouver, and in a few places on the Interior Plateau, recent volcanics occur. They overlie till and occupy postglacial canyons.

Land Use

Furs were the first natural resource exported from British Columbia. This trade was followed a century ago by the recovery of gold from placers in the Cariboo region, and soon other discoveries of the precious metal were made. Logging first began along the accessible coast, spreading to the interior after the construction of railroads. The development of copper, lead, zinc, and other minerals has been rapid after transportation became available. Fishing is a major industry at coastal points.

For agriculture the province has many handicaps. Northern British Columbia experiences frequent summer frosts, making it climatically unsuited for most crops. There is little cultivation along the coast because of the heavy rainfall, leached soils, forests, and scarcity of level land. Interior valleys have small rainfall, and irrigation may be necessary for successful farming. Furthermore, areas of arable land are widely scattered and often consist of isolated plots squeezed in between mountain ranges. Slightly over 4 million acres (2 per cent of the area) are used for agriculture, a little above 1 million acres being cultivated. The grazing of cattle and sheep is the chief industry on untilled land.

Four agricultural districts are recognized: the coastal valleys; the southern interior valleys; the Nechako district in the north-central interior; and the Peace River Block.[1] Of 370,000 acres in cultivation in the coastal valleys, about 95 per cent is located in the Lower Fraser Valley and the lowlands on southern Vancouver Island. The southern interior valleys have 420,000 acres of improved land, of which the Okanagan Valley has 160,000 acres. There are 90,000 acres under cultivation in the Nechako district and 200,000 in the Peace River Block. Dairying, hay, fruits, vegetables, and flowers are typical of the Fraser Valley and around Victoria. Orchard and small fruits, vegetables and seeds, dairying and small grains are characteristic of the southern interior valleys. About one-third of the cultivated land in the Okanagan Valley is irrigated. Unimproved land is used for grazing, and the livestock are taken to mountain pastures in the summer. The Peace River area is noted for its wheat, and the Nechako area produces excellent legume seed.

[1] Donald Kerr, "The Physical Basis of Agriculture in British Columbia," *Economic Geography*, Vol. 28, pp. 229–239, July, 1952.

CHAPTER

6

Climates of the
Pacific Northwest[1]

PHIL E. CHURCH

Climate is perhaps the most important environmental factor in the Pacific Northwest. Even casual observation indicates that the climatic elements throughout the region have obviously affected the natural vegetation, development of relief features, kinds of crops, and numerous human activities. As in the rest of the world, a number of controls combine to determine the characteristics of the climate in this area. Of these the most important are latitude, altitude, relation of land and water masses, ocean currents, mountain barriers, frequency and intensity of storms, frequency and trajectories of air masses, and the local topography. Within an area where one type of climate should be expected, the controls may vary so that a number of types result, though they all somewhat resemble the basic climate (Fig. 8).

Classification

The general location of the Pacific Northwest, on the windward coast in midlatitudes, is such that the characteristics of the climatic elements combine to give a type of climate known as "western margin cool temperate" (Herbertson), or "cool marine" (Koeppe), or "western margins of continents in higher middle latitudes" (Jones and Whittlesey), or "Csb" (Koeppen), or "BC's" (Thornthwaite). The essential features, as denoted by these classifications, are a small annual range of temperature for the latitude, an abundant precipitation, most of which comes during the rather mild winter, a relatively cool sum-

[1] The writer wishes to acknowledge the helpful assistance of Professor N. F. G. Davis, University of British Columbia, Vancouver, B. C.

All data have been taken from the U. S. Weather Bureau, Climatic Summary by Sections (1, 2, 3, 4, 5, 6, and 7), from "Establishment of Stations up to 1930."

mer, a long frost-free season, and wind from off the ocean nearly all year. This type may be considered as the main or basic climate for the whole area. Its best development is along the coast; it shows increasing degeneration from the basic type in direct proportion to increasing distance from the coast.

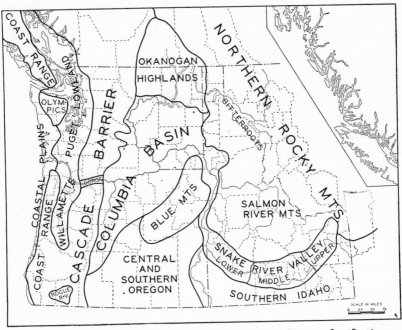

FIG. 8. Northwest physiographic divisions used in climatic classification.

Controls

The latitude determines the seasonal cycle and total amount of heat to be received from the sun. This should yield a mean annual temperature of about 42°,[2] and January and July means of 19° and 65°, respectively, at 50° north latitude. But the ocean and its currents and the air masses from over the ocean prevent the attainment of the expected average temperatures. It has been shown by Gerlach[3] that air masses from off the Pacific Ocean are present over Seattle no less

[2] All temperatures are given on the Fahrenheit scale.

[3] Arch C. Gerlach, "Distribution of Air Mass Types and Frequency of Change in the Western United States during 1937–1938," *Monthly Weather Review*, Vol. 66, 1938.

than 80 per cent of a normal year. As the air masses flow eastward, their properties are modified and changed by the parallel, high, and continuous mountain ranges which lie athwart the general trajectory of air flow.

The latitudinal shift of the wind belts during the course of the year results in numerous extratropical cyclones in this latitude during the winter, but during the summer the weather is controlled by the Pacific High; thus the summers are sunny whereas the winters are cloudy. In addition to the main mountain ranges, the local topography allows marked differences of weather, particularly temperature, to occur within short distances. This is especially true during calm, clear weather.

The ocean to windward affects the temperature and moisture content of the air traveling across it, the air bringing those acquired characteristics to the land. For this region, the control which is next most effective is the mountain barriers which stand so high that the temperatures are materially reduced on their slopes, moisture is wrung from the air on the windward side, and dynamic warming is permitted on the lee side. Furthermore, the mountains obstruct the flow and allow only the potentially warmer air from aloft to move to leeward. All these changes occur downwind.

TEMPERATURE

Mean Annual Temperatures

Along the west coast there is little difference in the mean annual temperatures (Fig. 9). From Brookings, Oregon (approximately 42° north latitude), to Prince Rupert (approximately 55° north latitude), a difference of 13° of latitude, 900 land miles, the mean annual decreases but little more than 7°, to 45° at the latter station. This temperature difference is about the same as that experienced in a difference of 2000 feet in the mountains. The flat north-south temperature gradient, owing to wind off the ocean, is in sharp contrast to that along the east coast, where the mean annual changes about 1° per 60 miles.

Inland the mean temperatures are more dependent upon altitude, effect of the mountain barriers, and distance from the ocean. Inland the mean temperatures decrease progressively. The lowlands west of the Cascades, the Columbia Basin below 1000 feet, the Rogue River Valley, and the Lower Snake Plains all enjoy temperatures above 50°.

The remaining subareas are too high or subjected to too protracted cold winters to average above 50°

The Columbia Basin between 1000 and 3500 feet, the Middle Snake Plains, southern and eastern Oregon, the Coastal Range in Oregon, and Idaho bordering on the Columbia Basin are the largest areas that

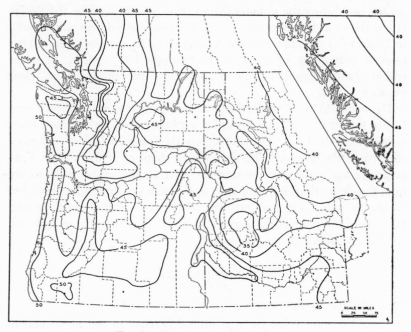

FIG. 9.   Temperatures of Northwest.

have mean temperatures between 50° and 45°. The Cascades (above 2500 feet), a portion of central Oregon (above 4000 feet), the Upper Snake Plain, and mountainous Idaho, Montana, and British Columbia largely experience mean temperatures between 45° and 40°. The highest mountains and high mountain valleys in Idaho and Montana average below 40°.

Large differences in temperature are found within short distances where the altitudinal difference is appreciable. Between Longmire and Paradise Inn (altitude difference 2800 feet) the mean drops from 44° to 38°.

Sea-Level Temperatures

By correcting the temperature (Fig. 10) for the altitude of each station above sea level,[4] the effect of the ocean and the mountains on the mean temperature may be shown. Unlike the actual mean annual temperature map, the sea-level isothermal map portrays an increase

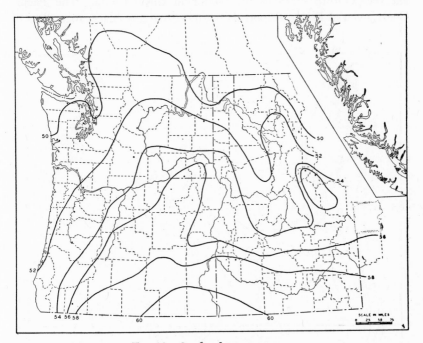

FIG. 10. Sea-level temperatures.

of temperature from coast to interior. The southwest trend of the isotherms along the coast indicates that the ocean exerts a cooling which is dominant from March to November.[5] The north and northeastward alignment of the isotherms on the lee side (east) of all major mountain ranges illustrates the barrier effect of the mountains in preventing the flow of cool ocean air during the warm season.

[4] For computing sea-level temperature 0.9° F. for each 330 feet (0.5° C. per 100 meters) was added (see C. F. Brooks, A. J. Conner, and Others, *Climatic Maps of North America*, Harvard University Press, Cambridge, Mass., 1936).

[5] *Ibid.*, Maps 3, 4, and 5.

January Mean

The temperature distribution during January (Fig. 11) shows a great similarity to that of the mean annual, that is, a rapid decrease of temperature eastward and very little increase southward. Within the latitudinal distance there is a difference of only 12°, a remarkably flat temperature gradient for winter in this latitude. The Pacific Coast, even at Prince Rupert, is warmer than any place, regardless of

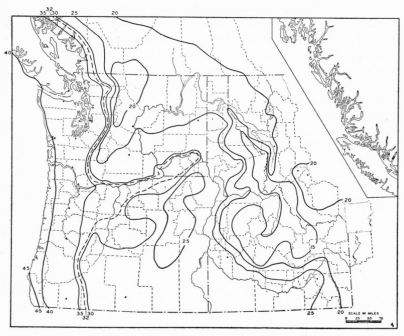

Fig. 11. January mean.

latitude, east of the Cascade barrier. The greatest change of temperature occurs along the windward slopes of the mountains whereas, on the lee side, there is little difference in temperature from the tops of the mountains to the floor of the valley below. This is especially true along the eastern flank of the Cascades. It is caused by an inversion of temperature in the cold, dry air in valleys. It is a common occurrence in winter to find a decrease of temperature as one ascends on the west side of the Cascades and a continued decrease of temperature as one descends on the east side.

Below 1000 feet in the Columbia Basin the mean temperature is above freezing. This is largely due to the low altitude and secondarily to the easy access, through the Columbia Gorge, of relatively warm air from the ocean.

The larger valleys do not show such pronounced inversions, and therefore have lower mean January temperature than the high, small enclosed valleys of Idaho and Montana.

A measure of the continentality of the eastern part of the region is illustrated by the Snake Valley in Idaho. In the western part (altitude between 2000 and 3000 feet) the mean temperature is from 25° to 29°, in the middle part (3000 to 4000 feet) the temperature is between 25° and 20°, and in the eastern section (above 4000 feet) the temperature is below 20°.

Lowest Temperatures Recorded

The coldest air (Fig. 12) comes from a traveling polar anticyclone which moves along the eastern edge of this area or to the east of the

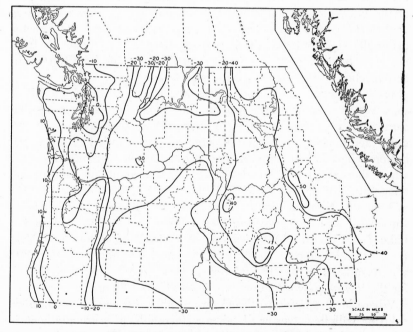

FIG. 12.   Lowest temperatures recorded.

great chain of the Rockies. This produces a pressure gradient which causes cold, dry, clear air to flow southwestward. Though this happens a number of times each winter, not always does such a flow cover the whole area. The frequency of cold flows decreases from northeast to southwest.[6] As the air flows toward lower latitudes it passes over a surface which is warmer; therefore, the minima temperatures are higher along the California-Nevada border. The marine air along the coast keeps surface temperatures so high during the winter (between 40° and 45°) that the cold air is warmed rapidly as it arrives there. Thus, the coast has relatively high minima temperatures.

The most pronounced factor in warming the air in its western motion, however, is the effect of the mountain barriers. Because of the north-south alignment of the mountain ranges only the potentially warmer air, which is above the top of the continuous ranges, can flow over. This air in its descent on the westward slope is then heated dynamically (approximately 5.5° per 1000 feet). The higher the mountain the warmer (potential temperature) the air that can flow over and the greater the descent. By damming off the bottom part of the polar air, the mountains thereby increase the temperature as well as reduce the amount of air flowing southwestward. This factor materially contributes to the decreasing frequency of polar air from northeast to southwest. During a normal winter, air from the northeast reaches Seattle about half a dozen times.

Whenever clear, dry air covers the area it is preceded by a fall of snow which remains on the ground, thus producing the best possible surface for nighttime radiation to lower the air temperature. Inversions then develop, and low temperatures are recorded at the valley bottom. The lowest temperatures are in the most protected valleys where there is no wind to stir the air. This accounts for the extreme temperatures of Bowen (−55°), Dillon (−52°), and Fortine (−49°) in Montana; New Meadows (−49°) and Obsidian (−44°) in Idaho; Cusick (−36°), Stockdill Ranch—near Winthrop—(−33°), Bumping Lake (−31°), and Wenatchee (−29°) in Washington; and Vale (−39°) and Wallowa (−38°) in Oregon. A temperature of −70° was recorded Jan. 20, 1954, at Rogers Pass, 40 miles north of Helena for the lowest known temperature in the United States.

Where low gaps form a break in an otherwise continuous barrier, cold air will flow westward when a favorable pressure gradient is present. The Columbia Gorge is a major gap of low altitude across the Cascades. The lowest temperatures west of the Cascades, Longview (−20°), are immediately tributary to the Gorge, and greater warmth is found in all directions from the south through the west to

[6] Arch C. Gerlach, *loc. cit.*

the north of this orifice. Wind of destructive velocity is often observed in the gorge when the air drains westward.[7,8]

Of lesser influence and effectiveness is the gap in the Fraser River in lower British Columbia. The air drainage basin of this valley is much smaller than that of the Columbia Basin. Nevertheless, with favorable pressure, cold air flows out as far as Georgia Strait and the San Juan Archipelago and accounts for the low minima (below 0°) in the northern part of the Puget Sound Lowland and southern British Columbia.

July Mean

During this month (Fig. 13) the reverse condition from that of midwinter is present; that is, there is an increase of temperature from

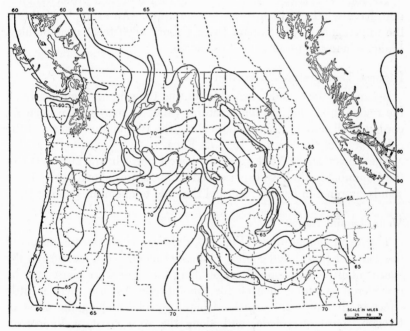

FIG. 13. July mean.

west to east. This amounts to more than 15° from the coast to the Lower Snake Valley, though the latter is more than 2000 feet high.

[7] D. C. Cameron, "Easterly Gales in the Columbia River Gorge," *Monthly Weather Review*, Vol. 59, 1931.

[8] A. B. Carpenter, "Subsidence in Maritime Air over the Columbia and Snake River Basins," *Monthly Weather Review*, Vol. 64, 1936.

The difference from coast to inland is largely owing to the blocking mountains and to the aridity of the summer air which permits high daytime maxima.

The immediate coast and adjacent portions of the Puget Sound Lowlands have temperatures below 60°, the greater part of the Puget Sound Lowlands have temperatures below 65°, but the Willamette and Rogue River valleys are between 65° and 70°. All the Columbia Basin, central and southern Oregon, and the Snake Valley are between 65° and 70°. In western Montana the temperatures are well above 65°.

All the higher mountain ranges, the Cascades, Olympics, Coast Ranges, and Rockies, have means of 65° or less. These lower temperatures are solely the result of, and dependent upon, altitude.

The high, enclosed, narrow valleys, by reason of their protected location, have relatively high mean temperatures. An example of this is the upper part of the Salmon River (above 6000 feet) near Stanley, Idaho, where the mean is well below 60°.

Highest Temperatures Recorded

Because of the usually clear skies during the summer over nearly all the region, high maxima temperatures (100° or more) have been recorded at all stations, except those along the Washington coast and the cold waters of the Strait of Juan de Fuca.

The Lower Snake Valley and the lowest part (below 2000 feet) of the Columbia Basin have experienced temperatures above 110°. Boise stands supreme in having recorded the only temperatures above 120°.

Mean Annual Range

The mean annual range (Fig. 14), difference between the means of the warmest (July) and coldest (January) months, is a measure of the continentality. The annual range along the immediate coast may be considered as purely marine for this latitude because there is little effect of the continent expressed here, especially along the coast of Oregon, south of Toledo, and along the west coast of Vancouver Island, north of Estevan. Along the latter portion of the coast the range is between 18° and 19° and along the former about 15°.

Eastward from the coast the annual range increases to the maximum amount of more than 50° in the middle Snake Valley. The Coast Range of Oregon and the Cascades are marked by an especially steep gradient, again illustrating the effect of the barrier control. Though wintertime temperatures in the topographically lowest parts of the

Columbia Basin are nearly those found along the coast, high summer temperatures produce an annual range of more than 40°. In the higher parts of the interior basins the range is about 45°, though central Oregon, by reason of a somewhat lower latitude, has a range of nearer 40°. This amount, more than double that along the coast, may be considered as a continental range.

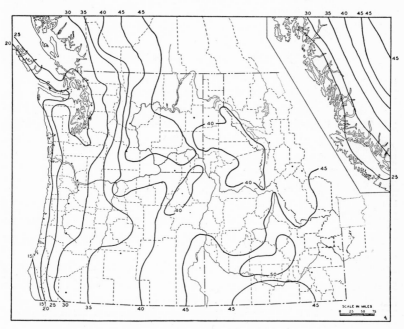

FIG. 14. Mean annual range.

Last Killing Frost in Spring

Within the region are wide differences of the average date of the last killing frost in spring (Fig. 15). The station extremes are February 11 at Tatoosh Island and June 28 at Stockdill. The primary controls determining the date for each station are altitude and exposure, except along the coast and the littoral adjacent to the inland waters. Isolines of the average dates, therefore, closely parallel the contour lines.

Along the coast marked differences occur, depending on the distance from the Pacific. A few miles produces differences of a week to a month. North Head, Washington, on the coast, is separated from Astoria by only 10 miles and yet the frost date of the latter is March 8 and the former February 17. On the lee side of the inland waters of Washington the last frost generally comes before April 1 along the immediate shore, but inland a few miles and below 1000 feet the frost is as late as the last of April. This is true in the lower part of the Columbia Basin also.

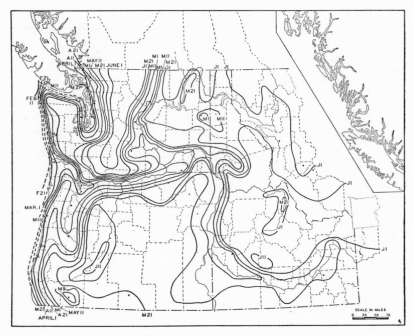

FIG. 15.   Last killing frost in spring.

Between 1000 and 4000 feet in Washington and Oregon, frost occurs any time during May, the earlier dates being at the lower altitude. Striking differences in the dates, and therefore stages of vegetative progress, are to be noted within short distances where changes of altitude are great. Snow may still cover the ground at Moscow when the lilacs bloom in Lewiston, 2000 feet lower. The first early vegetables come from Kennewick (altitude 500 feet), which is relatively free of late frosts; the same vegetables come later from the higher locations, where late frosts delay planting. In the Snake Valley, however, by reason of rapid warming in the spring, the last frost may be experienced before May as high as 3000 feet, and only in the highest enclosed valleys (above 6000 feet) are the frosts retarded until June.

First Killing Frost in Autumn

The isolines of average dates again closely parallel the contour lines but, for the area as a whole, there is less difference in the dates of the killing frost in the autumn than the last frost in spring (Fig. 16).

In Washington, where both the earliest and latest last spring frost occur (4½-month interval), there is a difference of about 3½ months

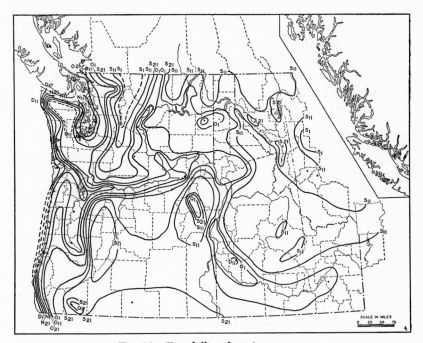

FIG. 16. First killing frost in autumn.

in the autumn frost. This is because autumn frosts occur during clear, calm weather, and nighttime loss of heat is the dominant factor in reducing the air temperatures to freezing. The loss of heat is about equally rapid within the altitudinal range of stations. Through this process freezing temperatures result in a valley, whereas the normal decrease of temperature with altitude may bring the slopes of a mountain to freezing temperatures on the same date.

When nighttime cooling reduces the temperature in a valley bottom, somewhat higher temperatures, perhaps above freezing, may result at intermediate slopes. The valley side may then have a later first frost in the autumn. This is frequently the case in enclosed valleys, irrespective of altitude, but the immunity to frost of the valley sides depends largely on the ratio of bottom width to drainage area of the sides; the narrower the valley, the more pronounced the vertical temperature differences.

The coast has its first autumn frost in late November or early December; so late that cranberries can be grown there. The Willamette-Puget Sound Trough and the lower Columbia Basin have their first autumn frost during the last week of October or first half of November. In the Snake Valley in Idaho the corresponding dates are first week of October, last week of September, and mid-September for the lower, middle, and upper parts. Between 1000 and 3000 feet in the Columbia Basin the frost generally occurs in the latter half of September, whereas at higher altitudes the arrival may be as early as the second week of September.

Length of Frost-Free Season

The length of the frost-free season (number of days between the date of the average last spring frost and first fall frost) reflects the wide differences of the determining frosts (Fig. 17). The extremes are 68 and 306 days (Stockdill and Tatoosh Island; 200 miles apart; altitude difference 2200 feet).

The length of the frost-free season clearly demonstrates that east of the Cascade barrier the land is the dominating influence, for example, short season, and that altitude plays an important part in determining whether the season shall be slightly more or much less than 4 months in length. The altitude of the Lower Snake Plains is low enough to permit a season of about 5 months, whereas, in the Columbia Basin, the season is about 4 months. Higher up, the season shortens approximately in direct proportion to altitude.

The coastal plain, except for a portion where the Oregon Coast Ranges abut the ocean, has more than 7 months without frost. This is directly ascribable to the temperature of the winter wind from off the water which is higher than 40°. But the decrease in length, progressively inland, is very rapid. Usually within the first 30 miles the season is shortened by a full month.

The Puget Sound Lowland and Willamette Valley show marked differences within short distances but the average season is about 7 months in length. The differences depend upon the location of the stations; for example, city or country, hillside or valley bottom, close to or few miles from water (Puget Sound, Strait of Juan de Fuca,

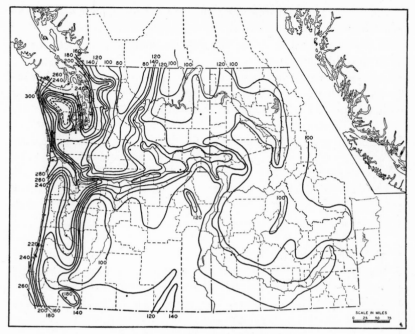

FIG. 17.   Length of frost-free season.

Columbia River, etc.). Thus local topography and proximity to water bodies produce or prevent a long frost-free season here.

PRECIPITATION

Mean Annual Precipitation

The outstanding characteristic of the precipitation (Fig. 18) over the whole area, except western Montana, is that more falls during the colder half year (November through April) than during the warmer half year (May through October). The colder half-year proportion decreases from west to east. Because one of the criteria of a marine climate is that greater precipitation occurs in winter than summer, the whole region has a marine precipitation regime as far inland as the Bitterroot Range. To the east of that barrier, a continental precipitation regime holds sway.

North Head, Washington, is the best example of a station along the coast least influenced by mountains. Its annual total (approximately 50 inches) indicates the amount that occurs along the coast at sea level. The recorded falls at other stations, being considerably more than at North Head, demonstrate that the amount is affected by the mountains.

The windward slope of the mountains (southwest) causes ascent of the unstable and nearly saturated [9] maritime air. This results in copious precipitation on the western slopes. North of the Columbia River more than 100 inches is common; it is here that the greatest amount of precipitation occurs in North America.

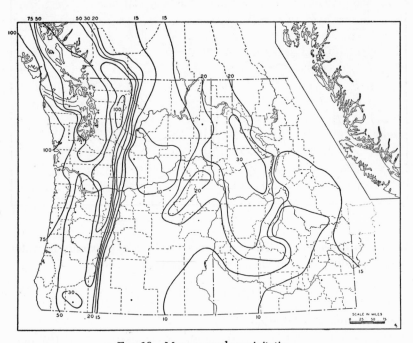

FIG. 18.   Mean annual precipitation.

The first mountain ranges receive the largest amount, and succeeding ranges (downwind) receive somewhat less. The precipitation then is governed largely by altitude.

The lee slope permits descent of air or increases the distance through which the rain must fall. The greater the latter distance, the greater the precipitation that evaporates and the less that reaches the surface of the earth. If the air on the lee slopes is actively descending, it is becoming warmed and, therefore, is a drying wind from which no

[9] H. C. Willett, "American Air Mass Properties," *Papers in Physical Oceanography and Meteorology,* Vol. II, No. 2, p. 30, 1933, Massachusetts Institute of Technology and Woods Hole Oceanographic Institute.

precipitation can come. Thus, the lee slope receives less precipitation, and the mountain casts a shadow of less rain. Paradoxically, this has been termed a "rain shadow"; a better term is "dry shadow." These shadows are very definite in the Northwest, especially in the lee (northeast) of the Olympics where the annual amount is less than 20 inches (Sequim, etc.).

The Cascades cast a "dry shadow" of considerable importance because the Columbia Basin is lower than the Cascades. The rainfall decreases with diminishing altitude in all directions to a minimum of about 6 inches just north of the confluence of the Snake and Columbia rivers. The low plains of the Columbia Basin, together with central and southern Oregon that receive less than 10 inches a year, form interior deserts. The Northern Rockies and the Blue Mountains proper, because of their altitude (equal to or higher than the Cascades), are more favored with precipitation, averaging 15 to 50 inches. In the lee of these mountains, or any of their spurs which lie athwart the moist westerly winds, are local "dry islands." Of these the largest is the Snake River Plain. Here again the altitude is the main factor determining the amount, for the lower portion receives about 10 inches or less, the middle 10 to 13 inches, and the upper portion more than 13 inches.

From the above it follows that the isohyets will generally parallel the coast and the windward slope of the mountains, but will cut across the mountain gaps, for example, Straits of Juan de Fuca, Columbia Gorge. On the "shadow" side the isohyets will more closely parallel the contours, with the least rain at the lowest altitude.

Because the precipitation comes during the colder half year, it is associated with traveling depressions which cross the Pacific from the China Sea.[10] The annual north-south swing of the normal cyclonic trajectory and the annual cycle of change in intensity of these storms provide little cyclonic precipitation during the warmer half year. The summer, though sunny and hot east of the Cascades, is relatively free of convectional storms because the air is too dry. Only small cumulus clouds (alto cumulus) can develop from daytime convection except where the air is ascending the higher mountains. Here summer thunderstorms are relatively frequent. The coolness of the lowlands west of the Cascades is so detrimental to convectional activity that

[10] H. G. Byers, "Air Masses of the Pacific," *Bulletin of Scripps Institute of Oceanography Technical Series,* Vol. 3, No. 14, p. 321, 1924.

only a few mild thunderstorms occur each year, and these are the result of frontal movements associated with cyclones.

Snowfall

With winter sea-level temperatures near freezing and with maximum rainfall during the colder half year, it is to be expected that at

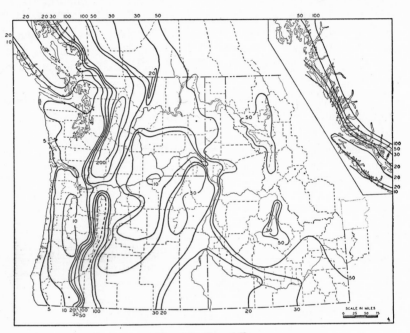

FIG. 19. Snowfall.

moderate and high altitudes, and especially on the windward slopes of the mountains, much of the precipitation will be in the form of snow (Fig. 19).

Along the coast there is little snow (average is about 5 inches) because of the lack of cold waves from the interior reaching so far west. The lowlands west of the Cascades, which are colder than the Pacific Coast Plains, have an average of about 10 inches. Even this is a small amount compared to the total rain during the same period. Here, as along the coast, there are few flows of cold air from the east to produce the necessary cold for snow.

Undoubtedly, considerable snow falls on the higher slopes of the Olympic Mountains—sufficient to allow snow fields and small glaciers to be present in spite of altitudes below 8000 feet. In the Cascades, the amount depends almost entirely on altitude and exposure, with an increasing amount being recorded up to a height of 5000 to 6000 feet. The zone of maximum amount may be above that, but, at present, there are no recording stations above 6000 feet. At 500 feet (Snoqualmie Falls) the winter total averages 16 inches, at 3000 feet (Snoqualmie Pass) nearly 400 inches, at 4400 feet (Mt. Baker) 492 inches, and at 5500 feet (Paradise Inn) 591 inches. Because of the great depth of snow in the Cascades, the State Highway of Washington finds it feasible to keep but three routes over the mountains, Snoqualmie, White, and Stevens passes, open all winter.

East of the Cascade barrier the amount decreases rapidly. In the Columbia Basin there are 10 to 35 inches, the amount increasing in all directions from a point near the confluence of the Snake and Columbia rivers.

In the Blue Mountains and Northern Rocky Mountain areas, the winter's fall is well above 50 inches, and in higher places the total may be more than 200 inches. In the mountains, railroads must build many miles of snow sheds and maintain snow-removal equipment to keep the rails open during the winter. As with rainfall, deep, enclosed valleys receive less snow than the surrounding mountains.

In British Columbia the situation is the same; to wit, about 10 inches on the immediate coast and a rapid increase of total fall with higher altitude. At Premier (altitude 1371 feet) the total is 466 inches.

The duration of the snow cover is somewhat proportional to the total amount. The lowlands, west of the Cascades, and the coastal plain have snow on the ground less than 5 weeks. This duration increases to 10 weeks in the lower part and to 15 to 20 weeks in the upper part of the Columbia Basin. In all the mountains where the snow depth is 50 inches or more, the duration on the ground is more than 20 weeks. On Mt. Baker (4400 feet) and Mt. Rainier (5500 feet) the season is at least 40 weeks long. Above 8000 feet snow lies on the ground all year.

The amount of snow is of utmost economic value especially for irrigation where natural precipitation is insufficient, and also for hydroelectric power. All irrigated districts are entirely dependent upon the snow melt, which is at a maximum at the time that the greatest amount of water is necessary for the growing crops. Because of this characteristic, it is not essential to store much water for the irrigating season and irrigation costs are relatively low.

The water power developed, and to be developed, is also largely dependent on the runoff of snow melt. That this maximum hydro-electric power should be maintained all year it is necessary to provide reservoirs to even out the early maximum discharge of the rivers.

In the Northwest numerous snow courses have been established where snow surveyors are busy in late winter measuring the water content of the snow cover to determine how much water will be available for irrigation, power, and other uses during the following dry season.

Sunshine and Cloudiness

From the records of the few weather-bureau stations that record sunshine and cloudiness it is possible to conclude that along the coast and the lowlands west of the Cascades the average amount of sun-shine is 40 to 45 per cent of the total possible. This figure would be further decreased in the coastal mountains, probably to 30 per cent. East of the Cascade barrier in the Columbia Basin, northern Idaho, and western Montana the yearly average is 52 and 59 per cent. In the Snake Valley, as represented by Boise, the high value of 65 per cent is realized.

Winter is the least sunny season over the whole area. Along the coast the sun shines about 20 per cent of the total possible time, and this amount increases slightly in the lowlands west of the Cascades. In the Columbia Basin, northern Idaho, western Montana, and the Snake Valley the percentages ar 28 to 43 per cent.

Summer is the sunny season. Seattle and Portland report an aver-age of 60 and 64 per cent, Spokane and Baker 77 and 75 per cent, Kalispell and Helena 69 and 70 per cent, and Boise 84 per cent.

Crops grow rapidly during the sunny summer and produce large yields when irrigated (two to four cuttings of alfalfa can be made, depending on the district). In appearance of the fruit and quality of the grains these crops are superior to crops raised in less sunny areas. Fewer pests and diseases attack the crops than in cloudier climates.

Wind

The mountain-valley character of the topography of the region, with the observing stations in the valleys, materially reduces the validity of wind observations because the surface wind will largely be directed either up or down the valley. For general wind directions isobaric charts of the average pressure then give a truer picture. These charts show that during the winter season the wind is from the southwest to south and in the summer from northwest to west. These directions are consistent with the rainfall regime; southwest wind has a high moisture content and is unstable (therefore rainy), and the northwest wind, being cooler than the surface over which it is traveling and descending (therefore warming), is dry.

Many local winds of all types are to be found because of the topography, mountain barriers, juxtaposition of land and water, snow surface versus bare ground, and mountain gaps of all sizes in addition to rapid changes in steepness and direction of the pressure gradient. Among them may be listed the following, the places where found, and season of occurrence.

Sea breezes (land breeze seldom observed because the water is too cold). Along the coast and the inland waters (summer).

Valley breezes. Any mountain valley (warmer half year).

Mountain breezes. Same as above.

Fall (katabatic or gravity) *winds.* Any mountain valley which opens out to a high, wide, snow-covered, large alpine meadow (spring and summer).

Gorge winds. Fraser, Columbia, Snake, Thompson, and other rivers, Strait of Juan de Fuca, fiords of British Columbia (any season).

Chinook (foehn) *winds.* On the lee side of any mountain, provided precipitation (rain or snow) falls on windward slope. Examples: A descending wind on east side of Cascades in winter; descending wind on west slope of Bitterroots or Cascades if snow or rain has fallen on east slope of the Rockies (rainy season).

Conclusions

The location of the Pacific Northwest in midlatitudes on the western margin of the continent with resultant onshore wind yields a marine climate. The distinctive characteristics of this basic type are greatly modified by distance from the coast, differences in altitude, mountain barriers, and local topography. The modifications are all toward increasing aridity and continentality, except on the windward slopes of the mountains, and are so pronounced that all marine characteristics have been obliterated on the eastern boundary of the area. As a result there is a large number of climatic types (Table 1).

The number of the climatic types and their characteristics have produced nearly all types of soil from the most acid to the most alkaline. The Northwest has the greatest commercial forests in the world (more board feet per acre), excellent grazing land, and even alkaline flats, all of which are the result of native vegetation controlled by climate and soil.

TABLE 1

SUMMARY TABLE OF CLIMATES OF THE PACIFIC NORTHWEST

Physiographic Regions	Climatic Areas	Temperature °F.				Precipitation*		Per Cent of Sunshine	Length of Growing Season (Days)
		Mean	Range	Jan.	July	Total—Inches	Total Snow Inches		
Plains									
Willamette Valley	Willamette-Puget Sound Lowland	more than 50	25 to 30	35 to 40	60 to 70	20 to 50	5 to 15	40 to 45	180 to 260
Puget Sound Lowland									
Pacific Coast Plain	Coastal Plain	50	15 to 20	40 to 45	55 to 60	50 to 150	0 to 8	30	180 to 310
Columbia Plain	Columbia Basin	45 to 50	30 to 45	25 to 35	68 to 77	5 to 17	10 to 40	50 to 60	130 to 210
Channeled Scabland									
Snake River Plains	Snake River Valley	40 to 50	45 to 50	15 to 30	68 to 77	8 to 15	10 to 50	60 to 65	100 to 170
Rogue River Valley	Rogue River Valley	more than 50	30	35 to 40	65 to 70	20 to 30	10 to 20	60	180
Plateaus									
Yakima Folds	Columbia Basin	45 to 50	35 to 45	25 to 35	63 to 77	10 to 20	10 to 55	40 to 60	80 to 200
Deschutes Plateau									
Tri-State Slopes									
Palouse									
Waterville									
Owyhee Plateau	Central and Southern Ore., and Southern Idaho	45 to 50	45	30	70	10	10 to 20	60	120 to 140
Basin and Ranges			40	25 to 30	65 to 75	10 to 15	10 to 55	60	80 to 150
Mountains									
Olympics	Olympics	35 to 45	25 to 35	25 to 35	50	30 to 200	8 to 300	30 to 40	80 to 120
Oregon Coast Ranges	Coast Range		25 to 35	25 to 35	65	40 to 150	5 to 300		100 to 150
Vancouver Island									
Cascades	Cascade Barrier	35 to 45	35 to 50	10 to 25	55 to 65	40 to 100	15 to 600	30 to 45	80 to 120
Okanogan Highlands	Okanogan Highlands					10 to 20	15 to 60	50	80 to 150
Blue Mountains	Blue Mountains					15 to 20	40 to 100	45 to 50	100 to 160
Northern Rockies	Northern Rockies					10 to 20	40 to 100	50 to 55	80 to 140
Middle Rockies	Southern Idaho					10 to 15		55 to 60	

* Throughout the Northwest the greatest precipitation occurs in the colder half of the year in all regions except the northern and middle Rockies, where it comes in the warmer half of the year as a result of continental influence.

Each climatic type will permit certain activities, will tolerate some and will restrict others. This is particularly true of all forms of agriculture and, to a lesser extent, of many other human endeavors. The large number of climates, each with its distinctive characteristics, has passively permitted or actively demanded the wide range of activities to be described in later chapters.

PART

3

Exploitation and Conservation
of Northwest Resources

INTRODUCTION

Resources of the Northwest have largely controlled the pattern of development and settlement of the region. Their orderly exploitation constitutes the basis for continued substantial regional growth. Principal resources include: soils, grasslands, minerals, fisheries, water for power and irrigation, forests, wildlife, and scenic attractions. The problems of utilization and conservation for these are discussed in the appropriate chapters.

Because of the large areas of mountains and deserts, only about one-tenth of the region possesses tillable soil. However, here are found most cities and villages and more rural residents than are in all the remaining 90 per cent of the Northwest. Noteworthy intensive cropping of land may occur near large cities and in irrigated districts. In contrast, the untilled grasslands support comparatively few ranchers, a condition that will endure unless the land is reclaimed by irrigation. Although both soils and grasslands have been damaged by erosion and mismanagement, much is being accomplished to conserve them so as to insure their continued contribution to the Northwest economy.

Northwest minerals account for many of the mountain settlements and have helped in the growth of several cities. Formerly the minerals were chiefly produced for export, but increasingly they are being further fabricated for local use. Export of metal manufactures can be expected to increase. Northwest mines depend more and more on the recovery of metals from low-grade ores, which will prolong production far beyond what was once considered possible. Discovery of new mineral deposits and development of new uses and cheaper processes of recovery will help insure that the mining industry will remain of importance long into the future.

Fisheries, once threatened with extinction from mismanagement, have been rehabilitated by the use of conservation methods. By-products are becoming a valuable addition to the income of processors of fish.

Water resources are in the forefront in rapid development at present. Numerous power plants are being built by both public and private capital, and as soon as new sources of energy are available, industry absorbs them. In the Northwest, hydroelectricity carries the power load rather than coal, oil, or natural gas. Irrigation development is making steady progress and thousands of new farms are being reclaimed from desert.

Forests and timber products lead all other resources in value and employment. Great improvement has been made in the complete use of wood, in the protection of the forest against fire and other enemies, and in forest reproduction and management. Continuance and expansion of these conservation measures will allow the timber and woodworking industries to maintain production and employment. The preservation of the forests is closely allied with the conservation of wildlife and the use of the region by tourists and for recreation. Hunting, fishing, tourism, and recreation are steadily growing industries.

Details concerning these natural resources and their use and conservation are dealt with in Chapters 7 to 15 of this part of the book.

CHAPTER

7

Soils and Their Conservation

W. A. ROCKIE

INTRODUCTION TO SOILS OF REGION

A hundred years ago the Pacific Northwest was a wilderness of timber, of grass, and of sagebrush. Bare land was virtually non-existent. West of the Cascades nearly every acre was tree-covered, except for a few scattered grassy meadows. East of the Cascades, the grass and sage-covered lowlands were interspersed with and surrounded by pine and fir-covered mountains and hills. There was little land in the entire region without a vegetative cover.

Underlying the blanket of growing plants was the rather continuous but highly heterogeneous mantle of wind-blown, water-washed, and otherwise accumulated broken bits of soil-making materials. This varied continuously as to its geological source, methods of deposition, texture, depth, and profile characteristics. From these many diverse origins, and under the many locally different climates in the region, the soils of the Pacific Northwest developed through the ages up to the time man began to cultivate and use the land.

The lowlands generally have a deep mantle of unconsolidated soil material; the mountains, usually a thin mantle. Usually the soil is more uniform as the topography is smoother, less uniform as it gets rougher.

The soils of the Northwest are highly variable everywhere. They vary with the geological formations, topography, precipitation, temperature, humidity, winds, sunshine, cloudiness, degree of drainage, and character of the plant cover beneath which they have developed. Sometimes they even vary with no apparent reason. Although study of the Northwest's soils began in the 1890's, and mapping started about 1900, only a very minor segment of the region has been covered to date. Much of the cultivated acreage has been soil-mapped, but practically none of the range and forest areas.

Because a vast number of variations in soil conditions exist, it is necessary in this generalized study to group similar soils together. Such groupings may be based upon differences in morphology, topography, site exposure, depth, profile, texture, organic-matter content, mellowness, color, alkalinity, crop adaptability, and still other characteristics.

Parent Material of Northwest Soils

Basaltic bedrock dominates the most ground area in the Northwest of any class of rock. It underlies most of the surface between the Cascades and the Rocky Mountains and is also common west of the Cascades. The Cascades are volcanic except for some sedimentary rocks in northern Washington. The Coast Range consists dominantly of dense sedimentary cover rock. The Rocky Mountains are chiefly of granite and other crystalline rocks.

Superimposed upon thousands of square miles of the lowlands within these three general areas of different types of bedrock (basaltic plateau, Cascade and Coast ranges, and Rocky Mountains) are extensive areas of loosely consolidated or unconsolidated lacustrine, alluvial, wind-blown, and outwash sediments. In fact, probably two-thirds of the surfaces within the region have a mantle of this secondary material. This is particularly true of the lands that are used for any phase of agriculture. The basaltic plateau, all the major valleys, and many of the lesser depressions within the Cascades, Coast Ranges, and Rocky Mountains also are well covered with these deposits. Even some of the mountain slopes have secondary sedimentary material, although most of them have a thin mantle of soil that is largely residual.

Soil Textures

Textures of the soil range from fine clays to coarse sands and gravels. In the Columbia Basin, the soil textures are generally sandy along the western border, becoming finer to the eastward. In general, the soils along the eastern border are loams, silt loams, and silty clay loams. West of the Cascades, soil textures in the glaciated portion are extremely variable, ranging from gravel to sand to clay. The nonglaciated portion, in which most of the west-side agriculture is located, is dominantly the heavier-textured soils, chiefly silt loams and clay loams. In the Rocky Mountains the soils are mostly sandy, heavy-textured soils being the exception.

Soil Profiles

The profile of a soil portrays the different zones or horizons from the surface downward into the unaltered parent material. Soil students recognize three separate horizons (A, B, and C) in soils (Plate 7B).

Horizon A is the upper or surface layer from which natural factors are removing, through erosion, leaching, and gravity, certain important chemical and physical constituents of the soil material.

Horizon B underlies this upper layer and receives, through precipitation and deposition, the materials that are being leached and washed downward from horizon A.

Horizon C is the underlying parent soil material, relatively unaltered by these weathering processes.

Development of soil profiles is a slow process even under the humid climatic conditions in western Washington and Oregon. It proceeds still more slowly under the semiarid conditions east of the Cascade Mountains, where the development of a mature soil from its inert beginnings might require a period of at least several hundred years.

Soil Is Alive

The soil is a *living* thing; it is the complex product of weathering, washing, and deposition, acted upon by bacteria, plants, and other forms of life.

Soil is always developing, always changing, from infancy to old age. The young soil has developed no horizons; the old soil has fully developed horizons. Soils age slowly in arctic climates and rapidly in hot climates. Therefore, a soil's age is not a matter of years but a measure of its progress from the original inert mineral material.

Effects of Plant Growth and Other Life

The soils of the Pacific Northwest attained their present development only after a long succession of gradual changes covering thousands of years. Plants furnish organic materials and together with climatic conditions assist in the development of soil from the inert mineral deposit. Both roots and decaying remains of above-ground parts of plants are a source of humus that helps to make a mellow soil.

During the period of natural development, compacted deposits of clay, silt, or sand become porous, mellow, and spongelike soils. The degree of soil development in any particular locality depends upon several factors, among which the following are of the greatest importance: the nature of the parent soil material; the length of time during which development has been under way; the nature of the plants growing thereon; the density of that vegetation; the abundance of digging rodents and worms, insect, bacterial, and fungus life, and several climatic factors, among which are rainfall, freezing, and thawing.

SOILS

There are many different ways of grouping soils, according to the purposes to be served. Two well-recognized classifications will be of

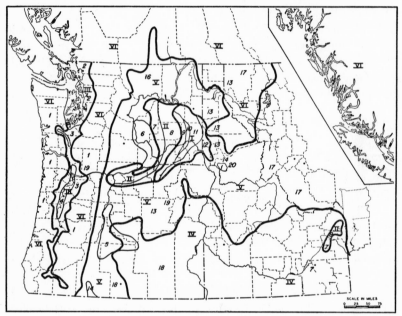

Fig. 20. Soil series and groups. See Table 1 for key to numbers.

value in a discussion of the soils of this region: (1) geographic and (2) taxonomic. The first includes soils of close geographic relationships, particularly as such characteristics determine their use adaptation. The taxonomic grouping (established by Dr. Marbut) is designed to place soils having similar morphology and theoretically similar genesis in the same groups. From the standpoint of soil types, the region has been divided into six major areas, corresponding closely to zones that have similar climatic conditions, common natural vegetation, and use capabilities. (See map, Fig. 20.)

Palouse-Walla Walla Area

The Walla Walla, Athena, Palouse, Thatuna, Nez Perce, and similar soils lie mainly in the 14- to 25-inch rainfall belt of the Columbia Basin wheat section of eastern Washington, northern Idaho, and northeastern Oregon, with a few small areas in the foothills of southeastern Idaho. In general these soils occupy roughly parallel narrow belts of rolling prairie uplands between the dry semiarid basin below them and the low-timbered mountains which rise above them. The elevation ranges from 700 to slightly over 3000 feet in Washington, Oregon, and northern Idaho, and from 3500 to 6000 feet in southern Idaho. Native vegetation consists principally of dense stands of bunchgrass and their climax associates. The cultivated land is devoted chiefly to grain, and the Spokane to Pendleton area constitutes one of the most productive wheat areas in the world.

Subhumid Soils

The groups mentioned represent progressive degrees of soil development under increasing rainfall and soil-maturing conditions from drier to wetter extremes. The soils are *pedocals* and therefore have a zone of lime carbonate accumulation (see Table 1).

Walla Walla Series. The soils of the Walla Walla series have been formed from wind- and water-laid sediments under conditions of weathering productive of zonal pedocals, but the original materials were deposited so recently that the soils have the least mature profile development of the upland prairie groups. The series is characterized by mellow, pervious profile, brown to dark-brown noncalcareous soils with lighter-brown, friable subsoils that sometimes become slightly calcareous in the lower subsoil.

Athena Series. Closely associated with the Walla Walla is the Athena series, a slightly more mature soil than the Walla Walla. Athena series soils are intermediate in characteristics between the Palouse and the Walla Walla. They are dark-brown soils developed under grass cover and under the influence of slightly more rainfall than the Walla Walla but less than the Palouse, probably between 16 and 20 inches. The surface soils have a high content of organic

TABLE 1

IMPORTANT SOILS OF THE PACIFIC NORTHWEST

Order	Suborder		Soil Groups	Soil Series	Occurrence Map, Fig. 20	
					Soil Area	Soil Series
Zonal Soils	Pedocals	Light-colored desert soils	Sierozem soils	Portneuf	II, IV	7
				Wheeler	II, IV, V	7
			Brown soils	Ritzville	II	8
		Dark-colored soils of semiarid grasslands	Prairie soils	Nez Perce	I	20
			Chestnut soils	Walla Walla	I	9
				Athena	I	10
			Chernozem	Palouse	I	11
	Pedalfers	Soils of the forest grassland transition	Degraded Chernozem soils	Thatuna	I	12
		Light-colored podzolized soils of the timbered region	Gray-brown Brown podzolic soils	Everett	III, VI	2
				Olympic	III, VI	1
				Melbourne	III	1
			Gray-brown podzolic soils	Helmer	I, V, VI	13
				Santa	I, V, IV	
		Soils of lateritic material	Red podzolic soils	Aiken	III, VI	3
Azonal			Lithosols	Underwood	VI, V	17
			Alluvial soils	Yakima	IV, V	6
				Willamette	IV	4
				Chehalis	III	3

matter and have a slight accumulation of lime at a depth of 50 to 60 inches. The Athena is easily cultivated and is one of the best wheat soils in eastern Washington and Oregon.

Palouse Series. The Palouse soils are most extensively and typically developed on the rolling hills of Whitman and Spokane counties, Washington. The climate is subhumid, with slightly higher rainfall than the Athena, generally from 18 to 22 inches, and the original vegetation was tall grass. The predominant surface of the Palouse soils is a dark-brown, friable, and granular silt loam. The subsoil is a tough, brown to yellowish-brown clay loam underlain by yellowish-brown silty clay loam, generally noncalcareous except in lower depths. Palouse soil is a typical chernozem (Table 1).

Thatuna Series. Soils in the Thatuna adjoin timbered, higher mountain slopes and have a more maturely developed profile than the

Palouse, from which they are differentiated by slightly lighter surface color and a compact leached gray subsurface layer and compact clay subsoil. The Thatuna was developed under a rainfall of 20 to 30 inches, and, as a result of leaching, the series falls in the category of a degraded chernozem.

Wheat-Summer Fallow Area

The soils of the wheat-summer fallow area are derived from wind-and-water-deposited materials.

SEMIARID SOILS. The semiarid soils have been developed under lower rainfall, 10 to 14 inches, than the Palouse-Walla Walla soils, and all are pedocals. They have lighter-brown to grayish-brown surface soil, show less mature development, and have a higher concentration of lime near the surface.

Ritzville Series. The Ritzville series of the mellow subsoil group is the deepest leached soil and has been developed under slightly more rainfall than the Wheeler series or its counterpart with compact subsoil, the Portneuf series. The Ritzville is a light-brown loam of uniformly mellow surface. The profile shows little difference between soil and subsoil, except that, at a depth below 30 inches, concentration of calcium carbonate may begin. The Ritzville includes the main area of low-rainfall wheat land in central Washington and northern Oregon. Although yields are usually moderate, large-scale farming operations are generally successful. Both wind and water erosion is often a problem.

Wheeler Series. The Wheeler series includes light-colored desert soils developed under a rainfall of 5 to 10 inches annually. This series is essentially unleached, showing concentration of lime carbonate in the surface few inches and differing in this respect from the slightly deeper leached Portneuf. The soil is well adapted to crop production under irrigation but under dryland conditions is generally marginal for cultivated crops, being devoted mostly to range. Erosion is a serious problem under all conditions of present use.

Portneuf Series. The Portneuf series, a rather extensively mapped soil, is distinguished from the Wheeler in the slightly deeper leaching and greater compaction in the subsoil. The soil is favorable for cultivation under irrigation, but erosion may be a hazard. Other similar unleached soils are extensively developed in southern Idaho, but have not been mapped and correlated. They differ from the Portneuf only in depth of leaching, being calcareous in the surface horizon.

Coastal Valleys Agricultural Area

The soils of the area west of the Cascades fall into three broad groups of pedalfers (humid-climate soils): the "red-hill" soils of western Oregon and southwest Washington; the glacial soils of northwest Washington; and alluvial soils.

RESIDUAL SOILS. The "red-hill" soils are residual, developed mostly from dark-colored lavas and sedimentary rocks. The Aiken and Olympic series are the dominant soils derived from igneous rocks; the Melbourne and Carlton series, from sedimentary rocks. Forest once covered most of these soils.

Aiken Series. The Aiken series is one of the most productive hill soils west of the Cascades. They are red, slightly podzolic (leached) soils and are related to the Olympic and associated with the Melbourne soil derived from the underlying sedimentary deposits. The Aiken soils are under timber cover with a rainfall of 40 to 90 inches annually.

The surface soil consists of red to brownish-red friable clay loam with a compact but not impervious subsoil which is bright red or slightly yellowish-red. Where topography is favorable for cultivation, the Aiken ranks at the top of the hill soils for the production of prunes, walnuts, cherries, filberts, and field crops.

Olympic Series. The Olympic soils have darker surface layer, more yellow in the subsoil, and are slightly less productive than the Aiken, which they closely resemble. Contrary to the general opinion, erosion does occur under clean cultivation, but this can be controlled more easily than on the associated Melbourne group.

Melbourne Series. The Melbourne series is derived from consolidated sediments (gray to grayish-brown shales and fine-grained grayish-brown sandstones), the principal rocks of the lower hills of the Coast ranges. The Melbourne soils are characterized by the brown or slightly reddish-brown surface horizons of generally friable structure. The subsoil below 10 inches is a moderately compact yellow to brownish-yellow clay or clay loam, mottled iron stains, grading into weathered bedrock at depths varying from 24 inches to 4 feet. The topography is sloping to hilly and in some places steep and rough. The main types of the Melbourne series are commonly used for pasture and are generally rated as marginal for cultivation. Serious erosion has occurred on this group of soils.

ALLUVIAL SOILS. The *Willamette* terrace and the *Chehalis* recent alluvium are the dominant water-lain soils of the area. They are level to gently rolling, having friable, slightly developed profiles and are well suited to intensive agriculture.

Willamette Series. The Willamette soils are among the most desirable in the Coastal area. They are mellow and friable and are moderately high in organic matter. The topsoil is brown, merging into a yellowish-brown heavy loam or silty clay loam. It originally supported a forest cover, but now is very largely under cultivation, including orchards, small fruits, vegetables, and general field crops. This series is very extensive in the Willamette Valley.

Chehalis Series. The Chehalis includes lands along many Coastal streams. They originally supported a heavy growth of trees and when cleared form a highly productive soil although often subject to overflow. Generally level to undulating, their surface is marked by sloughs and old stream channels. The topsoil is generally a very mellow dark grayish-brown highly organic silt loam to silty clay loam, which usually extends to depths of many feet with but minor variations. The Chehalis soils are used for general field crops, especially hops, potatoes, berries, truck crops, and orchard nuts and fruits.

GLACIATED SOILS. The upland soils of the northern (glaciated) part of the area have been developed largely from glacial material under ample rainfall and heavy forest growth. Most of the soils in this area were originally grouped in the Everett series, but some sections have been reclassified.

Everett Series. These slightly podzolic soils occupy the rolling uplands. The topsoil is light brown to reddish brown and medium light textured. The subsoil consists of gray to light-brown material, lighter in color and texture than the surface. Since the soil is developed from coarse gravel, it is porous and is usually excessively drained and strongly leached. The crop adaptations and yields on the glaciated uplands are limited because of their droughty nature and low rainfall during the summer season.

INTERMOUNTAIN GRASSLAND AREA. The soils of this grazing area were in the main developed under arid to semiarid rainfall (5–10 inches annually) and with a usual cover of grass, sage, and scattered juniper. Crops generally require irrigation, and their chief use is for grazing.

The Wheeler and Portneuf soils previously mentioned and the *Burke* are the most common and generally favor growth of grass. The Burke is a fine sandy loam in contrast with the *Ephrata* soil, whose surface is usually gravelly or stony, with a substratum of gravel. Both the Burke and Ephrata may suffer wind erosion, and dunes have developed which have become a menace to adjacent land. In southern Oregon and parts of southern Idaho are extensive areas of soils derived from pumice, an eruptive rock. This soil group has been tentatively called Deschutes series. Its internal drainage is excessive. Extensive overgrazing and attempts at cultivation have allowed serious deterioration from wind and water erosion.

Gem and Waha Series. The Gem and Waha series comprise dark-colored soils developed over basalt under grass cover and under rainfall of less than 15 inches. The Gem series is of slightly lighter color and higher lime content, which distinguishes it from the Waha. Typically the Gem has a dark brown or dark grayish-brown granular clay loam topsoil high in organic matter, and a medium-brown or yellowish, compact calcareous clay subsoil. Part of this soil is currently farmed by the wheat-summer fallow system. The soils of both this series and the less calcareous Waha, when used for raising wheat, become seriously eroded and require very careful management.

Brownlee Series. The Brownlee series is one of the residual soils developed from granite under low rainfall and with grassland cover. The surface usually is a dark-brown friable platy loam high in organic matter; the subsoil below 12 inches is a light-brown or pale reddish-brown noncalcareous gritty loam somewhat more compact and slightly heavier in texture than the surface soil. It has cloddy structure and is underlain by disintegrated granitic bedrock at shallow depths. On steep hills erosion has reduced its capacity for grazing.

Extensive bodies of ancient lake and river terrace soils occur within this area. Considerable acreage of grazing land of this type has been, or is being, placed under irrigation. These soils as a group do not have well-developed profiles. The *Sagemoor* is an example. This soil consists of light-brown to grayish-brown surface material overlying grayish-brown to gray subsoils, which grade into a stratified deposit of gray silt loam many feet in depth and with little difference between surface and subsoil.

MOUNTAIN FOREST. GRAZING AREA. The soils of this area have received more precipitation than those of the preceding group, probably 20 to 40 inches, at an elevation of 2000 to 8000 feet, and were developed under an open forest cover. They occupy a large area of thinly timbered mountainous country, including the east slope of the Cascade Mountains, the Blue Mountains, and much of the Rocky Mountains in Washington, Idaho, and Montana.

The steepest and most broken areas are characterized by *lithosols*, a group which because of youth, relief, or condition of parent material has no clear soil development, and consists in large measure of recently weathered rock fragments. Less-rugged mountain topography generally has more mature but still young soils showing somewhat more development of soil horizons. Because this is mainly range or forest land of small value little mapping has been done.

Underwood Series. These soils are residual from lava bedrock, where open woodlands were the usual native cover. These lands usually have gentle and undulating slopes. The surface soil is usually a reddish-brown sandy loam which merges, usually within 3 or 4 feet, into largely disintegrated but solid bedrock.

They are variously used for cereals, hay, and dry-land alfalfa, with some strawberries, fruit, and nut orchards, but are generally not too successful for crop production, primarily because of their shallowness. Generally speaking, they are among the poorer soils.

Moscow Series. These soils are residual from granitic and other crystalline rocks in foothills and mountains, generally too steep for safe cultivation and usually too shallow to be highly productive. The soil is a friable, yellowish-brown micaceous loam that is both droughty and of low fertility. It originally supported a stand of timber, and, where it has been cleared for cultivation, erosion becomes an immediate problem. It is fairly suited to the growing of close-growing cover crops, but even then is highly subject to summer drought. Underwood and Moscow soils are the two main series. Together, these soils probably cover less than 1 per cent of the area.

MOUNTAIN FOREST AREA. *Lithosols and Shallow Soils.* The mountain forest area has predominately shallow and stony soils consisting to a considerable extent of freshly disintegrated material, differing from place to place according to the character of the underlying rock. The climate is humid, rainfall ranging from 30 to 200 inches, with elevations from 1000 to 14,000 feet. The cover is dense forest. Severe erosion, due to denudation resulting from forest fires, overuse, and careless and destructive logging operations, and slight to severe erosion on other lands, resulting from man and animal activity, are constantly changing the physical constitution of the mountain soils.

Summary

The Pacific Northwest, from a soil-study standpoint, is a little soil world of its own. The great range in climate, topography, natural vegetation, and parent material supplies all the dynamic factors that produce members of most of the great soil groups of the world.

PROBLEMS OF SOIL DETERIORATION

During the hundred years or so since farming began in the Northwest, the inexhaustibility of the soil resource always has been the boasted pride of every community. For a long time not a soul questioned the truth of such a claim, but occasionally an observing person has left a written record indicating that "not all is well" with the land. Washing or blowing of soil from its croplands was recorded in a few technical reports on the Palouse printed before 1920, although neither of them indicated that it was viewed as a serious threat to the land. Today, when one sees a typical Palouse hillside toward the end of a bad erosion season, one is really impressed that a remedy for this damage is imperatively needed.

Land Problems Developed

Before 1930, practically no efforts had been made to stop soil washing or blowing in the Northwest. Local dustbowls had caused some dryland farmers to attempt to stop "blowing out" of their wheatfields, although their objective was pointed more toward growing successful wheat crops than conserving their soil.

More by accident than by design, a few Northwest farmers were practicing conservation measures in 1930. However, they displayed no enthusiasm. It was not then known what was needed for soil conservation, nor did these farmers realize how seriously better farming practices were needed. Actually, most of them thought that their farming methods were well adapted to their respective localities.

Of all the croplands in the Northwest, those in the Palouse and in the Blue Mountain foothills are most frequently in distress. Almost every year they show severe damage. Less often, the sandier dryfarm lands of the Big Bend and the Horse Heaven Hills show extreme vulnerability to "blow" conditions. Most of the other croplands of the Northwest are susceptible to erosion damage. From their experience and observation these farmers gradually became conscious of erosion and began to take steps to correct it.

Why Land Damage Occurs

The first concerted efforts in the Northwest toward soil conservation began about 1930, although earlier action would have been desirable. Around 1900, however, the necessity for conservation of the soil in the Northwest was practically inconceivable. But when man started to overcultivate croplands, overgraze rangelands, and overcut and burn the forestlands, the picture quickly changed.

Overcultivation of our croplands destroyed the original soil structure and more than half of the organic matter it originally contained, depleted much of the original supply of plant foods, and removed as much as 2 feet of soil from the surface through erosion and tillage.

Overgrazing of rangelands destroyed almost everywhere the very thin layer of humus-containing topsoil (generally less than 1 inch on rangelands), too generally destroyed the stand of bunch grasses that it originally supported, permitted those highly palatable plant species to be replaced by worthless and even poisonous weeds, and allowed several inches of soil to be lost through water and wind erosion.

Overcutting and burning of forestlands destroyed and/or removed from too great an acreage the forest cover which protected these lands, frequently left the soil without any protective cover, often with the aid of fire destroyed all the organic matter the soil contained, and on a more limited acreage lost all the original surface soil.

A rather direct result (at least in part) of the previously outlined losses from cropland, rangeland, and forestland are the many land damages that come from floods, from inadequate drainage, and from alkalinity and salinity. Other land damage results from the improper use of water by farmers who irrigate. Obviously conservation to correct these ills needs be an immediate objective.

Evolution of Soil Conservation

During the many years of agricultural research in the Northwest before 1930, many valuable farm practices had been learned, but most farmers either ignored or refused to accept the findings of research. Among initial attempts to evolve an acceptable conservation program, the principle of applying frequent green-manuring crop rotations stood out as having the highest potential value to the land. It was also very noticeable that the Palouse farmers were not using this outstanding practice, in large part because they had not been taught how to property use a green manure crop like sweet clover.

The present specific practices that are individual parts of conservation farming have evolved gradually, mostly since 1930. Some are the result of research at experiment stations; others are betterments of farm-born-and-proved research. All our present conservation practices are still in an evolutionary status. Every year finds some change for the better in one practice or another. These practices consist of two kinds: one is the real soil-improving practice; the other is designed to lessen erosion and, of itself, does not improve the soil in any respect.

Soil-building centers around the many green-manuring rotations, and also includes stubble mulching, cover cropping, fertilizing, grassed waterways, and all permanent or long-time plantings of any cover crop.

Other practices include strip cropping and terracing, rough dry tillage, diversion ditches, contour farming, subsoiling, drainage, irrigation, and water spreading (Plate 9A).

Soil Conservation as a Science

Soil conservation is our newest agricultural science. Soil erosion was not considered serious in the Northwest until 1930, when the Pacific Northwest Soil Conservation Experiment Station was established at Pullman, Washington, and was followed by others. These have helped to give scientific direction to everything involved in the protection, maintenance, and improvement of our land resources.

Land Damage Resulting from Cultivation

Cultivation has caused deterioration of soil structure, and losses in organic matter, plant food, and from erosion (Plates 7B, 8A, and 8B).

Loss of Soil Structure. When land is first plowed, the plant remains in the soil are a problem to the farmer, who considers the roots, stems, sods, and other pieces that will not pulverize as enemies to be destroyed. Actually, his soil problems probably increase about as rapidly as these undecayed and decayed organic materials disappear. Virgin soil loses structure every time it is tilled. Since the production of just one crop usually involves from three to eight workings, for certain crops even more, it takes but a few years to pulverize the soil.

All cultivated lands, unless they have received sufficient crop residues, green manures, or barnyard manures to offset the constantly decreasing soil structure and organic matter, quickly become a structureless soil that brings decreasing returns and sets the stage for heavy soil losses by wind or water erosion.

Loss of Organic Matter goes along with the loss of soil structure. Humus is the most easily lost, decayed vegetation next, and undecayed vegetation is last to go. The plant cover has been adding to the organic matter of the virgin soil for centuries and is the chief agency that transformed the once inert mass of mineral particles into a mellow plant-growing medium.

Most of the cultivated soils in the Northwest have lost from one-third to one-half of their original organic matter through several processes. These included stubble burning, erosion by both wind and water, oxidation, and leaching. Although these losses through stubble burning have been largely stopped, erosion is still a major problem.

Losses of Plant Food have resulted from erosion, leaching, crop removal, fire, and oxidation, although mineral salts generally are lost only through the first three means. Plant food deficiencies are constantly increasing under our management of the land; deficiencies of nitrogen, phosphorus, potash, sulfur, and calcium being especially common. The absence of certain trace elements, such as boron and manganese, or the presence of certain other trace elements, such as selenium, also has proved a very serious matter to agriculture.

Soil Lost by Erosion exceeds in importance the preceding losses, important as they are. Each year the average cultivated acre yields from $15 to $200 in new wealth, and properly managed and protected, the land can continue in production indefinitely. When erosion removes all or part of the soil mantle, this annual harvest of treasure ceases or declines. Many of our Northwest lands have only a thin layer of soil on bedrock. Loss of soil under such conditions causes irreparable damage to the land. Although the loss by erosion from lands having deeper soils is less critical, it is always tragic wherever it occurs. Most of the soils in this region are gravely injured for crop production when they have lost 6 inches of topsoil, and they are usually abandoned before they lose 12 inches of the surface layer because crops usually depend upon the top 9 to 12 inches.

Land Damage Resulting from Overgrazing

The rangelands of the Northwest tell a story of damage from overgrazing that began long before homesteading got under way in the region. Primarily, *too many animals* were grazed on *too few acres* for *too long a time* and at *wrong times*. The animals gradually ate the most palatable native forage species into the ground. The livestock used the range at any and all seasons and the land was never rested. Gradually the more palatable plants became weakened and died, their space being occupied by less palatable vegetation. Invasion of the area by weed species that not only were less appetizing to livestock, but which also proved more aggressive on the rundown land than the original native species, was the only possible result. With the ever-decreasing amount of plant cover, excessive trampling and packing of the soil followed. In time, this sequence of deteriorating range condition was followed by accelerated erosion.

Land Damage from Deforestation

During the period that has seen vast forested acreages in the Northwest denuded, either by logging or fire or both, little or no thought was given to the land. Some of this deforested land was cleared for cultivation, but much of it was abandoned.

These deforested lands have shown erosion damage in widely varying degrees. Naturally, the lands that were cleared for cultivation became the most vulnerable to deterioration, especially on slopes and hills. Damage on the level lands can be remedied by crop rotations. In general, logged-off land has not suffered much damage, because nature has quickly seeded down the disturbed portions of the forest floor to a wide mixture of plants.

When the forest destruction was the result of fire, however, erosion is much more severe than occurs after logging. The usual forest fire is sufficiently destructive that not only is the duff mantle destroyed, but all organic content of the topsoil is also destroyed. The result is usually that severe sheet erosion occurs the first year following a forest fire, with the amount decreasing in rather direct proportion as plants re-cover the land. In areas having highly erodible soils, steep slopes, and heavy burns, as in parts of northern Idaho, sheet erosion may still be severe after 25 years, but with soils of low erodibility and gentle slopes, as in much of the Tillamook Burn area in Oregon, erosion is well controlled within 3 to 5 years after a severe burn.

Land Damage from Floods

Floods in the Northwest cause minor damage to the land itself. Most of the losses are to man-made structures and other improvements.

STREAMBANK DAMAGE results from man's removal of nature's protective plant cover, including that on the valley bottoms. In some measure, the removal of plant cover from croplands, the reduction of plant cover on range from overgrazing and the removal of timber from forestland and the resulting deterioration in soil conditions, all tend to increase the level of the floods.

OVERFLOW DAMAGE results chiefly from: (1) the loss of crops; (2) the cost of removing debris from the land; (3) the cost of re-establishing a replacement crop, especially in the case of orchards and vineyards; (4) the task of mixing the new mantle of mud with the soil beneath; and (5) the loss of soil by scouring. All these may or may not result from any flood.

Other Land Damages

OBSTRUCTED DRAINAGE. Hundreds of drainage projects have been organized in the Northwest, but because people neglected proper maintenance, many of such projects have deteriorated. Inadequate maintenance of installed drains, inadequate levees, lack of tidal gates where needed, inadequate pumping facilities, and insufficient tributary ditches are common causes of deteriorated drainage facilities. Attaining successful drainage in such districts is one means of getting better land use on many of our lowland areas. In addition, we still have large land areas needing drainage on which no drainage work has yet been done.

IMPROPER IRRIGATION. Although there are 4 million acres of irrigated cropland in the Northwest, a surprising proportion of this area is not sufficiently well irrigated to produce capacity crop yields. Much of this shortcoming is due to (1) applying water by other than the best methods; (2) applying water at the wrong time; (3) applying too much water; (4) applying water to land that has never been prepared for irrigation; and (5) shortage of sufficient water either during the entire season or during critical drier periods.

ALKALINITY OR SALINITY. This condition is common in most of the Northwest except west of the Cascade Range. It commonly results from the evaporation from the land surface of considerable amounts of water where nature provides insufficient precipitation to leach the excessive amounts of residual salts downward beyond the plant-root zone. Usually it is intimately associated with the irrigation of arid lands.

Kinds of Erosion

When land is subjected to erosion by either water or wind, different kinds of land are affected in different ways and in varying degrees. Some of these types of erosion, generally man-induced, result from washing by water, others from drifting by wind, and still others from combined forces of wind and water.

Sheet erosion, gully erosion, and badlands are three degrees of soil washing; dust-blowing fields, soil-buried fence rows, and dunes are somewhat comparable stages of soil drifting (Plates 7B, 8A, and 8B).

SHEET EROSION has attained a serious stage on most of the sloping croplands and on some of the rangelands in the Northwest, although a negligible percentage of the area has yet had to go to less intensive land use. The steepest slopes in the Palouse are approaching that change. This condition tends to develop on all sloping croplands inadequately protected by vegetative cover. The original structure of the soil has been so completely destroyed on all our cultivated lands having silt loam or heavier soils that the soil tends to puddle badly during every wetting. Runoff and rilling are the inevitable results. Lowered production invariably follows in due course, and ultimately gullying and abandonment occur.

Irrigation, as most commonly practiced for row crops, carves out a rill with each irrigation. In certain areas in the Northwest, on especially steep irrigated slopes, as much as 20 to 30 inches of soil has been carelessly lost through sheet erosion during a single decade.

Sheet erosion on rangeland results from similar causes as on cultivated areas: inadequate cover, destruction of soil structure, and sufficient puddling to seal the surface. On forestland, the same principle holds, although usually with slightly different causes: removal or destruction of cover, fire burning out the organic matter, and the destruction of soil structure. The rangelands and forestlands of the region do not yet show widespread washing.

SNOWDRIFT EROSION is a highly localized but exceedingly severe and spectacular type of erosion common in the Northwest. It is simply a concentrated form of sheet erosion which begins at the downhill edge of the huge snowdrifts that are most commonly found in the Palouse area. Erosion is greatest, of course, when the soil beneath the drift is clean cultivated, finely pulverized, and without any cover.

SOIL SLIPS AND EARTH FLOWS are caused by very special conditions. Usually a combination of (1) very steep cultivated slopes, (2) completely saturated soil, (3) a slipping zone in some horizon of the soil section, and (4) an abundance of free water percolating through this zone will produce numerous soil slips on the wheatlands and occasionally elsewhere in the region. Sometimes the soil mass lets go and slides down a less steep part of the slope without appearing to flow, but simply slides on skids. This is the soil slip. In other instances, the entire moving soil mass is so filled with water that it moves like a fluid. This is the earth flow. These slips and flows vary in depth from a few inches to several feet. Examples of this phenomenon, usually on a small scale, generally less than 20 feet in width and usually moving less than 100 feet in distance, occur by the thousands every year.

GULLY EROSION occurs in certain soils having a very mellow profile, sometimes simultaneously with sheet erosion, but more commonly after sheet erosion has removed most or all of the topsail. As gullies develop, they lengthen and deepen so that they effectively divide and subdivide farm fields into ever smaller and less practicable land-use areas. Sooner or later, gullied cropland must be abandoned to a less intensive use.

STREAMBANK EROSION commonly follows logging, fires, clearing, and cultivation, which decrease the reservoir capacity of formerly forested headwaters; and overgrazing, fire, and cultivation, which speed up the runoff from the former grasslands. The original thicket along the streambank, which is, in considerable measure, gone today, also offered protection to most streambanks. The clearing and cropping of formerly wooded bottomlands allow increased runoff reaching these bared lands, so that they melt away more quickly and the rich alluvial soil goes down the creek or river. Streambank erosion may largely destroy our most valuable valley lands.

SCOUR AND DEPOSITION result when flood waters either deposit some of their load or increase the sediment in suspension by scour pickup from the land. Both are damaging in some degree and must be classed as part of the damage to the land.

WIND EROSION. Northwest farmers are now well convinced that long-continued cultivation of even the best soils under low-rainfall conditions is a hazardous practice. As the soil structure is more and more pulverized by each year of cultivation, it becomes increasingly vulnerable to attack by wind. Sandy soils break down more quickly than heavier soils, but, regardless of texture, *all soils will blow*. Large areas of farmland in the Northwest are highly vulnerable to wind erosion. As wind erosion becomes more severe, the ripply land surface becomes ever more dunelike. Ultimately, a typical dune topography results. The Northwest has many dune areas.

ESSENTIALS OF CONSERVATION FARMING

In general the main objective of farming methods and practices in the Northwest has been to grow the largest amount of saleable crops at the lowest possible cost. Some of the practices have proved to be exploitative, but until after 1930 the exploitation of land was given very little thought.

The essentials of conservation farming are (1) to use the land in keeping with its capabilities and (2) to protect the land in keeping with its needs. Therefore, if we combine the objective of agriculture with the essentials of conservation, we need (1) maximum crop yields, (2) minimum cost of production, (3) maximum safe land use, and (4) minimum measures of protection of the land.

Because of the complexity of the problem, ignorance of the best methods at the start, and the way the needs differ in some detail with every change in the soil, the slope of the land, the aspect, and the weather, progress in adapting conservation farming practices to each individual farm is very slow.

Before making recommendations of conservation practices for the different fields of any selected farm, the soil conservationist must first accurately and adequately classify all lands in this farm and secondly he must be able to prescribe adapted conservation farming practices for each of the kinds of land he has found on that farm.

PRINCIPLES OF SOIL CONSERVATION

When soil-erosion experimentation was first begun around 1930, two cardinal principles showed immediately.

The first of these two principles was and still is: *Effective prevention and control of soil erosion and adequate conservation of precipitation in any locality require that the use of the various kinds of land be in keeping with its capabilities and its needs.* The second is: *Efficient application of conservation measures to various kinds of land usually requires the assistance of a technician in the field.*

Naturally the capabilities, facilities, adaptabilities, and needs of the land owner-operator must be simultaneously considered. Almost without exception, when the above two principles have been carefully followed, the recommended use and practices have proved to be fundamentally sound and signally successful.

Conservation Farm Plan

Before making any recommendation for a certain tract of land, the conservationist must be able to classify the different kinds of land within that tract and determine the needs for each. He must know how to weigh the various factors that contribute in any material respect to this complicated problem, and then, finally, to prescribe specific treatments for each different kind of land that will correct the unwise uses and methods of farming.

For example, on a gently sloping portion of a field, a certain crop rotation and utilization of the crop residues may be all that is needed, whereas on a steeper portion of the same field an extra green manuring may be required every third year, and on a steep hill, a permanent cover of either hay or trees may be necessary.

Since no two farms are identical and no two farmers are alike, no two farm plans should be the same. The different kinds of soil and cover, varying slopes, and sites under different intensities and amounts of wind, precipitation, sunshine, humidity and temperatures require variant treatments. Usually several conservation practices protect and maintain the land against deterioration. The first step in making a conservation farm plan is to plot on a map, often a vertical aerial photograph, the physical factors of soil, slope, erosion, cover, and others that affect conditions, and, from knowledge of the many contributing factors, the technician evolves a particular combination of practices for each unit area on the map.

Land Capability Classes

Several systems of classification of the land's capacity are being currently employed in the Northwest, but that of the Soil Conservation Service of the U. S. Department of Apriculture classifies all lands into eight major types that are based primarily upon safety of use. Although, in theory, every acre of land fits into one of the eight classes (Plate 9B), in practice difficulties arise.[1] (Figure 21 shows land use.)

[1] These eight classes are described as follows:

Class I. Very good land that can be cultivated safely with ordinary good farming methods. It is nearly level and easily worked. Some areas need clearing, water management, or fertilization. Usually there is little or no erosion.

Class II. Good land that can be cultivated safely with easily applied practices. The usual requirements are rotations and fertilization. They may also include such measures as contouring, protective cover crops, and simple water-management operations. Moderate erosion is common under exploitative land-use.

Class III. Moderately good land that can be cultivated more safely with such protection as terracing, strip cropping, rotation, cover crops, and fertilization. Usually it is subject to moderate to severe erosion under exploitative methods of using the land.

Class IV. Fairly good land that is best suited to pasture and hay but can be cultivated occasionally, usually not oftener than 1 year in 6. Even when plowed only occasionally the most intensive erosion-prevention practices are required.

Class V. Suited for grazing or forestry with little or no limitations.

Class VI. Suited for grazing or forestry with minor limitations; needs protective measures.

Class VII. Suited for grazing or forestry with major limitations; needs extreme care to prevent land damage.

Class VIII. Suited only for wildlife or recreation. This land usually is rough, stony, sandy, wet, or highly erodible.

The major conservation farming measures (Plate 9A) now used in the Northwest are as follows.

CONTOUR FARMING. Plowing, planting, cultivating, and harvesting sloping fields on the level: that is, farming on the contour around hill-

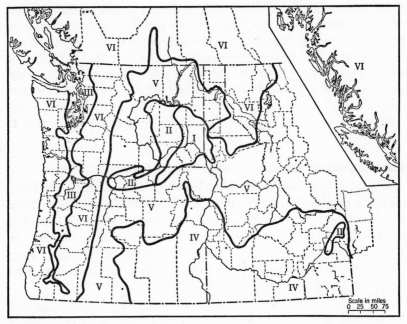

FIG. 21. Generalized land use in the Northwest. (*Photograph by Soil Conservation Service.*)

I. Palouse-Walla Walla area (largely agriculture with annual cropping predominant).

II. Wheat-summer fallow area (dryland agriculture predominant).

III. Coastal valleys agricultural area (agriculture, pasture and forest checkerboard).

IV. Intermountain range area (irrigated cases and summer fallowed foothills dotting this case rangeland).

V. Mountain forest grazing area (jointly used for forest and range with scattered agricultural areas).

VI. Mountain forest area (primarily dense forest cover).

sides with transverse furrows to fit the lay of the land, instead of straight up-and-down-hill furrows. Such furrows catch rainfall and allow much of it to soak into the ground. This conserves water and greatly reduces the amount of soil that is washed away. Part of the extra water which thus enters the soil is used by crops, and part is added to the underground water supply to feed springs, wells, streams, and ponds.

CONTOUR FURROWING has not been widely used in the Northwest and is limited to pastureland and rangeland. It involves making furrows on the level to hold rainfall. This helps the growth of pasture and range grasses. Where runoff has been excessive, this measure decreases the loss and in effect increases the rainfall.

CONTOUR SUBSOILING. Breaking up hard subsoil so that it can absorb more rainfall. This is done mostly on pasturelands to improve the grass stand. Subsoilers follow contours, and the intervals vary with land and cover. This practice gives best results when the subsoil is dry and brittle enough to shatter when the subsoiler passes through it.

COVER CROPS. Dense crops that prevent erosion of cultivated areas at times when there are few or no other plants for protection against wind and water erosion. There are summer covers, winter covers, and perennial covers. Legumes and grasses are used most commonly.

CROP ROTATIONS. Alternating production of various crops on a piece of land. On rich land it keeps the soil productive, and on rundown land it improves the soil. In a good rotation, one soil-building crop helps the next. For example, nitrogen, needed for plant growth, is added to the soil by legumes, such as clover, alfalfa, and vetch. After they have rotted, the nitrogen can be used for growth by plants that do not have the power to fix nitrogen, such as corn, sugar beets, and potatoes. Rotations often are integrated with strip cropping by shifting the close-growing strips and the tilled strips at fixed periods. In this way the soil is improved by the same cropping system used to stop erosion.

CROSS-SLOPE FARMING. This practice is an imitation of contour farming but is not sufficiently accurately done to qualify as such. Although not quite as effective, it is a valuable practice.

DIVERSION CHANNELS. Channels with a ridge on the lower side. The ridges sometimes are larger than field terrace ridges and are farther apart. Otherwise they are much the same. They are built with a low channel gradient across slopes to divert damaging or wasteful runoff.

DRAINAGE. Removal of excess water from wet land by ditches or by tile drains. Such artificial waterways must be kept free of silt by protecting the watershed from erosion or by desilting the water as it enters. Open ditches also must be kept free of plant growth and debris that stop drainage, or the benefits will be lost.

FERTILIZING LAND. Use of manure or fertilizer on land that needs additional plant food to stimulate plant growth.

FIELD AND GULLY PLANTING. Planting eroded or erodible land, which is unsuitable for cultivation, to trees, shrubs, grassses, vines, or other useful plants that will help stop erosion and will also conserve rainfall.

GRASSED WATERWAYS. Protected channels and outlets carry off excess water from terraces and near contour crop rows. These waterways are stabilized against erosion by grasses, legumes, and vines. They include meadow strips, grassed ditches, diversion ditches, and grassed channels at the ends of field terraces.

GREEN MANURING. Turning under legumes, grass, or grain crops improves the soil by adding to the supply of organic matter. The soil tilth is also improved.

GULLY CONTROL. Using plants and mechanical measures to stop eroding gullies. These measures reduce the rate of water flow. It is done by using (1) grass, vines, trees, and shrubs; (2) flumes and other devices to lessen the cutting power of waterfalls; and (3) dams for catching silt.

IRRIGATION. Spreading water on land by safe methods to increase crop yields. Applying water with sprinkler systems is the safest method.

IRRIGATION DEVELOPMENT AND IMPROVEMENT. Management of water for irrigation. The term includes building and improving water distribution systems on farms; land preparation, such as leveling; measurement and control of water; development or improvement of springs and wells; and disposal of waste water.

MEADOW DEVELOPMENT. Using land not suitable for cultivation to grow hay. The land should be plowed only to renew planting.

PASTURE DEVELOPMENT. Developing new pastures with selected grasses and legumes and different combinations thereof. It may include fertilization, liming, drainage, irrigation, fencing, clipping, spreading droppings, and other measures.

PASTURE IMPROVEMENT. Using measures that increase growth and improve quality of forage species. It includes such measures as deferred and rotation grazing, proper stocking, stock water ponds or wells placed to encourage better distribution of livestock, spacing of salt and bedding grounds for the same purpose, reseeding, liming and fertilizing, basin listing, and contour furrowing, water spreading, weed control, clipping, spreading droppings, and fire protection.

POND MANAGEMENT. Use of suitable measures (*a*) to protect ponds from erosion and siltation and (*b*) to aid production of fish and other pond wildlife.

RANGE MANAGEMENT. Includes deferred and rotation grazing and sometimes reseeding, as well as other supplemental aids to maintain the range at its optimum continuous and permanent production and to maintain the soil.

SHELTERBELTS. WINDBREAKS. Plantings of trees and shrubs in strips or belts usually 1 to 10 rows wide. The main purpose is to deflect wind current, thereby reducing wind erosion and snow drifting. Such strips of trees and shrubs also conserve rainfall through increased absorption by the soil, and protect fields and gardens, livestock, orchards, and buildings.

STRIP CROPPING. When designed to retard soil washing, contoured strips having heavy crop cover alternate with row crop strips. When designed to prevent soil drifting, similar strips are placed at right angles to prevailing wind. When combined with crop rotation, green manuring, and stubble mulch, it proves extremely valuable.

STUBBLE-MULCHING OR MULCHING. This practice is also called *trashy fallow*. It involves leaving crop residues and soil-improving crops at least partly on the ground instead of burning them or turning them under. These materials include grain stubble, straw, cornstalks, sweet clover, and other protective cover crops. Mulching protects the soil from erosion and baking, cuts down erosion and evaporation, lowers the soil temperature in summer, helps the soil to absorb more rainfall, decreases the degree of freezing, and aids growth of useful bacteria in the soil. The practice requires implements that do not turn the soil upside down.

TERRACING. Ridging land on or nearly on the contour. The farmer builds up low ridges or embankments of soil across sloping fields to intercept rainfall. Terraces with slight grade slow down runoff water resulting either in increased absorption or in guiding the runoff to safe disposal at the sides of the fields. This controlled excess water runs off slowly, causing relatively little erosion. Level terraces hold all the rainfall on the land, unless they are overtopped.

WATER SPREADING. Controlled spreading of runoff water in areas of low rainfall from the foot of slopes and from gullies and washes over nearby land that needs it. This is done by dikes, dams, and other means of directing water from one place to another. The object is to make use of all water in low-rainfall areas, rather than waste it.

WILDLIFE-AREA IMPROVEMENT. Management of area for best environmental habitat for wildlife may include special plantings of suitable species of food plants, protection of area against fire and grazing, and protection of wildlife against predators.

WOODLAND MANAGEMENT. Handling woodlands to secure maximum production possible under safe land use. Includes protection from fire, insects, disease, and injurious grazing, thinning, selective cutting, and harvest and improvement cuttings.

OTHER PRACTICES. Since this science is so new, other important practices will undoubtedly evolve and be added to the list with the passing years. Changes in the specifications of some of the above practices certainly will also occur.

NORTHWEST HISTORY OF SOIL CONSERVATION

Although prevention of soil erosion was advocated by a few farseeing persons in the United States ever since colonial times, the earliest known reference to this problem in the Northwest was by W. J. Spillman,[2] who used the term *soil conservation*, although at that time he meant just the prevention of soil erosion. Several Northwest bulletins mention soil erosion and soil blowing during the next two decades, but not until 1929–31 did it receive any important official attention in the Northwest.

With the study of erosion and its control which was started at Pullman in 1930, we have the first tangible progress in this direction.

The next forward moves came when the Soil Erosion Service (changed to Soil Conservation Service in 1935) started the following projects.

Palouse, Pullman, Washington, 1933.
Wildhouse, Athena, Oregon, 1934.
Squaw Valley, Montour, Idaho, 1934.
Badger Pocket, Ellensburg, Washington, 1935.
Chehalem Mountain, Newburg, Oregon, 1935.
Rock Creek, Condon, Oregon, 1935.

Soil conservation nurseries for selecting, breeding, and growing new plants for conservation were also started as follows: at Pullman in 1935; at Bellingham, Washington, Warrenton, Oregon, in 1936; and at Aberdeen, Idaho, in 1939.

[2] Department of Agriculture, *Farmers' Bulletin* 406, Pullman, Washington, 1910.

In 1936, through the Agricultural Adjustment Administration (now the Agricultural Conservation Program of the Production and Marketing Administration), government support of soil conservation was started through an entirely different channel with cash payments for conservation work on farms. These have continued from then until now. Under this program, a large majority of the Northwest's farmers

FIG. 22. Soil conservation districts in Pacific Northwest.

cooperated in the 1930's, but the percentage of farmers participating during the 1940's and early 1950's rather steadily decreased.

In 1940, the first farmer-sponsored soil conservation districts in the region were organized, and the efforts of the Soil Conservation Service toward conserving our soil resources swung almost entirely to work with these soil conservation districts (Fig. 22). By years, the number of these districts in the Northwest has grown as follows.

1939	0	1947	102
1941	33	1949	130
1943	48	1951	151
1945	64		

The people of the Pacific Northwest are showing an increasing interest in their land problems, and landowners and operators are steadily improving their farm practices. Present trends indicate that soil conservation is here to stay.

REFERENCES

Bennett, H. H., *Soil Conservation*, McGraw-Hill Book Co., New York, 1936.

Bennett, H. H., *Elements of Soil Conservation*, McGraw-Hill Book Co., New York, 1947.

Chase, Stuart, *Rich Land, Poor Land*, McGraw-Hill Book Co., New York, 1936.

Graham, Edward H., *Natural Principles of Land Use*, Oxford University Press, 1944.

Jacks, G. V., and R. O. Whyte, *The Rape of the Earth*, Faber & Faber, London, 1939. The American edition is entitled *Vanishing Lands: A World Survey of Soil Erosion*, Doubleday, Doran & Company, New York, 1939.

"Soil Conservation Society of America," *Journal of Soil and Water Conservation*, 1945 to date.

Marsh, G. P., *The Earth as Modified by Human Action*, Charles Scribner's Sons, New York, 1907 (first edition, 1884).

Mickey, Karl B., *Man and the Soil*, International Harvester Co., Chicago, 1945.

Sears, Paul B., *Deserts on the March*, University of Oklahoma Press, Norman, 1935.

Sharpe, C. F. S., *What Is Soil Erosion?*, Publication 286, U. S. Department of Agriculture, Washington, D. C., 1936.

Shepard, Ward, *Food or Famine*, The Macmillan Co., New York, 1945.

Thompson, Margaret, and Otis W. Freeman, *The Conservation of Northwest Resources*, Grange Cooperative Printing Assoc., Seattle, 1950.

U. S. Department of Agriculture, "Soils and Men," *The Yearbook of Agriculture*, Washington, D. C., 1938.

U. S. Department of Agriculture, *Soil Conservation*, Washington, D. C., 1935 to date.

Vogt, William, *Road to Survival*, William Sloane Associates, New York, 1938.

The Natural Grasslands
of the Northwest;
Their Importance and Management

A. L. HAFENRICHTER

Extent of Grasslands

The major areas of natural grasslands of the Pacific Northwest are found east of the Cascade Mountains. Nearly all the untimbered land in eastern Washington, eastern Oregon, southern Idaho, and western Montana once was a vast expanse of bunchgrass prairie.

In the original condition more than 90 million acres, or 140,000 square miles, of grassland covered this part of the Northwest. Waving seas of grass, often stirrup-high to a horse, greeted the early explorers.[1] A typical view of this bunchgrass prairie is shown in Plate 10A.

In some places, particularly in southern Idaho, and in portions of eastern Oregon and eastern Washington, sagebrush was scattered in the grassland. Grasslands merged rather abruptly into the forest at higher elevations, but throughout the timbered area they retained their identity at lower elevations, being present along the major drainageways in the Blue Mountains of Oregon and the Rocky Mountains of southern Idaho, western Montana, and northeastern Washington. The transition zone of separation between forest and grassland is short and characteristically represented in the browse-shrub and ponderosa pine types.

Importance of Grasslands

The Northwest grasslands support a large and important range livestock industry. They are the principal lands which have been converted to farming enterprises, and they afford protection to the water-

---

[1] J. C. Fremont, "Report of the Explorering Expedition to the Rocky Mountains in the Year 1842, and to Oregon and Northern California in the Years 1843 to 1844," *Document 166*, Blair and Rives, Washington, 1845.

shed of the Columbia River and its tributaries. Interspersed as they
now are with cropland where feed is produced, and adjacent to forest
lands that are grazed during the summer months, the grasslands constitute an essential economic link in Northwest agriculture.

The grasslands found by the early explorers in the Pacific Northwest
did not support great herds of wild grazing animals such as the buffalo
found in the Great Plains, although some antelope were found in
southern Oregon and wild horses were reported in eastern Washington.

Livestock was first introduced into the interior from posts and forts
in western Washington and Oregon about 1825, and about 10 years
later cattle, sheep, oxen, and horses began arriving with settlers who
came across the plains. The livestock population grew rapidly. In
1850 there were only 42,000 cattle and 15,000 sheep in Washington,
Oregon, and Idaho. By 1900 these numbers had increased to 1,177,000
cattle and 4,483,000 sheep. The number of sheep continued to increase for the next 10 years, whereas the number of cattle increased
but slightly.

Exact data for the numbers of beef cattle and sheep on range lands
are difficult to obtain, but it is estimated that in 1930 the grasslands of
the Northwest supported slightly more than 750,000 beef cattle, exclusive of young stock, and nearly 4 million sheep, exclusive of lambs.[2]
In eastern Oregon and Washington about 75 per cent of all sheep are
range flocks; in Idaho about 65 per cent are range flocks. Both classes
of livestock obtain much of their feed in the late fall and early spring
from the grasslands. About 50 per cent of the cattle and 75 per cent
of the lambs are marketed grass-fat or as feeders from the range; the
remainder are marketed after being fattened on fall pastures and
winter feed lots. These figures indicate the importance of Northwest
grasslands which, in addition to their value for grazing, are intimately
related to agricultural lands where winter feeds are produced and to
the forest lands that supply the summer range from about May 1 to
October 1 or later.

Large portions of the bunchgrass prairie of the Northwest were converted to croplands. The prairies were first plowed for wheat production about 1870, and by the turn of the century about 12 million acres

[2] A. E. Orr et al., "Trends and Desirable Adjustments in Washington Agriculture," Washington Agricultural Experiment Station Bulletin 335, 1936.

H. A. Vogel and N. W. Johnson, "Types of Farming in Idaho," Idaho Agricultural Experiment Station Bulletin 207, 1934.

H. D. Scudder and E. B. Hurd, "Graphic Summary of Agriculture and Land
Use in Oregon," Oregon Agricultural Experiment Station Circular 114, 1935.

in the semihumid areas had been converted to this use. During the First World War additional thousands of acres in the more arid areas were converted to wheat production. Under the impetus of high wheat prices, and high yield from new land, this proved successful. When prices returned to normal and wind erosion occurred, however, it was no longer economical or feasible to farm these marginal lands, and they were abandoned.

Late in the nineteenth century irrigation development began, and a total of about 5 million additional acres of grassland was converted to irrigation farming. It is estimated that nearly 1 million additional acres in central Washington that are now rangeland may be converted to other agricultural use when the water facilities being developed for irrigation are completed.

The grasslands of the Northwest have an important role in water-shed protection. They provide the essential vegetation cover for 40 to 50 million acres of watershed of the Columbia River system. On this river system are some of the largest storage reservoirs and power developments of the West. Many smaller reservoirs and diversion irrigation works are located on tributary streams. Numerous facilities to provide stock water and irrigation for hay meadows are located on individual ranches. All these developments are a recognized integral part of western agriculture and represent a large investment of private and public funds.

Reduction of storage capacity of reservoirs by siltation or by damage to irrigation or power developments by floods reflects itself in individual, community, and public welfare. Frequent floods affecting large areas, property, and human life are not widespread because the grasslands are most commonly located in areas with low precipitation; but localized torrential rains occur and damaging floods are reported from small grassland watersheds in the vicinity of Boise and Pocatello, Idaho, in the northern part of eastern Oregon, and in eastern Washington. Damage by siltation or floods occurs only on grassland watersheds where the vegetal cover is depleted or has been destroyed.

Ecology of Grasslands

The grasslands of the Northwest are known as the Palouse prairie climax.[3] This climax [4] is part of the great grassland formation of west-

---

[3] F. E. Clements et al., "Ecology," *Carnegie Institution of Washington Yearbook*, Vol. 38, pp. 134–140, 1939.

[4] The climax is a concept denoting a mature vegetation with a floristic composition and ecological structure developed through succession and capable of

ern North America that supports the vast range industry of the United States west of the 100th meridian. The Palouse prairie is characterized by being composed chiefly of perennial bunchgrasses. The sod-forming grasses of the Great Plains are absent except in the transition zone in western Montana and in a narrow transition area in southeastern Idaho. This prairie is a climax vegetation which has developed in relatively recent times. The chief factors that have caused it to be defferentiated from other plant associations in the grassland formation are rainless summers and cool growing seasons during spring and fall while moisture is available. The plants are usually dormant during the dry summers and cold winters.

The dominant species that give the bunchgrass aspect to the Palouse prairie climax are blue bunch and beardless wheatgrass (*Agropyron spicatum* and *A. inerme*) and two needlegrasses (*Stipa comata* and *S. occidentalis*). Associated with wheatgrass and needlegrass are Idaho fescue (*Festuca idahoensis*), Sandberg's bluegrass (*Poa secunda*), big bluegrass (*P. ampla*) or Nevada bluegrass (*P. nevadensis*), and June grass (*Koeleria cristata*). Two native forbs [5] usually occur—yarrow (*Achillea millfolium*) and balsamroot (*Balsamorrhiza sagitata*). The most common species of the prairie are shown in Plate 10*B*.

No great expanses of the climax prairie remain, but remnants may be found throughout the original area. These occur where protection from grazing or other disturbance has been provided, such as fenced rights-of-way, cemeteries, and monuments, on inaccessible or excessively steep land, or where good range management has been practiced.

Several experimental enclosures have been established during the past ten years, and in a relatively short time most of them have passed through successional vegetative stages to the true climax. A characteristic of these climax remnants is the luxuriance of the vegetation and the density of the ground cover as shown in Plate 10*A*. All the grasses in the climax prairie have been found to be palatable and

maintaining both its composition and structure indefinitely unless a major change in climate occurs. It is a stabilized association of plants that is inherently capable of perpetuating itself unless some natural factor or man-made process destroys the equilibrium between the plants and the environment. For a discussion of ecological terms the reader is referred to: J. E. Weaver and F. E. Clements, *Plant Ecology*, McGraw-Hill, New York, 1929.

[5] *Forbs* are herbs other than grasses, and at certain seasons they are quite conspicuous in the prairie.

nutritious, even the cured, dry forage known to ranchers as "standing hay." The luxuriance of the virgin prairie attracted the early explorers and was in part responsible for the rapid development of the range industry.

Climatic factors caused the development of the climax bunchgrass prairie in the Northwest, and because they are unique they also affect the use and management of the grassland as range. The rangelands are too steep, rough, shallow, or too dry to cultivate, and receive only 8 to 15 inches of rainfall during the fall, winter, and spring months; no effective rainfall occurs during the summer months.

During the fall and spring when the grasses are growing actively, they are intensely grazed, but the stock is moved to the higher forest ranges during the summer when the forage on the prairie is dry and water for the stock is scarce or lacking. Summer grazing is sometimes practiced where range is interspersed with cropland. Severe winters over much of the area prohibit grazing at this season and require that stock be given supplementary feed. Localized areas serve as winter range and are commonly located adjacent to breeding grounds in the river valleys under the protection afforded by the deep canyons. The valleys of the lower Snake River in the vicinity of Boise and Lewiston, Idaho, of the Columbia, the Snake, and Yakima rivers in Washington, and the Owyhee River in Oregon are typical examples.

Climatic hazards consist chiefly of recurring years with below normal precipitation and severe winters. With an already scanty rainfall, low-rainfall years have a pronounced effect on the volume of forage produced. Such years occur, on an average, as often as 1 to 3 years in 10 and may reduce yields as much as 50 per cent. They do not seem to have a pronounced effect on the composition of the prairie, although the density and vigor of the grasses are reduced often to a considerable extent and recovery in favorable years may be retarded.[6] Severe winters have adverse effects on livestock unless sufficient supplementary feed is available. In the early development of the range industry such seasons caused severe losses and emphasized the need for feed production.

Changes in Grassland

The present aspect of most of the grassland area is very different from the luxuriant climax reported by the pioneers. In a classification

[6] J. F. Pechanec, G. D. Pickford, and George Stewart, "Effects of the 1934 Drought on Native Vegetation of the Upper Snake River Plains, Idaho," *Ecology*, Vol. 18, pp. 490–505, 1937.

based on the general aspect to the observer, the rangelands of the Northwest as they occur today are divided into types and subtypes of which (1) perennial grasslands, (2) sagebrush, and (3) annual grass are the most common and important, whereas (4) meadows and other types, like the browse-shrub and weed, are less important because they are limited in extent (Plates 10A and 10B).

The perennial grassland type has the general appearance of the virgin Palouse prairie except that in many places the needlegrasses (Stipa spp.) are inconspicuous. This type occurs in many parts of the region, being typical and most extensive where it intersperses wheat-lands, approaches the timber transition zone, or is distant from water supplies. It consists mostly of perennial grasses denoting good grazing practice and has a grazing capacity of 6 to 10 animal months per acre.[7] This type can be seen in many parts of the Northwest along common routes of travel in eastern Oregon, eastern Washington, and western Montana. In southern Idaho it is located at the higher elevations above the Snake River plains.

The sagebrush type is now extensive in southern Idaho, southeastern Oregon, and central Washington. This type has increased at the expense of the grasslands and occupies some of the abandoned cropland. In its original condition it consisted of a rather sparse cover of sagebrush in a rich stand of the climax grasses and some palatable weeds. Today the sagebrush is much thicker and may even appear to be dominant. It has been shown that sagebrush invades grassland range and increases with great rapidity when the grasslands are heavily and continuously grazed in the early spring while the plants are growing.[8] Continuous early spring grazing has been a common practice, and as a result the palatable perennial grasses have disappeared or are greatly reduced in density and vigor; weeds, annual grasses, and often poisonous plants have replaced them. The grazing capacity of the sagebrush type has declined more than 65 per cent, nearly 9 acres being required per animal month of grazing as compared with 3 acres or less 60 years ago.

[7] Grazing capacity values of range types vary within limits depending chiefly on climatic conditions and intensity of use. Values for average grazing capacity in this section are taken from several sources, but for further information the reader is referred to R. E. McArdle et al., "The Western Range. III. The White Man's Toll," Senate Document 199, pp. 81–116, 1936.

[8] G. W. Craddock and C. L. Forsling, "The Influence of Climate and Grazing on Spring-Fall Sheep Range in Southern Idaho," U. S. Department of Agriculture Bulletin 600, 1938.

The annual grass range obtains its aspect or general appearance from cheatgrass (*Bromus tectorum*). This introduced low-value, winter annual was rare before 1890, but it is now generally distributed throughout the region. It has invaded poorly managed grassland, sagebrush, and other types and occupies a large part of the abandoned cropland. Typical examples are found on the breaks of the Columbia and Snake River canyons in Oregon, Washington, and western Idaho. This type is especially persistent where range fires are frequent on overgrazed ranges. It has a grazing capacity only slightly greater than the sagebrush range and is of value only in the early spring and late fall.

The grass meadows are not extensive but are vital to the livestock industry. Interspersed with other types in the valleys of the range lands where additional moisture is available or can be provided, they supply the hay essential to wintering stock. They may consist of stands of one of the big bluegrasses and wild ryegrasses (*Elymus triticoides* or *E. canadensis*) on moist meadows as is common in eastern Oregon, saltgrass (*Distichlis spicata*) and giant ryegrass (*E. condensatus*) if the alkalinity and water table are high, or sedges mixed with grass on wet meadows. Many have been converted to cultivated hay crops and irrigated. Other types occur but are close to or within the timber types and generally not extensive because the transition zones in the northwest are quite abrupt.

RESULTS OF CHANGES. These changes in aspect have been accompanied by a far-reaching change in forage value. In place of palatable and nutritious perennial grasses in the once extensive grasslands, are unpalatable shrubs and weeds in the sagebrush type and less-valuable species in the annual grass type. In addition, the whole plant cover is thinner, much soil has been lost by erosion, and water from rains and melting snow is lost as runoff instead of being absorbed. These conditions are illustrated in C and D of Plate 10A. It is estimated that the bunchgrass ranges have been depleted to less than half their original value.[9] In its original condition one square mile of the open range could supply 220 to 290 animal unit months of grazing, but at present the grazing capacity is estimated to vary from 70 to 140 animal months per square mile, depending on type. The rangelands are actually being required to support nearly twice this amount of stock; hence the prospect of further decline in value is imminent.

[9] E. H. Clapp, "The Western Range. I. The Major Range Problems and Their Solution," *Senate Document* 199, pp. 1–69, 1936.

In addition to reduced carrying capacity as a result of depletion, the value of the grasslands for the protection of watershed has also decreased. When the cover of vegetation on the grasslands is properly maintained, accelerated runoff and soil erosion do not occur; but depleted rangelands are constantly visited with these companion ills.

A study conducted on the Boise River watershed typically reveals the relation between plant cover, runoff, and soil erosion. Well-managed rangeland with bunchgrass cover absorbed an average of 99.6 per cent of the precipitation and lost only 6 pounds of soil per acre. Overgrazed rangeland in annual weeds absorbed only 39.2 per cent of the precipitation and lost 60.8 per cent as runoff with an accompanying soil loss of 15,280 pounds per acre.[10] The soil lost from overgrazed ranges contributes to stream siltation, and runoff water contributes to floods and abnormal stream flow.

Siltation affects navigation and reduces reservoir capacity. A typical example is the Arrowrock reservoir. Despite heavy sluicing, this reservoir lost by siltation 7500 acre-feet of storage capacity costing $100,000 to develop in the 12 years between 1915 and 1927.[11] The entire Boise River watershed of nearly 1.7 million acres supports a dependent irrigation area of 355,000 acres valued at 70 million dollars. About one-fourth of this watershed is overgrazed grassland on which sheet erosion is widespread and gullies are present to a serious degree.

The application of this illustration to the watersheds of other reservoirs that supply irrigation water for the 5 million acres of irrigated land in the Northwest is apparent. Underground water supplies also are reduced when accelerated runoff occurs, and loss of both water and soil from the grasslands reduces the ability of the range to produce plant cover and feed for livestock.

CAUSE OF CHANGES AND METHODS OF IMPROVEMENT. The depletion of cover, the consequent reduction in grazing capacity, and the change in kind and density of vegetation in the Palouse prairie grasslands are due to improper range management. The rapid rise in number of livestock during the last half of the nineteenth century, along with the free use of much of the range, and lack of a plan for constructive management of the grasslands caused depletion to be recognized as early as 1900. Despite several investigations, and reports and evidence

[10] G. W. Craddock and C. K. Pearse, "Surface Run-Off and Erosion on Granitic Mountain Soils of Idaho as Influenced by Range Cover, Soil Disturbance, Slope, and Precipitation Intensity," *U. S. Department of Agriculture Circular* 482, 1938.

[11] F. G. Renner, "Conditions Influencing Erosion on the Boise River Watershed," *U. S. Department of Agriculture Technical Bulletin* 528, 1936.

that the majority of stockmen recognized depletion and overgrazing,[12] about 85 per cent of the open ranges continued to decline in value during the 30-year period from 1905 to 1935.[13]

Since 1935 several federal government service agencies and state agencies have been working with organized groups of ranchers in a cooperative effort to effectuate remedial measures. Although it will be impossible to restore much of the grassland to more than 60 to 80 per cent of its original cover and grazing capacity, it has been demonstrated that relatively simple management procedures rapidly produce desired improvement if persistently followed. The most important of these are: (1) proper stocking, (2) proper seasonal use, (3) proper distribution of livestock, and (4) reseeding.[14]

Proper stocking includes adjustment of kinds and numbers of stock to the determined grazing capacity of the range. The grasslands of the Northwest are generally well suited for utilization by the two types of livestock most common in the region; cattle and sheep. Hence, after the grazing capacity of a range is determined by the range examiner who computes the kind and density of the vegetation and converts this to animal months per acre, the adjustment of numbers can be made. An essential requirement of adjusting numbers of stock to the grazing capacity is a recognition of the fact that this varies from year to year with variations in climate, particularly rainfall, and method of management. Therefore, safe stocking requires that the numbers grazed be about 25 per cent below the average forage production, or that the numbers vary with the season and the conditions of the range.

Since the Palouse prairie grasses depend chiefly on seed for their perpetuation and make most of their growth in the spring, proper seasonal use is obtained by deferred and rotation grazing. This is a particularly applicable practice in the Northwest. It provides for withholding grazing from one unit of the ranch each year until the grasses mature seed, and for grazing the units in rotation. Stock is removed from the range in the fall, when 20 to 30 per cent of the palatable

[12] W. A. Richards, F. H. Newell, and G. Pinchot, "Grazing on Public Lands," Public Lands Commission, *Senate Document* 189, *U. S. Department of Agriculture Forest Service Bulletin* 62, 1905.

[13] R. E. McArdle et al., "The Western Range," *Senate Document* 199, III, pp. 81–116, 1936.

[14] For a more complete discussion of management methods the student is referred to: J. T. Jardine and M. Anderson, "Range Management on the National Forests," *U. S. Department of Agriculture Bulletin* 790, 1919.

growth is still left. This method has received critical study and has been shown to be particularly applicable to Northwest ranges, where perennial bunchgrasses are the climax vegetation. Such treatment coincides admirably with the growth requirement of the plants.[15] Increasing the supplementary feed supply facilitates management in obtaining deferred and rotation grazing. By these methods plants are strengthened and new ones established.

Hardly a range has been surveyed and studied in the Northwest where improved distribution of stock would not be beneficial. Uniform distribution is accomplished by providing salt and water at regular but different intervals on the range, the use of well-located drift fences, and proper attention to herding. Uniform distribution relieves a common situation found on ranges whereby some areas are overutilized and depleted whereas others are underutilized and the feed wasted.

Reseeding severely depleted ranges may be necessary and has been successfully accomplished, but at disproportionate expense and with a high hazard of expectancy of establishing successful stands. This practice will probably apply best to abandoned wheatlands which must be reseeded if more than low-value annual grasses or weeds are obtained. The long, rainless summer season coupled with the fact that Palouse prairie grasses propagate by seed had been shown to mitigate against natural revegetation on plowed and abandoned land.

Results of Proper Management

The Northwest grasslands have responded in a remarkable degree to proper range management. The data from two contiguous areas on one ranch in eastern Washington are indicative of what may be accomplished in a short time.[16] One area on this ranch, when properly managed for one year, produced 2429 pounds per acre of green feed, 16 inches tall, whereas an adjacent improperly managed, unprotected area produced only 704 pounds per acre of feed, 8 inches tall. On another ranch, 1 year of good management increased the grazing capacity 22 per cent and the weight of grass per acre by 32 per cent; particularly striking was the fact that the perennial grasses, wheatgrass, Idaho fescue, and Sandberg's bluegrass, increased 30, 20, and 10 per cent in density, respectively, whereas the less valuable, annual cheatgrass decreased 25 per cent. The combined increase in the density of

---

[15] G. W. Craddock and C. L. Forsling, *U. S. Department of Agriculture Bulletin* 600, 1938.

[16] Unpublished data, Soil Conservation Service, Region 9.

all grasses was 15 per cent. These values were obtained on range-land that had previously lost 25 to 50 per cent of the topsoil by erosion and indicate the recuperative power of the climax species when proper management methods are determined and applied.

Not only do grasslands respond to expedients of good management by increase in growth and density of valuable perennial climax grasses at the expense of low-value annuals and weeds, but it has been determined that proper management increases economy of stock production. In one experiment, cows on overgrazed range produced a 73 per cent calf crop weighing an average of 197 pounds when four months old, whereas on properly grazed range an 84 per cent calf crop weighing an average of 257 pounds was obtained.[17] Thirty per cent more feed was required for the stock on the overgrazed range, and the market value of the lighter calves was less.

By proper management of the grasslands the vicious cycle of cover depletion, accelerated runoff and erosion, and reduced income per unit is reversed to a favorable cycle of improved cover and feed, conservation of soil and water, and increased income. By proper management many of the valuable perennial grasses of the Palouse climax prairie can be restored and maintained.

It will not be possible in most cases to restore the climax to its virgin condition and maintain it under grazing use. The aim of proper management should be to attain a sustained-yield forage production which will allow a sustained-yield livestock production. Good management will prevent invasion of annual grass, undesirable weeds, and sagebrush. It will recognize that continuous heavy grazing in the early spring and late fall is damaging to the growth and perpetuation of bunchgrasses. It will recognize that range fire should be prevented and that grasslands suitable only for range purposes should not be plowed for temporary crop production.

A well-managed range that results in sustained yields will have an adequate density of perennial climax grass species to afford adequate watershed protection, and give the highest sustained economic return.

[17] See also L. C. Hurtt, "Overgrazing Increases Production Costs," *American Hereford Journal*, Vol. 26 (9), pp. 58, 60–61, 1935.

M. H. Saunderson and L. Vinke, "The Economics of Range Sheep Production in Montana," *Montana Agricultural Experiment Station Bulletin* 302, 1935.

CHAPTER

9

Northwest Minerals

EDWIN T. HODGE and OTIS W. FREEMAN

The Indians of the Northwest made weapons and domestic artifacts from obsidian, flint, lava, and other rocks or minerals but knew nothing about the extraction of minerals from their ores. After the discovery of gold in California, prospectors scattered widely throughout the western mountains and tested the stream beds for placer gold. In the late 1850's or the decade of the 1860's were recorded discoveries of gold placers in many sections of Idaho, Oregon, Montana, northeastern Washington, and British Columbia. Soon the miners discovered the veins of gold-bearing quartz and of silver, lead, copper, and other metals, but until railroad transportation was provided the mining of quartz was generally too expensive to be profitable. The building of railroads permitted the opening of base-metal mines early in the 1880's, and the Northwest has been an important producer of copper, lead, and zinc in addition to gold and silver ever since. The mining industry led to the exploration and settlement of mountain sections years before this would have happened otherwise. Mining provides freight for the railroads, aids the construction of highways and development of hydroelectric power, furnishes much of the wealth to construct our large cities, and affords a market to the farmers for part of their crops.

The total value of metals produced in the Northwest approximates $265,000,000 annually, divided as follows: British Columbia, $125,-000,000; Montana, $50,000,000; Idaho, $50,000,000; Washington, $25,-000,000; and Oregon, $5,000,000. In addition, coal, cement, rock, phosphates, and other nonmetals were produced to a total value of many millions of dollars. Since the beginning of mining, the entire output of minerals from the four northwestern states is valued at over $6,000,000,000, of which gold, silver, copper, lead, and zinc account

160

for $5,366,000,000 to the end of 1950. The Butte mines have produced in excess of $2,778,000,000 in metals, and the Coeur d'Alene mining region in Idaho has had an output of over $1,335,000,000. At present, the four northwestern states produce one-fourth of the lead, nearly one-half of the silver, one-twelfth of the copper, one-ninth of the gold, one-eighth of the mercury, one-fourth of the zinc, and nearly all the antimony produced in the United States.

In British Columbia the total production of metals to the end of 1951 exceeds $2,000,000,000, and including coal and other nonmetallics, the minerals have a total value from 1852 to the end of 1951 of $3,000,-000,000. The total value of all the minerals from British Columbia in 1951 was a record-breaking $164,000,000.

Origin of Mineral Deposits

Mineral deposits result from geologic processes. Hence it follows that, if the chemist, physicist, geologist, and paleontologist can determine the characteristics of mineral deposits and how they originated, additional deposits can be located and the ore mined economically. Ore deposits are formed during periods of geologic activity, when the crust of the earth is being altered by fracturing and folding, and when hot liquid rocks (magmas) are cutting their way to the surface. The most important deposits of metals are found in the older rocks near where igneous (molten) rocks have cooled and solidified as intrusive masses. In addition to the veins and other ore deposits formed by chemical processes underground are those formed by mechanical processes or concentration on top of the ground.

The term placer is given to mechanically made deposits formed at or near the surface by streams coming from areas of mineralized rock. Weathering releases minerals that largely resist change, like gold and platinum, and they then may be carried away by moving water and deposited in quiet reaches of the streams along with sand and gravel, forming a placer. Both stream and beach placers exist in the Northwest.

Coal is the principal mineral fuel occurring in the Northwest. By its association with coarse, cross-bedded sandstones, it seems the coal was formed from beds of vegetable matter that accumulated in deltas and floodplains. When such deposits are mostly under water decay is prevented, and when buried under a load of sediments the organic matter is slowly changed by heat and pressure into coal. Small deposits of natural gas have been discovered in the Northwest, but no petroleum in commercial quantities has yet been found west of the

Great Plains or north of central California, except a small quantity in Alaska.

Another group of deposits are associated with surface water. Minerals in solution may be precipitated by chemical interaction, evaporation, and the activities of bacteria and little plants called diatoms. Examples include deposits of carbonates and sulfates, mostly of sodium, in the beds of dried-up lakes, and deposits of limestone, iron, and other substances made by springs. Probably the bulk of the phosphate deposits are the result of the interaction of solutions.

The ore deposits formed underground in bodies of rock include the greater portion of the metallic mineral deposits in the Northwest. All rocks are more or less cracked, fractured, and broken. At times major fractures called faults have been sites where one portion of the earth has moved in relation to another. It is along such lines or zones of weakness that chemical solutions have passed and often deposited minerals of commercial value as in the Coeur d'Alene district. Sometimes deposits are formed from the mineral matter of the rock itself, for example clay, magnesite, and certain iron ores. The introduction or intrusion of foreign chemical matter into rock by igneous activity results in forming many of the Northwest's most important metallic ore bodies. These are mainly vein deposits formed in cracks and fractures by precipitation from hot ascending waters derived from volcanic rocks. Where igneous intrusives directly contact other rocks, ore deposits may be formed by alteration, replacement, or deposition of material in the invaded rock, and many large ore deposits have this origin.

In places the earth's crust has been folded and fractured and tilted upward to form mountains. Later erosion of the mountains exposed the hidden veins and lodes. As a result, older mineral-bearing rocks may now be exposed on top of the ground. This is important in an area where lava, lakebeds, and other rocks would normally cover the surface and hide whatever minerals might be below.

Ores are combinations of minerals that can be mined and sold at a profit. An ore commonly contains one or more valuable minerals and others that are worthless, called "gangue."

The price of a metal depends upon its abundance and the cost of mining and extraction (smelting). Thus, 6 tons of iron ore which is mined with power shovels from open pits can be purchased for the price of 1 ounce of gold. Nonmetallic substances such as coal, salt, feldspar, or building stone are used practically in the form in which they are extracted from the earth.

MINERAL DEPOSITS AND PRODUCTION

Coal

The coal of the Northwest has never received the exploitation expected, owing in part to competition with imported low-cost petroleum and local water power. Its qualities make it a possible source of raw material for the electrochemical and electrometallurgical industries.

Production in the Northwest states since the inception of coal mining totals over 130 million tons varying from lignite to high-grade bituminous and a little anthracite. The estimated total coal reserves in the United States part of the Northwest amount to about 64 billion tons, mostly in the state of Washington. In 1918 over 4 million tons were produced, but output has fallen. In 1950 it amounted to 1.2 million tons, some of which was exported to Japan. Research in utilization, both in firing and in the chemical industries, might assist in the revival of this industry. Competition with private power and imports of oil and higher grades of coal from British Columbia and Utah have hurt the industry. There are large reserves of coal in Alaska, but production is small.

Several types of coal occur in the Northwest and adjacent areas.

a. Metallurgical coking coals occur in western Washington; on Vancouver Island, British Columbia; in the Bering River and Matanuska coal fields of Alaska, all close to tidewater; and at Crow's Nest Pass, Alberta, Canada.

b. Bituminous coals of good grade are found in all the above districts and in central Washington.

c. Lignite coals are found extensively in Montana, western Washington, and near Coos Bay in southwestern Oregon.

d. Semianthracite coal occurs in quantity in the Cascade Range of western Washington, especially in Lewis County.

Oregon has numerous scattered coal fields, but only the one near Coos Bay has recorded a steady but small production.

Washington coal is mined extensively on the Puget lowland at Bellingham, at several centers in King, Pierce, Thurston, and Lewis counties, and on the eastern side of the Cascades in Kittitas County (Roslyn, Cle Elum, Easton), which leads the state in production.

Montana has more coal, 407 billion tons, than any other state west of the Mississippi, the bulk being lignite, although some is bituminous coal of coking grade. This is 11.5 per cent of that of the United States and 8 per cent of that of the world. With few exceptions the Montana coal is located in the Great Plains, not included in this study, but it furnishes fuel to western Montana and to a small extent to other parts of the Northwest.

Coal deposits are widely distributed throughout British Columbia and reserves may amount to many billion tons, with most of the production coming from three localities in the southern part; East Kootenay in the Rocky Mountains; and Nicola-Princeton and Vancouver Island in the coast district. The total coal produced from the province through 1950 was 112 million tons and the annual output amounts to 1.8 million long tons per year, valued at over $10,000,000. The coal is of good quality and some is of coking grade. Much of the coast coal is close to tidewater and is supplied to ships' bunkers, and some is exported to the United States.

Petroleum and Natural Gas

No commercial deposits of petroleum and very little natural gas have been found in the region, despite considerable exploratory work. Outside the region oil and gas occur in quantities on the Great Plains of Montana and Alberta. Petroleum is piped from Alberta to Vancouver, British Columbia, for refining there and at Ferndale, Washington. Imported oil is also refined at Anacortes, Washington. A pipeline is planned to bring natural gas into British Columbia and Washington. Some Montana petroleum is refined at Butte and Spokane, and oil products are imported to Spokane by pipeline from Utah.

Limestone and Building Stones

Limestone of high quality is widely distributed. Deposits are worked around Puget Sound both in Washington and British Columbia, in northeastern Washington and southern British Columbia, in northwestern and northeastern Oregon, and in southern Idaho and central Montana areas to supply cement plants, pulp mills, smelter flux, and lime for the manufacture of chemicals. A variety of lime products are used at Portland in chemical plants.

The largest cement plants are located at Trident and Hanover, Montana; at Bellingham, Concrete, Grotto, and Seattle in western Washington; at Metaline Falls and near Spokane in eastern Washington; near Pocatello, Idaho; at Gold Hill, Lime, and Oswego, Oregon; and near Victoria, British Columbia. Portland cement production totals about 10 million barrels a year for the four Northwestern states.

British Columbia's output of cement and lime is valued at over $4,000,-000 annually.

High-grade marble occurs near Northport, Washington, and in the Wallowa Mountains of Oregon, but neither marble nor limestone is quarried to any large extent for building purposes.

Because of the small demand the output of granite and other building stone is small, being restricted mainly to monumental and decorative purposes. Small granite quarries are operated near Spokane. Lavas and other stone are locally crushed for roads and other construction use in response to local demand.

Phosphorus and Fertilizer

The Northwestern states contain 93 per cent of the *high-grade* phosphate reserves of the United States and more than half of the world's known supply. There are proved resources of over 5 billion tons in southeastern Idaho and 400 million tons in Montana, whereas for the world as a whole only 10 billion tons are known. Phosphate rock is mined commercially in southeastern Idaho and near Garrison, Montana. The Garrison phosphate rock is mined and shipped to Trail, British Columbia, and phosphate rock from Conda, Idaho, is shipped to Anaconda, Montana, for processing. At these cities sulfur fumes from smelters are manufactured into sulfuric acid, which on being added to phosphate rock changes the material into superphosphate, a plant fertilizer. About 800,000 tons of rock phosphate, worth $5,000,000, are mined each year. This is one-tenth the output of the United States. Phosphates are manufactured also by hydroelectric power, and electrolytic processing plants are located at Pocatello and at Don, Idaho.

Magnesite and Magnesium

The huge deposits of magnesite that occur near Chewelah, Washington, are, as far as is known, the largest deposits on earth. The material is calcined in rotary kilns at Chewelah and shipped east for making firebrick and the furnace linings for open-hearth furnaces that manufacture steel. Magnesite also occurs in the East Kootenay near Marysville, British Columbia.

Deposits of dolomite (magnesium limestone) are known in northeastern Washington and have been utilized for the extraction of magnesium in a plant at Mead, a suburb of Spokane. Magnesium is one-tenth lighter than aluminum and is being put to so many new uses that Northwest production should continue at a high level.

Aluminum

Although the region lacks important deposits of bauxite, the common ore of aluminum, about one-third of the United States output of this metal comes from the Pacific Northwest because of the available cheap hydroelectric power. The bauxite is mined in South America and Jamaica, calcined to reduce weight, and then shipped to reduction plants in Washington, Oregon, and Montana located near ample sources of power. Two additional plants are under construction at Kitimat, British Columbia, and The Dalles, Oregon. Possible minor sources of aluminum ore are known in the Northwest, but production is insignificant.

TABLE 1

ESTIMATED CAPACITY OF NORTHWEST ALUMINUM PLANTS, POUNDS PER YEAR

Mead	240,000,000
Wenatchee	170,000,000
Vancouver	152,000,000
Troutdale	151,000,000
Kalispell	108,000,000
Longview	50,000,000
Tacoma	50,000,000
Total	1,124,000,000

Clay and Kaolin

Good clay deposits are scattered over all the northwestern states and in British Columbia. Numerous deposits of brick or pottery clay and shale are known, and several plants, usually near the larger cities like Seattle and Vancouver, British Columbia, have been erected to supply local demand for common brick and tile. Willamina on the west side of the Willamette Valley is the largest plant in Oregon. Plants are also located near Spokane and north of that city at Clayton. The total value of clay products in the Northwest is over $15,000,000 annually.

Heretofore, many of the high-grade kaolins have been imported from England for paper fillers and ceramic manufacture. Deposits of clay, estimated at 100 million tons, are located in eastern Washington and in Latah County, Idaho. These clays are of pottery and paper-filler grade, but only building materials are manufactured from them at present.

Iron and Steel

A market for iron and steel, now supplied by importations, is in excess of 1 million tons a year in the Northwest. Considerable supplies of iron ore adapted to electric smelting are locally available and the industry has possibilities for expansion.

Deposits of iron ore are widely scattered and as far as known are of moderate size. Occurrences of iron include Columbia County, Oregon, close to Bonneville Dam and scattered ore bodies in northern and west-central Idaho. In British Columbia iron ores are found on Vancouver Island, Texada Island, and along the coast of the mainland. Ores have been discovered near tidewater in Alaska. In Washington iron ore occurs near Snoqualmie Pass in Whatcom County, on the Skagit River in the northern Cascades, and in Stevens and Okanogan counties. In the early 1950's shipments of iron ore began to be made to Japan from Northwest sources.

Iron and steel plants are in operation at Troutdale, Oregon, and Seattle and Vancouver, Washington. They use scrap iron and some imported pig iron mainly for their sources of iron. The furnaces are mostly of the electric type, although one at Seattle uses fuel oil. Several smaller fabricating works are located in various parts of the Northwest. A market exists for considerably more steel than is produced, especially since more rapid deliveries and lower freight rates from producer to consumer help to compensate for original higher costs when shipped from midwest and eastern points.

Ferroalloys

This is an age of alloy steels given special qualities by the addition of one or more other metals. These steels can be made in the electric furnace from raw materials either available in the Northwest or from convenient foreign sources. The main ferroalloy metals are chromium, manganese, molybdenum, tungsten, silicon, titanium, vanadium, nickel, and cobalt, of which several occur in commercial quantity in the Northwest.

CHROMIUM. Chromium comes from the mineral chromite and is needed for stainless and noncorrosive steels that will withstand high temperatures. Considerable chrome is used in tools and for armament. Deposits of chromite are scattered throughout the Northwest and Alaska, but because of high costs the mines usually operate only in times of war or high prices. In eastern Oregon chromite has come from Wheeler, Grant, and Baker counties. Important deposits are located in the Klamath Mountains in Oregon and Del Norte County, California, both in bedrock and in alluvial black sands along beaches and rivers. A chromite processing plant at Coos Bay operates when needed. Large deposits of low-grade chromite occur in southern Stillwater County, Montana, and there has been some production from the property.

An electrolytic plant at Mead, near Spokane, manufactures ferrosilicon and alloys containing chromium. Other plants producing ferrosilicon and ferrochromium are located at Tacoma, Portland, and Rock Island near Wenatchee.

MANGANESE. Manganese ores are regularly mined at Butte and Phillipsburg, Montana, and less-important deposits in the Olympic Peninsula and in Idaho are worked when demand and prices for the metal encourage production. Montana usually accounts for over 90 per cent of the domestic output of high-grade manganese, which, however, is only a small fraction of the total consumption, most manganese needed being imported. Over 100,000 tons of ore containing 35 per cent or more of manganese comes from Butte and Phillipsburg annually. A ton of steel usually contains from 12 to 14 pounds of manganese, and plants to supply eastern furnaces with ferromanganese are located at Anaconda and Black Eagle near Great Falls.

TUNGSTEN. This metal has been mined at intervals in considerable quantities in northeast Washington and central Idaho. The Yellow Pine mine in Valley County, Idaho, mined tungsten ore from 1941 to 1945 when the known ore body was exhausted. In 1944 this mine was the largest tungsten producer in the United States and only four mines in the country have exceeded its total output. The Ima mine in Lemhi County, Idaho, and the Germania mine in southern Stevens County, Washington, have produced important amounts of tungsten. Some of the metal has come from Jardine District in Montana near Yellowstone Park. Tungsten occurs in northern and southern British Columbia, and shipments have come from near Salmo and other operations.

COBALT. The only mine operated for its values in cobalt in the United States is the Nightbird at Cobalt, Lemhi County, Idaho. The ore also carries values in copper and is smelted at the only cobalt smelter in this country, at Salt Lake City. Cobalt is valuable for making tools and other alloy steels.

OTHER ALLOY METALS. Occurrences of molybdenum are scattered throughout the Northwest and some development has taken place, but production has been insignificant.

One small deposit containing 25 per cent titanium is known in western Washington, and many iron ores and placers in the Pacific Northwest may contain compounds of titanium, but there has been no commercial production. Some production of nickel has come from the Fraser Valley, 100 miles from Vancouver near the little towns of Choate and Yale. Nickel ores occur near Riddle, Oregon, and are being explored to determine the possibility of their economic utilization. Beryllium has been found near Deary, Idaho, and other places in Idaho and Washington, but no worthwhile production has yet resulted. Vanadium is recovered as a by-product from the processing of phosphate rock at Anaconda.

ANTIMONY. The most important property operated for antimony in the United States is at Stibnite, Valley County, Idaho. Stibnite (antimony sulfide) is the chief antimony mineral, and the mining town is named after it. Here a smelter for antimony was built in 1949 to handle the ore and concentrates. About 5000 tons of antimony are produced at Stibnite annually. The antimony ores at Stibnite carry values in gold which help pay costs of operations. Some antimony is recovered as a by-product from smelting lead, silver, gold, and copper ores in Idaho.

Gold

Placer mining for gold in the 1850's and 1860's was the first metallic exploitation in the Northwest. It was succeeded by lode mining, and in value of output gold is a leading metal in many districts of the region. In all, nearly $600,000,000 in gold has come from deposits in Montana, Idaho, Oregon, and Washington since mining began. Gold was first mined in British Columbia from placers in 1858, and production to date totals almost a half-billion dollars.

The Wallowas and Blue Mountains in northeastern Oregon have accounted for two-thirds of the total state production, with the remainder mainly from the Klamath Mountain region, with a small output from the Bohemia district in the central Cascades. The Blue Mountains area contains some twenty-seven districts where gold quartz has been found in some quantity.

In the northern Cascades of Washington, gold had been mined in the Blewett, Swauk, Peshastin, and the Monte Cristo districts, and in several parts of Whatcom and Okanogan counties. The principal placer districts are in the Wenatchee Range from which has come $3,000,000 in gold, and from bars along the Columbia River in Stevens and Ferry counties. Mines at Republic, Ferry County, since 1900 have produced from veins more than $11,000,000 in gold. The Orient district, Stevens County, has several mines with values in gold and silver.

Chelan County, Washington, leads the state in output of gold, the largest producer being the Gold King near Wenatchee and the Holden mine near the head of Lake Chelan where gold is associated with copper and zinc ores.

In British Columbia the main gold camps are in the southern part of the province at Bridge Creek, 150 miles north of Vancouver, Sheep Creek and Hedley in the interior, and Zeballos on Vancouver Island. The Nelson, Kamloops, and Ymir districts also are productive. Placers are important in the Cariboo region and in the northern part of the province. In 1950 the output of gold was approximately $12,000,000 from British Columbia, of which about 95 per cent was from lode deposits.

In Idaho are numerous deposits carrying gold and silver. In Owyhee County the Silver City and other districts have produced ore valued at more than $40,000,000. Several districts in Lemhi, Custer, Butte, Blaine and Valley counties have occurrences of gold, but no locality has exceeded $1,000,000 in total output. At one time Idaho was among the principal placer mining states in the Union, and a large amount of gold is still obtained from placer deposits, central Idaho and Boise Basin leading in this respect.

Montana had the richest placers in the northwestern states. Bannock, Virginia City, and Last Chance Gulch were discovered in 1862, producing a great influx of miners. Mining of gold quartz began in the 1870's. One-third of the gold produced comes as a by-product from the Butte district, and much of the rest of the gold is obtained mixed with other metals. The total gold production has amounted to upwards of $400,000,000. Among the important districts are gold-silver veins at Marysville and other centers near Helena, Boulder, Phillipsburg, and near Yellowstone Park at Cooke City.

The Northwest has been interested in Alaska mining since the end of the last century, and after the "gold rush" to the Klondike and Alaska began in 1898 Seattle became the leading supply city and shipping port for the Alaskan mines. From 1880 to the present the value of minerals coming from the northern territory exceeded a billion dollars, of which gold accounts for about two-thirds. The annual production of all minerals considerably exceeds the purchase price of $7,200,000 for Alaska.

Silver

Idaho leads all the states of the Union in the production of silver, and Montana is in third place. The Northwest, including British Columbia, is one of the most important silver-producing sections of the world. Idaho produces one-eighth of all the silver mined in the United States. Here it is associated with lead, copper, zinc, and antimony ores and is widely distributed. Shoshone County ranks first, followed by Lemhi, Custer, Bonner, and other counties. The largest producer of silver in the United States is the Sunshine mine in the Coeur d'Alene district. Northeastern Washington has obtained silver in moderate amounts from ores of other metals. The only silver in Oregon is a by-product of the mining of complex ores.

The silver of Montana has come primarily from the copper and zinc ores at Butte. The ores are complex and extraction of the metals begun in 1875 gave difficulty in early years. Since 1875 Butte has produced nearly 600 million ounces of silver and from Phillipsburg and other districts in Montana have come about 200 million ounces. The total value is nearly three-fourths of a billion dollars.

In British Columbia most of the silver ($7,666,000 in 1950) is a by-product from gold, copper, lead, and zinc mines. Properties rich in silver alone, as in the Slocan district, are operated mostly when the price of silver is high.

Copper

The Northwest is a huge producer of copper. Although Butte is the most famous, the metal comes in smaller quantities from a number of sources. Copper occurs as a principal element in some ore, but often is, like gold, silver, lead, and zinc, one of several elements obtained from a complex ore. In addition to copper, these ores yield sulfur, from which sulfuric acid can be made.

In Montana the Butte district is the most productive copper camp in the world, having yielded from 1882 to the present over $2\frac{1}{2}$ billion dollars in copper, silver, gold, zinc, and minor metals. In addition to the high-grade ore that for 70 years supplied the bulk of Butte's wealth, there are enormous tonnages of low-grade ore. In the early 1950's a big shaft was sunk and cheap methods of mining and extraction developed that will extend the life of the Butte mines many years.

In Washington copper occurs in the northern part of the state. The largest producer is at Holden, from which 2000 tons of ore per day are concentrated. The concentrates are then transported by trucks and lake barges to the railroad for shipment to the Tacoma smelter. There are other copper occurrences in the northern Cascades and in Stevens County where copper-bearing veins have been developed, notably in the Bonanza mine near Bossburg.

Copper ores are smelted and electrolytically refined at Tacoma, Washington. This plant treats Alaskan and British Columbia ores imported by water, and concentrates from interior sources coming by rail. An even larger smelter is at Anaconda (Plate 11A), which handles the ores from Butte. Great Falls, Montana, has a large electrolytic copper refinery and other works, including an electrolytic wet-process plant that handles complex ores containing copper, lead, zinc, gold, and silver. Here cheap, abundant power is available from several falls on the Missouri River.

In Oregon a small production of copper has come from Waldo, southwest of Grant's Pass, and from deposits on the Snake River and in the Wallowa and Powder River districts. Most of the Idaho copper is a by-product of the silver ores of the Coeur d'Alenes, although a small production has come from occurrences in the northern and central parts of the state.

Most of the copper in southern British Columbia comes from two large operations. Until the discovery and development of the Rhodesian copper deposits, the Britannia mine, 30 miles north of Vancouver on Howe Sound, was the largest copper producer in the British Empire. It is still operating steadily and in depth much zinc ore has been found. About 900,000 tons of ore per year are concentrated at Britannia Beach; the copper concentrates are shipped to Tacoma for smelting and refining and the zinc concentrates to Trail. Gold, lead, cadmium, and pyrite are valuable by-products. The Copper Mountain Mine and Mill, near Princeton, 100 miles east of Vancouver, produces 1.8 million tons of ore per year, containing 26 million pounds of copper and some gold and silver. The total British Columbia output of refined copper is about 50 million pounds annually valued at over $10,000,000.

Lead and Zinc

The Pacific Northwest is a leader in lead and zinc mining. From the Coeur d'Alene district of northern Idaho have come well over a billion dollars in lead, zinc, and silver. The more persistent ore bodies have been followed for several thousand feet and average about 9 feet wide, some veins reaching 40 feet in thickness. Other lead and zinc districts in Idaho include Warm Springs in Blaine County in the southcentral part of the state, and the Bay Horse in Custer County. A large smelter and an electrolytic zinc plant are operated at Kellogg to treat the ores of the Coeur d'Alene and other districts. By-product metals produced by the Kellogg plants include gold, bismuth, antimony, and cadmium.

In Washington, lead and zinc ores, without much silver, are mined near Northport and Colville in Stevens County and in the Metaline district, Pend Oreille County. The mines at Metaline Falls supply 13 million pounds of zinc and 8 million pounds of lead annually, worth around $3,000,000. The zinc deposits at Metaline extend into British Columbia, where the Reeves McDonald mine produces 17 million pounds of zinc, 4 million pounds of lead, and some silver and cadmium.

In Montana the mining of lead began in 1880, but zinc from complex ores was not profitable until the Anaconda Company perfected an electrolytic "wet" process to recover the metal, and then Butte became the chief source of zinc in the state. Butte also leads in production of lead, the metal being a by-product from other ores. Lead is also mined in noteworthy quantities in Sanders, Flathead, Jefferson, and Broadwater counties and at Neihart and Barker in the Little Belt Mountains. Lewis and Clark County is second to Silver Bow (Butte) in zinc production.

The production of lead and zinc in Oregon is small, although there are some occurrences in the west slopes of the Cascades on the north Santiam River and at Bohemia in Lane County and in the eastern part of the state.

In British Columbia the Sullivan Mine at Kimberly in the Selkirk Mountains is the largest single lead and zinc producer in the world. This mine is responsible for the large majority of the lead and zinc production of the province and boasts of a total output of metals in excess of a billion dollars. It employs 2100 men in the mine and mill and produces 2.7 million tons of ore annually. The mine's lead output amounts to 290 million pounds, and that of zinc to nearly 250 million pounds annually, valued at $38,000,000 and $30,000,000 respectively. The total British Columbia production of lead in 1950 had a value of $45,000,000 and that of zinc $49,000,000.

TRAIL SMELTER. One of the most important operations connected with the mining industry of British Columbia is the smelting and refining of ore at Trail on the Columbia River about 10 miles upriver from the Washington border. This is now one of the most complete metallurgical works in the world and employs 3200 men. The smelter treats mainly lead and zinc ores from the Sullivan Mine and miscellaneous sources. The lead refinery has a capacity output of 575 tons a day. The zinc refinery is the largest single producer of electrolytic zinc in the world, with 400 tons a day. One of the interesting by-products from Sullivan ores is cadmium, which is used to make a fusible alloy. In addition, values in silver, gold, antimony, and bismuth are recovered, along with many tons of sulfur. Sulfuric acid and phosphate and ammonium nitrate fertilizer are other products. The abundant sulfur fumes and the cheap electric power available are factors in the manufacture of fertilizer, for which phosphate rock is imported from Montana (Plate 11A).

Mercury

Mercury (quicksilver) deposits that comprise a belt in the Coast Ranges of California, extend northward into Oregon and Washington along the western flanks of the Cascades. Still another ill-defined belt runs through northern Nevada, southeastern Oregon, and southern Idaho. The Ochoco Mountains of Central Oregon comprise another district. Mercury is recovered as a heavy liquid by distilling the sulfide ore called cinnabar. To save freight the distillation plants usually are located at the mines.

In Oregon mercury has come mainly from the foothills of the Cascades in Douglas and Lane counties, also east of Prineville, Crook County, and close to the southern boundary of Malheur County. Black Butte, in Lane County, had a steady output for many years. The largest producing quicksilver mine in the United States at one time was the Bonanza Mine in Douglas County, and this mine is still the leader in output of mercury in Oregon.

In Washington deposits near Morton, Lewis County, have been somewhat productive and prospects are reported in Kittitas and Chelan counties.

In Idaho mercury has been produced in considerable quantities near Stibnite, Valley County, and at the Almaden mine near Weiser. Cassia County also has deposits but the output has been small.

Production of mercury in the Northwest depends primarily upon prices. The mines open in times of high prices and close when the price of quicksilver drops.

Production of mercury began in British Columbia in 1940 and the total output in the next few years was worth about a million dollars.

Minor Minerals

ARSENIC, BISMUTH, AND CADMIUM. Arsenical copper ores from which arsenic can be recovered occur extensively in Montana and with other ores elsewhere in the region. White arsenic is a by-product of the Tacoma smelter and of the Anaconda copper smelter. Bismuth is another valuable by-product recovered at the Anaconda, Trail, and Kellogg smelters. Cadmium is a by-product from the zinc ore treated at the Trail and Kellogg smelters. About $1,500,000 worth of cadmium is recovered yearly at Trail. No mines are operated for their values in bismuth and cadmium alone.

PLATINUM. The principal production of platinum and closely similar metals comes from the Goodnews district of southwestern Alaska, where the output, all from placers, totals around a million dollars per year.

In southwestern Oregon, a little platinum is obtained from beach-placer deposits associated with black sands. It is also obtained in the smelting of copper ores at the Tacoma Smelter. A little platinum is recovered in placer operations in British Columbia.

TIN. Seward Peninsula, Alaska, produces the only tin mined by the United States. The output comes from placers and amounts to under 100 tons annually.

SILICON. Deposits of high-grade silica rock exist in eastern and northwestern Washington and in various parts of central Idaho. Important shipments are made from Newport and Denison, near Spokane, some of which is used in ferrosilicon. Other uses of silica include glass, silicon carbide, and alloy steel.

GYPSUM (calcium sulfate) is known in eastern Idaho and Montana and was formerly mined at Gypsum on the Snake River in Oregon. The mineral is mined in Iyoukeen Cove at tidewater in Alaska. In Montana two plants for the preparation of gypsum products have been constructed near Lewistown in Fergus County: one at Heath and one at Hanover. Between Kamloops and Vernon, British Columbia, large deposits of excellent quality are worked and some gypsum is shipped to Spokane for processing. Stucco, plaster, calcimine, wall-board, and brick are manufactured from gypsum. A plant at Seattle makes these from material brought by boat from California.

SALINE MINERALS. Lying on top of the lavas in the southeastern part of Oregon, southern Idaho, eastern Washington and southern British Columbia are areas in which saline deposits have collected. These deposits have resulted from evaporation of undrained lakes in arid regions. The salines include salt, borax, sodium carbonates and nitrates, sodium sulfate, and small amounts of potassium salts. Sodium sulfate and sodium carbonate occur in certain dry lakebeds of south-central Oregon and north-central Washington. In these states an intermittent output once came from plants near Warden and Oroville. Near Clinton in British Columbia soda and magnesium sulfate are produced. Borax was formerly produced from hot springs at the southern end of Steens Mountain.

PUMICE is mined in central Oregon and to some extent in Washington and is used in the manufacture of building stocks. Perlite, used for insulation and as an aggregate for plaster and concrete, is being quarried near Terrebonne in central Oregon.

DIATOMACEOUS EARTH. This material, made up of the siliceous cells of diatoms, is used principally as an insulator, absorbent, filter, filler, and abrasive. Large deposits of high-grade diatomite are located in central Washington and in central and eastern Oregon. It is known in British Columbia. This mineral also occurs in many counties in southern Idaho and in Nevada. It is produced in Deschutes County, Oregon, in Washington at Quincy, and in Badger Pocket, Kittitas County.

VERMICULITE. This is a peculiar decomposition product of mica, sold under the trade names of Zonolite and Unifill, that is mined near Libby in northwestern Montana. On being heated vermiculite expands and exfoliates into thin, paperlike flakes that are used for heat, sound, electrical insulation, and in the manufacture of wallboard. The annual production from the Libby deposits exceeds 100,000 tons, valued at over a million dollars.

GEMS. Sapphires have been mined at Yogo Gulch, Judith County, Montana, and are famous for their brilliancy and depth of color. The annual value was for many years nearly one-quarter of a million dollars, but production is now small, largely because of competition with synthetic gems. A few sapphires are recovered by placer operations near Helena and Phillipsburg.

A considerable agate industry has been developed in the Northwest, especially in the western part of Oregon, with the leading center at Newport.

Miscellaneous Minerals

Among the minor minerals produced in the Pacific Northwest are mica, carbon dioxide, Iceland spar, garnet, and fluorspar. There are prospects of strontium, monazite, and other minerals. Mica has been mined at intervals at the Moscovite property near Moscow, Idaho, and it occurs in British Columbia. The high grade of the material may compensate for lack of roads and remoteness. Near Goldendale, Washington, carbon dioxide gas is condensed from natural-gas sources and sold for Dry Ice and other commercial uses. A variety of calcite called Iceland spar, used for certain optical instruments, is found near Big Timber, Montana. Garnet, used for abrasive purposes, is mined near Fernwood and other places in northern Idaho. Fluorspar has been mined near Darby and Superior, Montana, and Forney in central Idaho, and the mineral occurs in other places in the Northwest. The mineral barite is supplied by one Idaho company. An occurrence of strontianite is located in Whatcom County, Washington. Monazite sand, a source of thorium, formerly used for gaslight filaments and a possible material for making atomic energy, is being mined from placers near McCall, Idaho, and occurs also in the Boise Basin and other places in Idaho in probable commercial quantities. There is reported to be 200 million tons of gravel containing 0.2 to 0.3 per cent of monazite in two counties of Idaho. Uranium, a source of atomic energy, has been reported from several localities in the Northwest, including Jefferson County, Montana, the phosphate beds in southeast Idaho, and near Hazelton, British Columbia, but no real production has resulted.

CHAPTER 10

Fisheries of the North Pacific

HOWARD H. MARTIN

The coastal waters of the Pacific Northwest are one of the few great areas in the world, where natural conditions favor a maximum of marine life. Like its positional counterpart, northwest Europe, it has a fortunate combination of broad continental shelf and warm and cold ocean currents, an environment in which phytoplankton and zooplankton thrive and multiply, providing the basic foodstuffs for the higher forms of marine animals. The pastures are enormous. The rugged littoral from Cape Blanco to the tip of the Aleutian Chain, and north of the Aleutians to Bering Strait, has thousands of islands and hundreds of protected bays, fiords, and inland passages. Great rivers like the Columbia and the Fraser offer thousands of miles of spawning grounds for anadromous fish. Some inland waters such as Puget Sound are cold and deep; others like Willapa Harbor are warm and shallow. Lakes and streams are also available for fresh-water species.

With such a diversity of habitat it is not surprising that there is a wide diversity of commercial fish. The latitudinal span is sufficient to encompass the codfish and the whale of the Far North as well as the warmth-loving tuna of southern waters. In between are almost the entire range of temperate and cold-water types, including many of the demersal or deep-sea dwellers, pelagic or surface-swimmers like the herring, river-running fish such as the shad and smelt, and the more sedentary mollusks and crustaceans. Some North Pacific fish, including salmon and halibut, are found in sufficient abundance to take first rank in the world.

Fishing Bases

Nearly every harbor has a fishing fleet. Astoria, one of the oldest centers, is home port and marketing point for most of the Columbia River fleet. With its many canneries, icing plants, and reduction works, Astoria perhaps has a heavier per capita investment in fishing than any other city of its size along the coast. Ketchikan, Alaska, is another town almost entirely dependent on fishing. Vancouver and Prince Rupert, British Columbia, and Bellingham and Aberdeen, Washington, are other cities with extensive fishing interests.

More vessels, however, are based on Seattle than on any other port, and most North Pacific fisheries products, fresh, frozen, or canned, eventually pass through Seattle warehouses, which provide ample storage.[1] The great center for the fleet is the Fishermen's Terminal at Salmon Bay, 84 acres in extent. Here the moorage facilities can accommodate 1000 vessels such as trollers, purse seiners, and trawlers. During the winter, boat owners overhaul their gear, make repairs, install new fittings, paint the vessels, mend their nets and trawls, and get ready for the opening of the next season (Plate 11B).

SALMON

The Annual Salmon Run

Just as the codfish is associated with New England, salmon has become one of the symbols of the Pacific Northwest. Every spring and summer the rivers from California to Bering Sea are the scene of one of the world's most spectacular fish runs. Millions of salmon converge at the river mouths, swarm across the bars, and move steadily upstream. Rapids and waterfalls are no deterrents. Driven by the spawning urge, salmon dart through swift waters and around great

[1] A single day's arrival by vessels of fresh and frozen fish in Seattle on July 15, 1952, was as follows.

	Pounds		Pounds
Halibut	182,500	True cod	12,975
Salmon: red,		Black rockfish	12,680
white, silvers	56,350	Red rockfish	5,940
English sole	24,240	Sablefish	8,330
Petrale sole	4,660	Ling cod	7,530
Rock sole	4,540		
Dover sole	1,820		

Arrivals by truck including salmon, crabs and oysters are not included.

boulders, leaping falls of considerable height. A long run of a thousand miles up the Columbia to the headwaters of the Salmon River in Idaho generally begins in March or April. The short runs of Vancouver Island, where the spawning beds may be only a few hours from salt water, may not begin until late in the autumn. The salmon finally reach the original stream or lake where they were hatched several years before. Scooping out a shallow nest, they deposit and fertilize the eggs, then cover them with a protecting layer of gravel. Pacific salmon take no food after leaving salt water. Spent by the journey and the final act of reproduction, the parents lie quietly in eddies and die within a short time.

The eggs generally hatch in about 2 months, the fry emerging from the gravel in the spring. Depending upon species, the young salmon remain several months, sometimes as long as 3 years, in fresh water before beginning their trip to the ocean. The salt-water phase of their life cycle lasts from 2 to 6 years, again depending upon the variety. Over 95 per cent of their growth is made in the sea, but their marine feeding grounds are not definitely known. Coho and Chinook salmon have been taken at depths as great as 90 fathoms. Chinook from the Columbia have been tagged off the Queen Charlotte Islands and later recovered in the Columbia, and other varieties migrate long distances through the passages of southeastern Alaska.

Species of Salmon

Five species of salmon are found in the Pacific Northwest, including Alaska. Sockeye or red salmon, weighing 4 to 10 pounds, have long been the favorite. An ideal cannery fish from the standpoint of size and color, the sockeye formerly provided most of the American pack and still accounts for about one-quarter of it. The great Chinook or King salmon, averaging over 20 pounds and sometimes weighing 100, are sold fresh as well as canned. Coho or Silverside are less popular for canning because of their lighter-colored flesh. Humpback or pink salmon, weighing 3 to 5 pounds, are the most plentiful, particularly in southeastern Alaska, where they are caught in great numbers; they now provide two-fifths of the pack. Chum or Keta, light in color and once regarded as inferior, are now taken by many canneries. Steel-head trout are frequently caught and sold as salmon.

Since food of an appealing color generally appears most appetizing, red salmon, such as those caught in Alaska and other areas, command the highest price. Pink or white salmon are not so attractive but have excellent food value; they now make up a larger share of the catch than the higher-priced red.

The Canning of Salmon

When the adult salmon reach the coasts before the annual spawning run, they are in prime condition. Packing plants are located from northern California to western Alaska, usually near river mouths. By means of traps, gill nets, and purse seines, the fish are caught by the thousands. Traps, now illegal in the state of Washington, are widely used in Alaska as well as in Oregon. Whether taken in trap or seine, the salmon are brailed out into huge scows often containing as many as 35,000 fish, which are then towed alongside the canneries (Plate 12A). Conveyors hoist the fish to the cannery bins above the work floor.

TABLE 1

CANNED SALMON PACK OF NORTH AMERICA, 1952

(Cases of 48 pounds)

From *The Pacific Fisherman*

Species	Alaska	Puget Sound	Columbia River	Coastal Areas	Total U. S.	British Columbia	Grand Total
Red or sockeye	1,279,748	122,709	10,336	877	1,413,670	499,174	1,862,844
Pink	1,172,419	2,635	.....	.....	1,175,054	675,836	1,850,890
Chum or keta	955,439	311,509	10,898	12,821	1,290,667	84,547	1,375,214
Coho or silver	193,625	168,297	30,062	5,550	397,534	64,095	461,629
Chinook or king	55,842	6,673	94,769	1,802	159,086	9,064	168,150
Steelhead	31	......	18,980	.....	19,011	3,752	22,763
Total	3,657,104	611,823	165,045	21,050	4,455,022	1,286,468	5,741,490

The modern cannery is completely mechanized, using high-speed mass-production methods. An ingenious machine known as the Iron Chink [2] butchers salmon at the rate of 60 per minute. Head, tail, and fins are removed, and rotating knives and brushes finish the cleaning work. The salmon on a moving conveyor are then cut into suitable pieces and fed into the cans by a filling machine. The cans are weighed, the tops clinched on, and then sealed in a vacuum sealing machine. An assembly line of this type can deliver a stream of cans to the cylindrical cooking retorts at the rate of 120 to 150 cans per

[2] This machine, invented by a Seattle mechanic about 1905, is called the Iron Chink because it took the place of the many Chinese cutters who formerly did the work by hand.

minute. Steam-cooked for 90 minutes or more, the cans are then cooled, labeled, packed in cases (the standard-sized case contains 48 pounds), and are ready for warehousing or distribution.

There are scores of canning companies in the Northwest, but eight or nine leading packers market about two-thirds of all the Alaska and Pacific Northwest salmon. Regardless of source, the larger part of it eventually reaches the Port of Seattle for distribution.

Trade in Fresh Salmon

Although most of the Northwest salmon are caught for the canneries, several million pounds are iced or frozen for sale fresh, particularly in the Pacific Coast states. Most of the fish for this market are taken by trolling, the Chinook or King salmon and the Silver being the favorites and bringing the highest prices. Both these varieties feed on small fish such as pilchard or herring, and can be taken on hand lines, using bait or spoon hooks. The trollers dress and ice their catch, generally landing it in Seattle, where several companies specialize in this business. Portland, Vancouver, British Columbia, and Astoria also buy and distribute fresh salmon. Traps are occasionally used, and some fish are taken by seines and gill nets. Part of the catch is also frozen preparatory to making smoked, mild-cured, or kippered salmon.

Northwest Salmon Pack

Canning in the Northwest began at White Cliffs on the lower Columbia River in 1866, with a small experimental pack of 4000 cases. Wherever sold, this new type of foodstuff met with such favor that operations were immediately increased manyfold. Canneries were built along the Columbia, in Puget Sound waters, and on all the rivers along the coasts of Oregon and Washington. The small coastal rivers reached a peak of about 250,000 cases in 1911; the pack in the same area is now only 20,000 cases per year. The Columbia River, a steady source since the 1880's, reached its maximum of 634,000 cases in 1895. Since then the teeming Chinook runs in the Columbia have shrunk, but this species still provides three-quarters of the 200,000-case pack. The Puget Sound area, with the richest salmon waters within the United States, has had an even more drastic decrease. Canning started here in 1877, reaching its maximum of 2.5 million cases in 1913. The great runs of sockeye and pinks were canned to the extent of over 1 million cases per year from 1899 to 1919. This steady decline in the Northwest States was somewhat offset by the rapid rise of Alaskan fishing, which was more than sufficient to satisfy the market.

Alaska Salmon

Located along 10,000 miles of coast line, the salmon fishery of Alaska is one of the richest natural resources of the North Pacific. It has an average fresh-fish value of $20,000,000 to $25,000,000 annually; when packed it has an annual value of well over $80,000,000.

The first salmon cannery in Alaska was established on Prince of Wales Island in 1878, and by 1888 the pack exceeded that of the Columbia River. More and more canneries were established in the North to take advantage of the seemingly inexhaustible supply, the industry finally reaching a peak of 6,677,000 cases in 1918 under the stimulus of war prices. During the ensuing decade the pack dropped to an average of 4.5 million cases per year, then began to increase, reaching an all-time peak of 8,454,000 cases in 1936, and has been averaging 4 million cases subsequently. One-half of the Alaska salmon are taken in fixed or floating traps, one-quarter by gill nets, and the other one-quarter in purse and beach seines. Very little trolling is done in these northern waters. Among the territory's most important salmon areas are Bristol Bay, the Kodiak district, and Prince William Sound; Ketchikan has long been the great canning center of southeast Alaska (Plate 12B).

Steamers from Washington and Oregon go north each summer with equipment and supplies, returning in the autumn with heavy cargoes of canned salmon. Seasonal workers who formerly traveled by steamer or cannery tender are now largely flown in. The annual "salmon airlift" begins in mid-May, transporting some 4000 fishermen, machinists, and cannery workers to Alaska. The runs begin in July and are mainly over in September, the crews being flown out at the end of the season.

Since 1950 there has been a marked trend toward the use of large freezer ships which go north with a flock of smaller fishing vessels. Frozen in brine and stored, the salmon are later processed at packing plants farther south. Some of these mother ships have combination freezer-and-cannery facilities. Freezer ships provide greater flexibility of operation than the shore cannery with its fixed location, and they may be used in other fisheries such as tuna, which run at a different season.

Overfishing Brings Regulation

In its early years this industry was unregulated, and cutthroat competition was rife among canners. Certain streams were blocked so completely by traps that virtually no fish reached the spawning beds. After a few years of heavy packs, followed by diminishing runs, the canneries had to be abandoned. Most streams showed some decrease, and apprehension was felt lest the profitable Alaska fisheries follow the Atlantic salmon industry into oblivion.

For many years there was a struggle between interests in favor of unrestrained operation and fisheries experts who pointed out the necessity of restriction in order to save the industry. The proponents of stronger regulatory measures were, as usual, accused of "trying to lock up the resources of Alaska," but in 1924 the White Bill gave the U. S. Fish and Wildlife Service supervisory and enforcement powers over all fishing in the northern territory. The most important feature of the bill provided for at least a 50 per cent escapement of all salmon entering the rivers to spawn.

Management for Restoration and Stabilization

Since salmon with few exceptions return to the home stream, each of the Alaskan rivers is now managed separately. A badly depleted area may be closed for a term of years, and the regulations relaxed when the run again approaches normal. For instance, the 1934 regulations closed 93 fishtrap sites, at the same time opening a number of previously closed fishing grounds to seines and other forms of gear. Despite this seemingly drastic restriction, the 1934 pack exceeded that of 1933 by 2 million cases.

The red-salmon area of Bristol Bay, one of the most valuable fishing waters in Alaska, has needed special care. The Bristol Bay sockeye matures in a 5-year cycle, and there was a steady decline in the 1920–25–30 runs, although other years remained close to normal. In order to give this particular cycle a chance to rebuild, the Fish and Wildlife Service limited Bristol Bay to a very short season in 1935; the larger spawning escapement that year improved the 1940 run, although it was still far below the average. Traps are prohibited in this area, all fishing being done with gill nets. In addition to regulating the type of gear the Fish Service maintains patrol boats in Alaskan waters.

Under these wisely flexible regulations, the Alaskan salmon pack has been kept up with a minimum of interference with individual fishing rights. Although it is difficult to satisfy all interests, regulation has met with general approval, largely because it has stabilized the industry and placed it on a permanent basis. Few Alaska operators would now care to go back to unrestrained competition.

Sockeye Decline in Puget Sound and the Fraser River

Although the Alaska salmon situation has been improving, the Puget Sound catch has decreased to one-third of its former size. All species of salmon are caught in the Sound, but the sockeye is regarded as the most important. In the main, the sockeye entering Puget Sound are bound for the Fraser River Basin of British Columbia, which is exceptionally well supplied with suitable spawning lakes and headwaters. On their way through the Sound to the Fraser the sockeye are exposed to an array of cannery traps, to numerous purse seiners clustered around the entrance, and to gillnetters in the mouth of the Fraser.

Since both Canada and the United States had vital stakes in the imperiled Fraser runs, a treaty was proposed in 1907 providing for a joint commission to investigate the problem. The measure was passed by Canada but defeated in the United States Senate. During the ensuing 30 years two similar treaties were approved by Canada but held up by certain American interests, while intensive fishing continued and the Fraser River-Puget Sound sockeye pack dropped to new low levels.

The Sockeye Salmon Treaty

In 1937 a treaty was finally ratified providing for the creation of the International Pacific Salmon Fisheries Commission. By this time the sockeye runs were so small that drastic rehabilitation was necessary. Canada made the entire Fraser Basin available for restoration and propagation, the cost to be borne jointly. The research staff of the Commission studied the sockeye through two complete cycles (1938–46) and, with the data obtained, drew up the necessary measures for control.

Escapement Problem at Hell's Gate

One of the basic difficulties on the Fraser dated back to 1913 when railway construction at Hell's Gate dumped a rockslide into the Canyon. The stoppage was so complete that sockeye were largely cut off from the spawning beds of the upper Fraser, the runs dropping from an estimated 4 million fish in 1913 to a few hundred in the low-water-level years.

Regarding the slide as a permanent obstacle, the newly formed Salmon Commission completed two fishways through the canyon in 1946, and within a few years the sockeye runs began to increase.

Many barren lakes and streams were also restocked with fingerlings from hatcheries. In 1952 a third high level fishway was completed, giving spawners access to the upper river at all stages of water. With continued good management the Fraser may again become the world's richest salmon river.

Bonneville and Grand Coulee

Included in the problem of salmon conservation on the Columbia are two dams, Bonneville and Grand Coulee, each of them higher than any obstacle formerly surmounted by anadromous fish. The 30-foot Rock Island dam on the middle Columbia south of Wenatchee is equipped with three fish ladders which provide passage for salmon on their way to the spawning grounds. Both the McNary Dam near Umatilla, Oregon, and the 55-foot Bonneville on the lower Columbia have an elaborate system of fish ladders and elevators. Once above Bonneville the fish have access to various tributary waters, including the entire Snake River system. Passes have also been constructed so that fingerlings on their way to the sea can reach the lower side of the dam safely.

The 350-foot Grand Coulee Dam on the middle Columbia, however, is an impassable obstacle. Salmon runs are completely blocked at this point, since it is impracticable to convey fish over a barrier of this height. Some 1100 linear miles of salmon streams in the upper Columbia basin of Washington, Idaho, and British Columbia were lost for spawning.

To counteract this reduction, a large Federal hatchery with acres of rearing pools was built near Leavenworth, Washington. Adult salmon on their return journey to the upper Columbia are intercepted at Rock Island Dam, stripped of their eggs, and the eggs fertilized. Fingerlings reared in the hatchery pools are taken by tank truck to suitable planting areas in understocked rivers such as the Wenetchee, Entiat, Okanogan, and Methow, streams tributary to the Columbia below Grand Coulee Dam. The young salmon thus artificially propagated and planted in new home streams join the down-river migration to salt water, later returning as adults to the parent stream to spawn naturally. By careful management augmented runs are being built up in various middle Columbia tributaries, and artificial propagation has become a permanent part of the effort to sustain spawning stocks.

Celilo Falls, famous Indian fishing reserve on the Columbia River (Plate 1A) will be drowned out when a new hydroelectric dam is completed at The Dalles.

To help counteract some of the losses in spawning area the Washington Department of Fisheries is improving some 300 miles of lower Columbia tributaries not previously available to salmon.

HALIBUT

One of the standard food fishes of America is the halibut, a great deep-sea flounder, dark on its upper or right side, white on the left or under side. The North Atlantic halibut banks supplied the American demand for many years. It was not until around 1890, after the inauguration of fast transcontinental rail service between Puget Sound and eastern United States, that Pacific halibut reached the market in quantity. With the steady decline of the Atlantic grounds, shipments from the Northwest increased. The proportion of Pacific to Atlantic halibut is now approximately 40 to 1.

Life Cycle of Halibut

Salmon mature in 4 or 5 years, but most halibut do not reproduce until they are 12 or 15 years old; approximately half of them mature at 12 years, and only a few as early as 8 or 10 years.

The parent fish gather in schools along the edge of the continental shelf and spawn during the winter, December to March. After the tiny halibut are hatched they work gradually toward shore, spending the early part of their lives in relatively shallow water, before settling down to much greater depths. Their migration range is small, a fish usually spending its entire life in or near one bank. Halibut live to 25 years and have been known to reach an age of 38. When caught they weigh anywhere from 4 to 200 pounds, but a few giants reach 300 or more. A record fish of 1936 tipped the scales at 325 pounds.

The Halibut Fleet of the North Pacific

The halibut banks follow the continental shelf from northern California to the Bering Sea. The fishing fleet, consisting of some 350 boats, is both American and Canadian, the latter taking about one-quarter of the North Pacific catch. Over half the vessels operate out of Seattle. Prince Rupert and Vancouver are the main home ports for Canadian vessels; Ketchikan, Petersburg, and Juneau, Alaska, and Astoria, Oregon, have smaller fleets.

Vessels, of sturdy design to withstand all sorts of weather, range in size from 35 to 90 feet and are nearly all Diesel powered. The smaller ones which fish the southern grounds nearer to port have crews of two to six, but the larger vessels carry eight or ten men. Hand-line fishing from dories long ago disappeared. Halibut are now caught on long bottom lines strung with a series of shorter lines baited with herring; this unit of gear, called a "skate," is usually set at depths varying from 50 to 175 fathoms. Modern vessels operate as much as 8 miles of lines carrying 4000 hooks, the heavy gear being raised and lowered by a power-driven winch. The larger and better-equipped vessels with considerable cruising radius operate as far away as the Gulf of Alaska and out around the Aleutian Islands.

Marketing the Catch

Dressed almost as soon as they are taken off the hook, the halibut are packed in crushed ice in the vessel's hold. The run to port is made as rapidly as possible. With its proximity to the richer banks Prince Rupert handles most of the Canadian catch. In order to avoid the long trip home, American vessels based on Seattle often unload their catches at Prince Rupert and then hasten back to the banks. The port and shipping center for most of the catch, however, is Seattle.

The fish are sold at auction, usually to large wholesale houses with their own docks and refrigeration plants. There the fish are unloaded, sorted, graded, and packed in ice in 200-pound boxes for shipment. Small halibut weighing less than 10 pounds are classed as "chickens," those 10 to 60 pounds as "mediums," and those over 60 pounds as "large" or "whales" (Plate 12B). So systematic and efficient is the handling that a cargo of halibut may reach Seattle in the early morning, be auctioned and unloaded before noon, graded and boxed in the early afternoon, and sent east by fast railway express that night.

The flesh of the halibut is unusually firm and is well suited to long-distance transportation. Sixty per cent of the catch is shipped at once as fresh fish; the rest is frozen and held in storage for gradual release. Like the better-known cod, the halibut has a liver rich in vitamin oils, which pharmaceutical companies buy at high prices. Since the early 1940's this fishery has averaged 55 million pounds, about three-quarters of it American, the remainder Canadian.

Depletion on the Halibut Banks

In the early 1900's most of the fishing was on the southern grounds within a radius of about 500 miles from the base ports. As the abundance declined in this area, vessels pushed farther north into Alaskan waters returning with even larger cargoes. Peak production was reached in 1915 with 63 million pounds. To keep up the catch both

Americans and Canadians went farther and farther to sea, fishing more intensively. Finally the limits of lateral expansion were reached and three definite evidences of depletion appeared.

1. Few halibut were being taken on the southern grounds, which had been worked longest and hardest.

2. The proportion of mature fish was decreasing, a larger share of each catch consisting of "chicken" or small, immature halibut.

3. The catch per skate or unit of gear had declined alarmingly. In the early days the average catch per skate was about 300 pounds, but soon after 1920 it dropped to 60 pounds.

Since the normal supply was still reaching market, the public was not aware of any depletion. Fisheries experts, however, pointed out the basic unsoundness of the situation and the probability that the Pacific banks were faced with a decline similar to that already present in the Atlantic. Authorities were convinced that this situation could not continue indefinitely without reducing the Pacific halibut to insignificance.

THE INTERNATIONAL PACIFIC HALIBUT COMMISSION. Accordingly, the International Fisheries Commission was created in 1924, with a membership of two Americans and two Canadians.[3] It was given authority to study halibut and recommend conservation measures. By research the long-concealed life history was obtained, and it was then possible to make recommendations for control and restoration.

Several regulatory measures have been applied.

1. A closed period during the winter spawning season. The halibut season now opens between May 1 and 17 and closes in less than 2 months.

2. The creation of certain nursery areas where fishing is entirely prohibited and which serve much the same purpose as wildlife refuges.

3. A catch limit which may be raised or lowered at the discretion of the Commission; 54 million pounds is the present quota.

4. The division of the fishing grounds into four areas, with separate regulations for each. These areas are:

I. South of Willapa Harbor.
II. Willapa Harbor north to Cape Spencer, Alaska.
III. Cape Spencer to the Aleutian Islands.
IV. North of the Aleutians in Bering Sea.

[3] A treaty signed in March, 1953, changed the commission's name to the International Pacific Halibut Commission and increased the membership to six, three from each country. For the first time, Alaska is to be represented.

Area I has suffered the most drastic depletion, and few halibut are taken there. Areas II and III have quotas of 25 million and 28.5 million pounds respectively and now provide most of the catch.

Regulation Brings Increased Abundance

All the regulations have been strictly enforced and are now generally favored by the fishing industry. Knowing in advance the poundage to be marketed throughout the year has also helped to stabilize prices. The average catch per unit of gear is 2½ times greater than in 1930. Even in this relatively short period the stock of adult fish on all banks has shown an appreciable increase, and the fishery is on a sustained yield basis.

SHELLFISH

Oyster Culture

The natural habitat of the oyster, a shallow bay or estuary where the tides sweep in and out to bring food, is found in several places along the North Pacific. Puget Sound had its native beds of small Olympia oysters, but they were overexploited and the industry was declining. Oyster seed, of a type long cultivated in Japan, was imported and planted in Willapa Harbor. The venture was a success; the oysters grew large and plump, and individual cultivators embarked on a new seafood business.

With its 100 square miles of shallow tide flats, Willapa Harbor is ideal for the introduced Pacific oyster. At low tide large acreages of bay bottom are laid bare, making it easy for cultivators to inspect and harvest their crops. For some years new oyster "seed" had to be imported annually, but in 1936 the first big set of young oysters occurred. Oyster culture has also spread to some of the tide flats in Puget Sound, Coos Bay, and Grays Harbor. Plantings of oyster seed from Japan, interrupted by the war, were resumed in 1947, some 50,000 cases being imported annually.

Although there is a big coast trade in fresh oysters, the Pacific bivalve is also planted, cultured, and harvested for canning. Large barges can be floated over the shallower beds at high tide, filled when the tide is out, and towed to canneries located around the bay. In deeper waters the crop is tonged from the bottom. At the cannery oysters are opened by shuckers or placed in large cylinders where they are steamed open. The small towns around Willapa do 80 per cent of the Northwest canning, which averages around 100,000 cases. The Northwest oyster industry is worth $2,000,000 annually.

Clams

Two varieties of clams, the razor and the hardshell, make up the catch of this valuable shellfish. The razor clam is best known but is found only in a few restricted areas along the north Pacific coast, including the hard sand beaches of Washington, north of Grays Harbor, and the Alaska coast near the mouth of the Copper River. Smaller amounts are taken along the Oregon coast.

The Pacific razor clam, famous for its size and the whiteness and firmness of its meat, buries itself in clean sand and must be hand-dug with a spade, the harvesters often working knee-deep in the surf. When tides are quite low the diggers make their best bags. During the Washington clam season, from March 1 to June 1, thousands of harvesters are busy, selling both to the fresh trade and the canneries. The Washington pack of razor clams has dropped from 50,000 cases per year to a scant 15,000. Fresh clams are relished along the Pacific Coast but are seldom shipped to the eastern United States. The pressure on this edible mollusk was greatly intensified in the decade 1930–40, and various beaches had to be closed to commercial diggers, with quotas firmly enforced. In 1951 Copalis was the only beach open to clamming, and the commercial quota was limited to 500,000 pounds.

Alaska razor clams in the Copper River district and on Kodiak Island are taken entirely for canning, which began in Cordova in 1916. This ground has also been worked so intensively that the Fish and Wildlife Service puts the packers on a quota which varies from 25,000 to 50,000 cases annually.

Hardshell clams are found in various beds around Puget Sound, and canneries operate in several Sound cities such as Port Townsend and Sequim. British Columbia also has a small hardshell pack.

Crab and Shrimp

With three special centers of crab fishing, the lower Columbia, Coos Bay, and Yaquina Bay, Oregon has long been the Northwest leader. For many years crabs have ranked second only to salmon in Oregon fishery production, and more meat has been sold fresh than has gone to the canneries. Washington, with Grays Harbor, Willapa Harbor, and various Puget Sound crab grounds, has at times (as in 1948) outranked Oregon. Alaska has a large canning and freezing industry, with Cordova on Prince William Sound as the chief center. Here the

Dungeness type of crab has long been the mainstay, but the catching and quick freezing of the giant Alaska king crab is beginning.

Six or seven commercial varieties of shrimp are found in the bays and sounds of the Northwest, with Alaska, British Columbia, and Puget Sound as the main sources.[4] These small shellfish are caught either by trawls or seines. Most of the Alaska take is canned, but the demand for fresh and frozen shrimp is increasing.

MINOR FISHERIES

Albacore Tuna

The catching of albacore off the Oregon-Washington Coast has assumed large proportions. For the 30 years preceding 1937, the canning of yellowfin, skipjack, albacore, and bonito as tuna was a California business. All types of tuna were taken in warm waters from California far south along the Mexican west coast. Trollers off the mouth of the Columbia began to take albacore in quantity about 1937, and salmon packers in Astoria canned them. Firmest and whitest of the tuna family, albacore accounts for almost the entire Northwest catch, individual fish averaging 15 to 20 pounds in weight. The Washington-Oregon albacore is a warm-weather fish; the run does not begin until July, reaching a peak in August. Albacore are usually taken with hook and line using bait and short powerful poles with which to "boat" the fish. Purse seines are also used to some extent.

Tuna canning methods differ considerably from those used for salmon. When boated the albacore are frozen in brine; at the cannery they are dressed, washed, cooked in live steam, and cooled. Trimmers remove the skin, bones, and dark meat, separating the fish into four parts, each called a loin. Cut into sections by a guillotine knife, the tuna is then packed in cans, sealed, and given another brief cook to sterilize it. Many new tuna-canning units have been built in Astoria and Grays Harbor, which at present are leading centers. The average annual pack for Oregon-Washington is 444,000 cases. British Columbia began tuna canning on a commercial scale in 1948.

[4] Shrimping in Puget Sound is an example of methods too severe for replenishment. Each new bed discovered was cleaned out and then abandoned; today the Sound produces less than one-quarter of the shrimp caught during the 1900–15 period. Hood Canal is the best remaining shrimp ground inside the Sound.

Herring, Pilchard, Shad, and Smelt

Another pelagic fish, the herring, is common along the Pacific Coast, Alaska, and British Columbia, providing nearly all the catch, valued at $7,000,000 annually. Purse seining is the most common method of taking herring, thousands of barrels being processed for food, oil, meal, fish bait, and fertilizer. Canadian purse seiners are active in the north Pacific during the annual run, and have by far the largest production. British Columbia herring, canned for overseas shipment, was in high demand during the war, but most of the present catch goes to reduction plants. Alaska herring intended for food are salt packed and eventually landed in Seattle for further processing. Alaska markets three-quarters of the total United States herring.

TABLE 2

FISHERIES OF THE PACIFIC NORTHWEST, 1948

(U. S. Fish and Wildlife Service)

Catch (in thousands of pounds and dollars)

Varieties (Selected)	Oregon		Washington		Alaska		British Columbia *		Total
	Pounds	Value	Pounds	Value	Pounds	Value	Pounds	Value	Value
Salmon	18,814	3910	38,796	9164	338,367	23,142	145,168	19,952	56,168
Halibut	629	101	13,253	2570	34,960	5,095	18,753	2,725	10,491
Herring	117	4	475	20	174,449	1,853	416,967	5,184	7,061
Albacore (tuna)	17,447	3583	4,430	1517	132	32	21	2	5,134
Crab	10,069	1047	22,712	2402	3,355	159	1,669	140	3,748
Flounder (soles)	13,424	683	13,824	809	248	7	12,853	727	2,226
Oysters	59	10	9,638	1900	7		1,695	187	2,097
Ling cod	1,054	128	7,559	1051			6,585	486	1,665
Sablefish	706	107	2,875	485	6,512	707	2,180	242	1,541
Grayfish		426		727					1,153
Shark	600	413	761	489	1,985	35	5	18	955
Clam	119	60	786	366	1,222	128	1,982	53	607
Rockfish			10,890	488			1,163	42	530
Cod	34	1	6,287	257	2,337	73	1,717	71	402
Shrimp			42	11	2,834	226	353	70	307
Smelts	930	80	3,631	195			56	6	281

* Dominion Bureau of Statistics, Ottawa.

Sardines (or pilchard), taken in purse seines in the same manner as herring, were formerly caught freely along the British Columbia and, to a lesser degree, the Washington and Oregon coasts. Most of the Northwest catch was landed at oil and fishmeal reduction plants.

After reaching a peak of 96,000 tons in 1944 the sardine catch declined rapidly and is at present insignificant.

The Columbia River and the coastal streams of Oregon have a shad run each spring, and a few carloads including shad roe are shipped East. Columbia River sturgeon, once heavily fished for their roe, are now growing scarcer. The spring run of silvery smelt in the Cowlitz River of Washington is welcomed both by commercial fishermen and by thousands who dip them up for food or sport.

Demersal or Bottomfish

The most famous deep-sea fish, the true cod, is less significant in the Pacific than in the Atlantic. Formerly caught with hand lines in Alaskan waters and especially in Bering Sea, the cod is now taken by trawls. Other varieties of bottomfish caught in large quantities include sole (English, petrale, and Dover), ling cod, red and black rockfish, and ocean perch. The sablefish, formerly called Alaska black cod, is caught in quantity; with its fine flavor and rich meat it is growing in favor.

Like the halibut, these so-called bottomfish are taken by means of deep trawls dragged along the ocean bottom. With rising prices many of these little-known demersal varieties find a ready market, and the Pacific Northwest trawl fleets, based mainly on Puget Sound and the Columbia River, are increasing their operations. Many new varieties of bottomfish are reaching the American market in the form of fillets. Livers and viscera are a rich source of vitamin oils.

Reduction Plants

One of the most interesting trends is the increase in reduction plants turning out oils, fishmeal, and fertilizers, as well as many other special products. Formerly a sideline in the Northwest, fish reduction is now one of the most profitable phases of the business, since it can use many inedible varieties as well as scraps left over from canning and other processing operations. Astoria has several plants of this type. Sharks are taken on hook and line or by harpoons like those used in whaling. With its high vitamin content shark-liver oil is in demand by drug houses. Dogfish (grayfish) livers, also rich in vitamins, are processed in Seattle, Tacoma, and Anacortes. Fish-liver landings at Seattle, chiefly from halibut, sablefish, dogfish, and ling cod, reach 1.5 million pounds per year. In this increased attention to by-products the fisheries industry resembles the meat industry, which finds a use for everything that enters the packing plant.

Whaling

Whaling has long since disappeared from the North Atlantic but is still pursued along the Alaskan coasts and in Bering Sea. A small whaling fleet from Victoria, British Columbia, still operates in the North Pacific, the Canadians using a shore station on the Queen Charlotte Islands. Small killer boats with harpoon guns hunt these northern waters for sperm, finback, and humpback whales. The carcasses of the great mammals are towed to the shore station for reduction; the oil is tried out, whale beef canned for export, and various types of feeds and fertilizers prepared for market. The take of the fleet is 300 to 400 whales annually.

Fur Seals of the Pribilof Islands

The Alaska seal (in reality a sea lion) forms the basis for a unique fur industry. The rocky Pribilof Islands of the Bering Sea have the largest rookies in the world. In winter the seals swim far south in the ocean, returning in early summer to their home grounds where the pups are born. Seal skins have long brought high prices, and from 1880 to 1911 hunters of many nations congregated around the Pribilofs to indulge in indiscriminate killing outside the 3-mile limit. There was grave danger that the herd would be exterminated. After an unsuccessful attempt in the early 1890's to make the Bering Sea a closed area under its sole jurisdiction, the United States in 1911 negotiated a treaty with Great Britain, Russia, and Japan. This agreement, the North Pacific Sealing Convention which prohibited pelagic sealing, was signed just in time, the herd having been reduced from a roughly estimated 3 million to a scant 150,000.

The present United States control includes both protection and management. Since seals are polygamous and sexes are born in equal numbers, a large proportion of the bachelor seals are surplus and can be killed without impairing the natural increase. Three-year-old bachelors provide the bulk of the 65,000 skins taken annually, and the carcasses are made into meal and oil, Canada sharing in the profits. Under this sensible system of control by international agreement, the seal herd has been stabilized at 1.5 million, now regarded as the optimum size.

RESTORATION PROGRAM

Protection for all Northwest Fisheries

Since fisheries play such a large part in the economy of the Northwest, public interest demands that they be preserved unimpaired as a permanent regional resource. Many years of effort have finally culminated in programs of rehabilitation for salmon and halibut. Equal care is needed for many other valuable food fish, now plentiful in North Pacific waters but in danger of overexploitation. Herring, pilchard, sturgeon, whales, shrimp, crabs, razor clams, to mention only a few, already show varying degrees of depletion.

The life history of each species differs to such an extent and the pressure upon them is so diverse that it is impossible to apply identical conservation measures. Each fishery must be regarded as a separate problem. The remedial measures for all, however, tend to have certain similarities, which may include:

1. A program of scientific research until the complete life history is known.
2. Flexible regulations which may include one or more of the following measures:
   a. A quantity limit on the catch.
   b. A closed season for part of the year, or possibly for a term of years if the stock is badly depleted.
   c. Refuge zones or nursery areas where fishing is prohibited.
   d. Restrictions on the size or the age of the catch.
   e. Restrictions on type of gear.
3. Legislation against stream and coastal pollution.
4. Increasing the young stock by means of hatcheries, if practicable.
5. Securing the cooperation of the fishing industry and the public by a program of education.

As it is always easier to preserve an original stock than to rebuild an exhausted one, fisheries experts try to act before exhaustion is reached. Preservation of the Northwest fisheries depends largely upon public willingness to recognize the danger, grant adequate appropriations for research, and submit to reasonable regulation. The ultimate goal of all such measures is a sustained yield and a permanent abundance.

REFERENCES

The Pacific Fisherman, published monthly, Seattle, Washington.

International Pacific Salmon Fisheries Commission, *Annual Reports,* New Westminster, Canada.

International Fisheries Commission, *Regulation and Investigation of the Pacific Halibut Fishery in 1950,* No. 16, Seattle, Washington, 1951; No. 20, Seattle, Washington, 1953.

Miscellaneous scientific and economic reports on Pacific Northwest fisheries, U. S. Fish and Wildlife Service, Washington, D. C.

Water Resources
and Their Development

R. M. HIGHSMITH and J. GRANVILLE JENSEN

Water has been, and will remain, a key resource in Northwest development. Irrigation agriculture supports most of the settlement on the arid lands between the Cascade and northern Rocky Mountains, and farmers elsewhere have found supplemental irrigation profitable for shallow-rooted crops. The Northwest is dependent upon hydroelectricity for energy to a degree not matched in any other region of the United States. Urban centers and industries now secure their large water requirements from clear mountain lakes and streams or suitable ground-water supplies.

Although most areas have had sufficient water, problems are beginning to appear in its use. Continued growth of Northwest population and industry will require additional development of water resources.

INVENTORY OF WATER RESOURCES

The water resources of the Northwest are great but unequally distributed. Runoff from watersheds varies from less than 1 inch in the arid portions of the interior to over 100 inches in areas of heaviest rainfall on the Coastal Mountains. The aggregate annual volume of streams reaching the Oregon and Washington coast is estimated to be 280 million feet (Fig. 23).

On the average, the Columbia River system, draining a total of 259,000 square miles, discharges 180 million acre feet annually at its mouth or about 65 per cent of the total Northwest runoff. Streams draining the Puget Sound Basin and the Washington and Oregon Coast ranges supply the remainder from an area of about 36,500 square miles. The Northwest also has large ground-water resources.

198

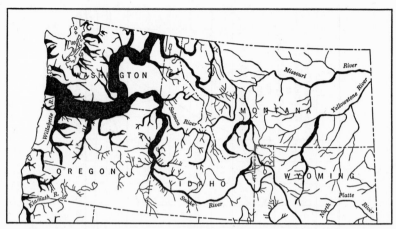

FIG. 23. Northwest hydrography, showing streams in the Northwest and discharge by width of line.

Surface Water

The Northwest is blessed in the Columbia River system, which has qualities that favor its management and use. Favorable qualities include: (1) large, firm volume of water; (2) small amount of silt carried by stream, which extends the life of storage reservoirs; (3) a relatively steep gradient; (4) numerous dam and storage sites; (5) passage of the system through a large portion of the arid sector of the Northwest; (6) a relatively deep channel, extending far inland; and (7) maximum runoff during the growing season.

The drainage basin of the Columbia River includes three-fourths of the area of the Northwest. The river system draws about 65 per cent of its water supply from the Northern Rockies, where part of the precipitation is stored in the form of snow and ice for warm-season release (see Fig. 24). The main stem rises in Columbia Lake in British Columbia, 2652 feet above sea level, and is joined by the Kootenai River and the Pend Oreille River before it reaches the international line. The Columbia River enters Washington carrying an annual average of 73 million acre feet of water, and, after crossing the state in a series of broad bends, takes a westward course through the Cascade Mountains to the Pacific Ocean.

The Columbia's major tributary, the Snake River, drains 190,000 square miles in the southeastern half of the Columbia Basin, and annually discharges nearly 37 million acre feet into the main stem. The Willamette River is the principal tributary west of the Cascades

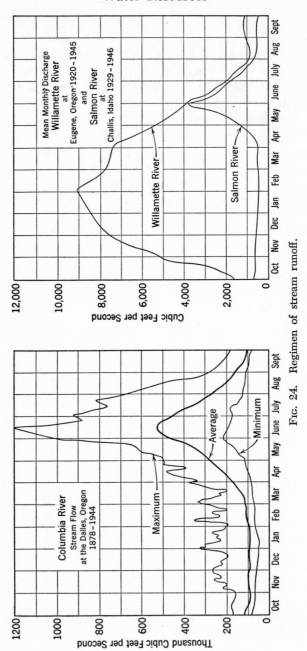

FIG. 24. Regimen of stream runoff.

supplying an annual runoff of almost 22 million acre feet. Other tributaries and their approximate volumes are graphically shown on the map of hydrography, Fig. 24. The Puget Sound and coastal streams of Washington and Oregon are small in comparison to the Columbia; however, considering the size of their drainage basins, their flow is great. In Washington, the Skagit River discharges annually 2 million acre feet from 1340 square miles, the Snohomish 5 million from 1790 square miles, and the Chehalis 3 million acre feet from 1420 square miles. In Oregon, the Rogue River has an annual runoff of 8 million acre feet from 5000 square miles of mountains, and the Umpqua has nearly as large a discharge and area. The west-side streams receive a major portion of their runoff from cool-season rains; thus their peak flows come during late fall, winter, and early spring in contrast to the late-spring and early-summer high flow of the dominately snow-fed streams rising in eastern portions of the region (Fig. 24).

For most of the streams, flow varies considerably during each year and from one year to another. Thus, for the Columbia River at The Dalles during the 70 years ending with 1948, maximum flow has been 1,240,000 second-feet (flood peak of June 6, 1894) and minimum flow has been 35,000 second-feet. These two magnitudes are 637 and 18 per cent respectively of the average of 194,600 second-feet. During the same period, yearly runoff has ranged between 225 and 85.5 million acre feet, in 1894 and 1926 respectively. These magnitudes are respectively 160 and 61 per cent of the average. However, variability in flow differs greatly among the numerous tributaries of the Columbia. For example, the adjacent John Day and Deschutes rivers in north-central Oregon may be considered. Measured flow of the John Day has ranged from 1420 per cent to less than 1 per cent of the mean, whereas that of the Deschutes has ranged only between 750 and 58 per cent of the mean. In proportion to drainage area, water yield of the Deschutes has been 239 per cent of that from the John Day. These examples suggest the complex and diverse problems to be solved in effectively managing the streams for optimum use of their waters.[1]

Ground Water

Water beneath the surface in the ground-water zone constitutes a significant portion of Northwest water resources. Detailed appraisals

[1] Statistics supplied by Arthur M. Piper, Staff Scientist, Pacific Northwest, U. S. Geological Survey.

of ground water cover only a few acres; however, available reports suggest that in numerous basins and valleys of the region individual wells of adequate construction will yield in the order of 500 gallons per minute with favorable low content of dissolved solids, generally under 600 parts per million, sufficient in quantities and quality to supply most domestic and stock needs.

Significant ground-water supplies are available in the Willamette-Puget trough and on the alluvial floors of most of the larger coastal valleys. Annual replenishment is well in excess of present ground-water draft and the surplus is discharged into streams or lost by evaporation chiefly during the dry season. Variations in subsurface materials result in marked local differences in ground-water supplies. The quality of the ground water of most of the Willamette Valley is suitable for domestic uses and irrigation, and abundant quantities can be tapped with shallow wells in the recent deposits along the streams. Similarly, ground water can be tapped at relatively shallow depths in the alluvial-filled valleys of the Puget Sound Basin, and at somewhat greater depth in glacial sand and gravel formations, as on the prairies south of Tacoma.

East of the Cascades the depth and quality of ground water varies with geologic conditions, and in the Columbia Basin farmers have secured water for irrigation and domestic use from wells.

The Spokane Valley and the Snake River Plain of south-central Idaho are favored with outstanding ground-water resources. There is a substantial ground-water flow, estimated between 1000 and 1200 cubic feet per second, through the broad, deeply filled glacial-outwash channel in which the Spokane River flows. The Spokane River gains from 600 to 800 cubic feet per second from springs in a 20-mile reach above Spokane Falls, and the Little Spokane receives an additional 300 to 400 cubic feet per second from springs north of Spokane.[2] These ground-water discharges tend to maintain a higher late-summer flow than would exist otherwise in the Spokane River.

In south-central Idaho there is a tremendous ground-water flow beneath the Snake River Plain which is the principal source of inflow to the Snake River between Blackfoot and King Hill, Idaho. A considerable portion of rain falling on this part of the plain, of streams discharging into it, and of water used for irrigation continually recharges the reservoir formed by the porous lavas blanketing the area. The bottom of this subsurface reservoir is the impermeable basement

[2] Appendix D, Corps of Engineers 308 Report, *Spokane River Basin*, p. D-21.

rock of an ancient Snake River Valley. The ground waters moving toward the trough tend to concentrate in buried channels of the ancient valley and discharge through many springs along the north wall of the Snake River Canyon between Milner Dam and Bliss.[3] It is estimated that 3.5 million acre feet a year enter or re-enter the Snake River downstream from Milner Dam in the form of ground water. The depth to the water table under the Snake River Plain averages more than 200 feet and varies chiefly with the contour of the land surface; in some extensive areas it exceeds 400 feet, and in one is known to be greater than 1700 feet. But in an area of about 1000 square miles the depth to the water table is less than 50 feet.[4] The concentration of dissolved solids varies from 200 to 600 parts per million throughout all the plain, except in the vicinity of Twin Falls, where it ranges from 500 to 1300 parts per million, probably as a result of poor drainage conditions.[5]

PRESENT DEVELOPMENT AND USES OF WATER

The economy of the Pacific Northwest is dependent primarily on the use of its water resources for domestic and industrial supplies, irrigation and other agricultural needs, hydroelectric power, transportation, commercial fishing, and recreation. The last two uses are considered in other sections and, therefore, will not be treated in this chapter.

Domestic and Industrial Water Supplies [6]

Northwest communities and industries have had relatively few problems in obtaining abundant and good-quality water supplies, since most are situated near sparkling, clear mountain streams or can draw upon ground water. Approximately 2 million people in 311 cities and towns obtain all or most of their drinking and household water from surface sources. The total demand on surface-water resources for domestic uses is estimated to be at least 250 million gallons daily. Four hundred and nine water systems using ground-water sources serve an additional three-quarter million persons with an estimated 100 million gallons daily!

[3] House Document 473, 81st Congress, *The Columbia River*, pp. 100–101.
[4] Appendix G, Corps of Engineers 308 Report, *Upper Snake Basin*, p. G-30-34.
[5] House Document 473, *loc. cit.*, p. 102.
[6] Figures from U. S. Public Health Service.

Industrial plants using small quantities of water depend largely upon public systems to supply their needs. Many concerns requiring large quantities of water, such as pulp and paper mills, the aluminum plants, the Hanford Atomic Works, and others located outside public system service areas have developed their own supplies. The total Northwest daily industrial water demand is estimated to be about 1¼ billion gallons. Approximately 80 per cent is obtained from surface sources. Most surface waters can be satisfactorily treated for industrial use, but some industries prefer ground water because a standard quality can be obtained with a standard treatment.

Irrigation

Irrigation agriculture is an important component of the farming economy of the Pacific Northwest (Plate 13B). Approximately 4.5 million acres, comprising about one-quarter of total Northwest cropland, are irrigated in the arid sectors between the Cascade Range and the northern Rocky Mountains (Fig. 25). In addition, an estimated 200,000 acres west of the Cascade Range are receiving supplemental irrigation during the dry summer season.

EAST OF THE CASCADES. The dry, hot summers, relatively long frost-free seasons, fertile soils, favorable relief for diversion and cultivation, and the dependable sources of water have made irrigation developments profitable ventures east of the Cascades. For example, Yakima County, almost wholly dependent upon irrigation, is the leading agriculture county of Washington and usually ranks fifth or sixth in income among the agricultural counties of the nation.

The major portion of the irrigated land is found along the tributaries of the Columbia River. Figure 25 shows the distribution of irrigated land in five sub-basins of the Columbia Basin east of the Cascades. The greatest development is in the Upper Snake River Plain, where nearly 1.6 million acres are under irrigation. In the central sub-basin, almost 1.2 million acres are irrigated, mostly in the Boise, Payette, Owyhee, and Malheur valleys. The Clark Fork-Clearwater sub-basin has a total of 420,000 acres under irrigation, over half of which is in the valleys of the Bitterroot and Flathead rivers of Montana. Slightly under 600,000 acres are irrigated in the central Washington sub-basin, of which 500,000 acres are in the Yakima Valley. In the Middle Columbia sub-basin about 333,000 acres are devoted to irrigation with notable concentration in the Deschutes Valley and large blocks in the Walla Walla, John Day, Umatilla, and Hood River valleys.

Significant irrigation developments are also found in the lakes and Klamath basins of south-central Oregon, which are outside the Columbia Basin. The total land in irrigation agriculture is about 400,000 acres.

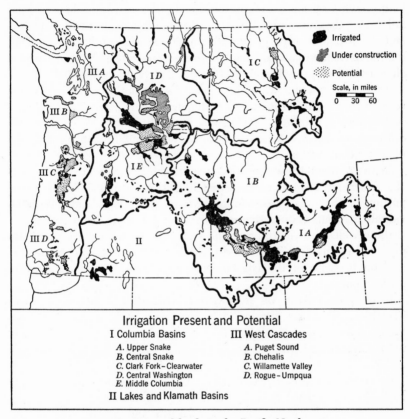

Irrigation Present and Potential

I Columbia Basins
A. Upper Snake
B. Central Snake
C. Clark Fork – Clearwater
D. Central Washington
E. Middle Columbia

II Lakes and Klamath Basins

III West Cascades
A. Puget Sound
B. Chehalis
C. Willamette Valley
D. Rogue – Umpqua

FIG. 25. Irrigated lands in the Pacific Northwest.

The bulk of the irrigated acreage east of the Cascades is found within relatively large projects. However, hundreds of individuals and small groups of individuals with private systems take water from the small streams of the region.

WEST OF THE CASCADES. In the Rogue River Basin 65,000 acres are irrigated largely in Jackson and Josephine counties. Approximately 19,000 acres are under irrigation in Dungeness Valley in the northeastern corner of the Olympic Peninsula. Total rainfall in these areas is between 16 and 20 inches and comes principally during the cool season.

The possibilities of increasing farm returns have stimulated interest in supplemental irrigation in the Willamette Valley,[7] the Chehalis Valley, and the Puget Sound Lowland, where the effectiveness of the long growing season is greatly reduced by the prevailing lack of rainfall during the 3 summer months. Although fall-sown, early-maturing, and deep-rooted crops grow well under natural conditions, summer rainfall is inadequate for shallow-rooted crops. Such crops, whose chief period of growth comes after the first of June, require about 1 inch of supplemental water per week during hot weather. Pastures require from 16 to 24 inches of water during the season for optimum production, depending on efficiency of application. Truck crops require about 12 inches and can be grown profitably only with supplemental irrigation.

In the Willamette Valley the area irrigated expanded from about 12,000 acres in 1930 to an estimated 100,000 acres in 1951. The major portion of the present development is on floodplain land with individuals or small cooperative organizations pumping from streams or shallow wells and distributing the water to the land with aluminum pipe and sprinklers. Pump-and-sprinkle irrigation is even being carried on in some of the coastal valleys to increase summer pasture production.

FUTURE EXTENSION OF IRRIGATION. One of the largest areas of irrigable land in the Northwest is contained in the Columbia Basin Project now being developed by the Bureau of Reclamation. The irrigation system is designed to serve 1,029,000 acres which lie within a 2,500,000-acre expanse of the Central Plain. At present 503,000 acres are included in development plans, the remainder being withheld partly by the Federal Government in the Wahluke Slope area adjacent to the Hanford Atomic Works for health and safety reasons and partly by wheat farmers on the higher fringes (Fig. 26).

Size and continuity of congressional appropriations will determine the rate of development, and since these vary, the Bureau of Reclamation necessarily has several alternative plans. It is currently operating under a plan which will bring approximately 160,000 acres under irrigation during the decade of the 1950's.

The first lands to receive water are in the south end of the project. In 1948 a pumping system for 5552 acres began operating northwest

[7] See Richard M. Highsmith, *Water Planning in the Willamette Basin*, 1950 Yearbook, Association of Pacific Coast Geographers.

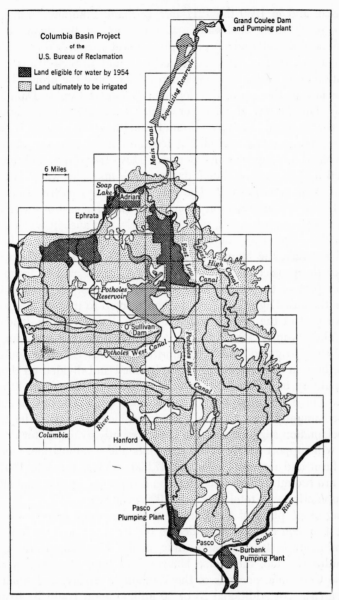

FIG. 26.   Columbia Basin Project.   (*Map from U. S. Bureau of Reclamation.*)

of Pasco, and in 1950 the 1211-acre Burbank Pumping Unit, east of Pasco, received its first water. Construction of the main irrigation system is sufficiently advanced to deliver water to 87,000 acres of land in the northern part of the project area and present plans call for irrigation of an additional 70,000 acres throughout the project by 1958.

The key to the entire development is Grand Coulee Dam (Plate 13A). This largest of all concrete dams impounds water and supplies the necessary power. From Lake Roosevelt, which is formed by the dam, water is lifted 280 feet and flows into the equalizing reservoir in the upper Grand Coulee. This reservoir, 27 miles long, is formed by two earth-and-rock dams, which impound water in the old glacial meltwater channel. The irrigation water is carried southward from the equalizing reservoir through a rocky area east of lower Grand Coulee by means of canals, siphons, tunnels, and ancient water courses (Fig. 26). About 2½ miles north of Adrian the water supply is divided between the 80-mile West Canal which irrigates the western part of the project and the 130-mile east Low Canal to irrigate the greater part of the eastern and southern sections. Sometime in the future the east High Canal will be constructed to irrigate lands in the eastern part of the project which are now devoted to dry-land farming. The 3½-mile O'Sullivan Dam south of Moses Lake will impound runoff from irrigated land to the north to be reused farther south.

The land in the project has been classified and divided on the basis of capability into farm units which, in general, vary from 40 to 160 acres. There are provisions for a few small units of about 10 acres in each community area, especially for intensified farming. The Bureau of Reclamation suggests that the land presently available for development will support nearly 6700 farm units and a population, including both farm and nonfarm, of about 47,000. When the total 1,029,000 acres are brought under irrigation the farm units will be doubled and the population will total nearly 100,000 people.

Long-range plans of the Bureau of Reclamation include a total of about 4 million acres to be added to the irrigated land, including the Columbia Basin Project, large areas in the Mountain Home district of southern Idaho, the Horse Heaven and John Day sectors of the Middle Columbia, portions of the Willamette Valley, and small scattered areas. An additional 25 or 30 million acres could be irrigated, but the feasibility has not been established.

Water for Power

Utilization of water for generation of electric energy is unusually important to the Northwest (Fig. 27). Over 98 per cent of the 25.4 billion kilowatt-hours produced in Washington, Oregon, and Idaho during 1950 was developed from falling water,[8] compared with only 29 per cent for the United States. Moreover, "hydro" supplies an unusually large share of the total energy of the region, providing about 30 per cent as compared with only 4 per cent for the nation. Hydroelectric development in the Northwest as the main source of basic energy came in large part from the deficiencies of the region in petroleum, natural gas, and suitable deposits of coal for large-scale utilization. Thus, attention was early turned to water as the only local energy resource that could be developed extensively and permanently.

The first development of water for power was the direct harnessing to turn water wheels of gristmills and small sawmills. Of the many small sites developed in the early days the fall in the Willamette River at Oregon City (Plate 14A) is outstanding as the place where electric energy was first transmitted by wire for use some distance away from the immediate site. Visitors stopping at the roadside turnout overlooking the fall read the historic marker, as follows: "Oregon City— once known as Willamette Falls—was the site of an Indian Salmon Fishing Village. The falls furnished the power for a lumber mill which began operation in 1842, a flour mill 1844, a woolen mill 1864, and the first paper mill in the Pacific Northwest in 1867. The first long-distance commercial electric power transmission in the United States was from Oregon City to Portland in 1889."

THE ERA OF DEVELOPMENT BY PRIVATE ENTERPRISE. With increasing population in the Northwest and the growing significance of electricity, private and municipal utilities developed numerous waterpower sites to generate electricity for sale in the urban centers. Through the first three decades of the twentieth century the emphasis was on sites close to the urban centers which could be readily developed at low cost for installation and transmission. Five major areas developed chiefly by private and municipal utilities stand out in the pattern of water-power plants as shown on the map (Fig. 27).

[8] Coal provides only about 10 per cent in the Northwest compared with nearly 50 per cent for the nation; petroleum about 45 per cent compared with 35 per cent for the nation; wood, some 15 per cent of the Northwest energy compared with an insignificant amount for the nation, and in the future it is likely to provide a smaller share.

1. The concentration of nineteen major plants tributary to the Puget Sound urban area. These include the installations of the Seattle City Light, especially Diablo and Ross Dams, fifth highest in the world (Plate 14*B*), on the Skagit River in the northern Cascade Mountains.

2. The twenty installations that serve the Lower Columbia and Willamette Valley regions. Development has concentrated on streams

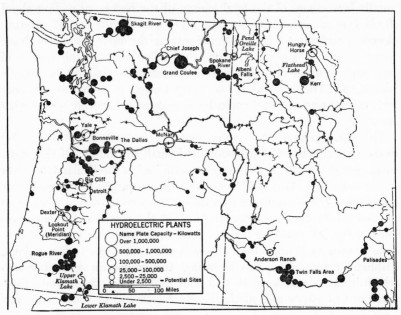

FIG. 27. Hydroelectric plants. Based on data from Bonneville Power Administration and Federal Power Commission reports, December, 1951. Circles are not proportional. Open circles, projects under construction.

flowing from the Cascade Mountains, especially the Clackamas and McKenzie rivers and the Willamette mainstem in Oregon, and on the Lewis River in Washington. Included in the group is the Federal plant at Bonneville.

3. The notable concentration on the upper Rogue and Umpqua rivers, developed chiefly by the California-Oregon Power Company.

4. Seven sites on the Spokane River, developed by the Washington Water Power Company to serve the Spokane urban region.

5. The upper Snake River with some twenty installations, chiefly developed by the Idaho Power Company.

THE ERA OF FEDERAL DEVELOPMENT. The era of Federal power generation began with the completion of Bonneville Dam in 1938

(Plate 14B) and Grand Coulee Dam in 1940. These enormous multiple-purpose dams produce low-cost electric energy for sale to industry and utilities through the Federal power marketing agency, the Bonneville Power Administration. In 1950, 56.7 per cent of the total energy flowing into the Northwest power pool was generated by Federal plants at Bonneville and Grand Coulee, 35.7 per cent by private companies, and 7.6 per cent by municipal utilities (24.9 billion kilowatts).

Great installations on the Columbia River have come only with the era of Federal Government development. Construction by the Federal Government has made possible projects requiring investments of several hundred millions of dollars. In addition, construction of the projects by the Federal Government makes practical the development of multiple-purpose dams planned and constructed to provide benefits not only in power, but also in irrigation, navigation, flood control, fish, and recreation. Grand Coulee Dam, built by the Bureau of Reclamation, and Bonneville Dam, by the U. S. Corps of Engineers, are in full operation; Hungry Horse, McNary, Chief Joseph, and The Dalles dams were under construction in 1953.

Low-Rate Energy. Federal projects on the main stem of the Columbia River have resulted in availability of large amounts of electric energy for sale to utilities and large industrial users on a 100 per cent load factor basis at the very low rate of $17.50 per kilowatt-year in 1952. The low cost of producing energy is a result of favorable physical conditions and Federal financial advantages including allocation of investment charges to several purposes, of which the most important are:

1. The great volume of water, even in the lowest water season.

2. The relatively steep gradient for so large a stream, and canyon sites in which dams can be built to develop the head by rapid steps and to store water.

3. Sites that can be developed without prohibitive cost for relocation of townsites and transportation routes without flooding valuable farm areas, since development is, as yet, in early stages and settlement sparse.

4. Federal financing.

5. Dams that are multiple-purpose and, therefore, properly have a share of the capital and operating cost charged to nonpower aspects such as flood control, navigation, and irrigation.

6. Operation on a high load factor.

PROBLEMS OF WATER FOR POWER. The low-water season on the Columbia comes in winter, from October through March, when consumer demand is at its peak; thus, there may be inadequate electric energy, especially firm power peaking capacity, during this period. During the high-water runoff period large amounts of power are always available to be sold as interruptible electric energy.

From the standpoint of water-resource development the solution to the dilemma is twofold. There must be more dams and power houses installed and there must also be far more water-storage capacity for management of runoff. Only with large summer storage will it be possible to draw the greatest service from the waters of the Columbia. Stored water will help control floods and, at the same time, by release during the low water season from October to March, will greatly increase the effective generating capacity of the several power installations downstream. It should also be noted that the streams of the western Cascades have their peak water flow during the winter. Consequently, a greater development of power on these streams with winter peak capacity would be of benefit.

POWER POTENTIALITIES. In spite of the spectacular developments that have been accomplished by private and public enterprise, only about 10 per cent of the potential hydro has been developed. Statements of potential vary because of such factors as the following. What development cost is economically feasible? How much water storage will be constructed? How much natural runoff will be available? How effectively will the total river development be coordinated? What percentage of the time is the energy to be available?

Potential power development in the Columbia River Basin alone is variously estimated as from 25 to 40 million kilowatts, compared with about 60 to 100 for the entire United States. The Northwest is usually credited with having some 35 to 50 per cent of the total potential hydro power of the nation.

Under the comprehensive plan for the Columbia River the Bureau of Reclamation and the U. S. Corps of Engineers currently propose to develop a total installed name-plate capacity of 11.6 million kilowatts on the Columbia River system. Development of Northwest potential water power will play a part in conserving the nation's nonrenewable fuels. Falling water, being inexhaustible, should be developed for power to the fullest practical extent but with reasonable regard for other water uses. For example, some streams should be reserved for recreational uses, others for fish-spawning grounds, and in some cases existing water rights, and future irrigation, needs to be considered.

In British Columbia no dams have yet been built across the main Columbia River, although a number of excellent sites have been surveyed. Notable among these is that of Mica Creek, where a 600-foot dam would create a reservoir 80 miles long, with potential power estimated at 660,000 kilowatts. Chief development has been on Kootenay River from Kootenay Lake to its junction with the Columbia River. Here are located sixty hydroelectric developments, five belonging to the Consolidated Mining and Smelting Company and one operated by the city of Nelson. The total installation power of these plants is 300,000 kilowatts. A dam under construction on the lower Pend Oreille River will have a capacity of 153,000 kilowatts, with provision for doubling output at a later day. The power will be used by the smelter at Trail.

A large power development constructed in the early 1950's at Kitimat, in western British Columbia, supplies energy to a huge aluminum plant.

Water Utilization for Transportation

The deep inlets and bays, the Columbia, and numerous lesser streams serve as highways of trade and commerce. Although the importance of the rivers is less since the coming of railroads and trucks, the rivers and harbors still constitute a valuable resource.

Puget Sound provides access far into the land for the largest of ocean-going vessels. Utilizing this waterway, ocean commerce is able to meet the railroads at favored inland situations and has led directly to the development of urban centers, including Bellingham, Tacoma, Everett, Seattle, and Olympia. In addition, ocean-going vessels can enter Lake Union and Lake Washington by way of Ballard Locks at Seattle. Numerous lesser inlets of the Pacific Coast also provide harbors and have led to the development of seaports, including those of Grays Harbor, Astoria (at the mouth of the Columbia), Newport, and the towns on Coos Bay.

Altogether, there are an estimated 600 miles of navigable river waterways in the Northwest, chiefly on the main stem of the Columbia and its two tributaries, the Willamette and Snake rivers. Improvements of the Columbia River began in the middle of the nineteenth century, when industrial leaders of Portland became seriously concerned over the potential loss of their water-borne commerce to Seattle and Tacoma, which were favored by their deep harbors. Even before Federal assistance was procurred Portland business leaders raised several hundred thousand dollars to construct jetties at the river mouth in the hope that the river would clear its channel. In 1877 the U. S. Corps of Engineers initiated the first Federal improvement projects on the river.

The existing projects provide a 35-foot channel 101 miles inland to Portland on the Willamette River. A channel with controlling minimum depth of about 14.5 feet extends 190 miles inland to The Dalles. Vessels pass Bonneville Dam by locks built in 1937 with width clearance of 76 feet. The Bonneville Locks were the highest single lift north of Panama until the completion of those at McNary Dam. Beyond The Dalles a 7 foot minimum channel extends as far as Pasco, Washington, 328 miles from the Columbia mouth. Celilo Falls and rapids just above The Dalles are passed by a narrow lock and canal with controlling width of only 45 feet. This serious handicap to river transportation will be eliminated by the slack water which will be created by The Dalles Dam now under construction and will increase the utility of the Columbia River waterway to Pasco in the Inland Empire. Projects proposed by the Corps of Engineers for the Snake River will provide sufficient depth of water for barge traffic as far inland as Lewiston, Idaho.

On the Columbia few ocean vessels now go beyond Vancouver, Washington. Above Vancouver the principal traffic is carried by barges, which annually transport over a million tons of bulk cargo as far as Pasco (Plate 14A). By far the greatest movements are petroleum products transported upstream and wheat and logs downstream. Above Pasco, river traffic is limited by low water, rapids, and scattered settlement. Numerous lakes such as Chelan and Pend Oreille, as well as other rivers, are used locally. For example, many log rafts are hauled to mills at Coeur d'Alene, Idaho, down the St. Joe River and across Lake Coeur d'Alene. Above Grand Coulee Dam, log rafts are floated on Lake Roosevelt to sawmills.

The Willamette River was of great importance in the early days of the Northwest as it passed through the most significant of the settlement areas. As early as 1872 a canal and locks were constructed to pass vessels around the falls in the river at Oregon City. These locks, using much of the original machinery, are still in constant use. Today the Willamette offers a 35-foot channel to Portland, an 8-foot to Oregon City, a 5-foot to Albany, and a 3½-foot channel to Corvallis.

The only use of the river above the falls is for movement of log rafts and a few pleasure boats. There is more active use between the pulp and paper mills at the falls and Portland. Over 2 million tons, chiefly logs, pulp, and paper originating at the plants at the falls, annually pass through the locks.

Portland, Oregon, with its 35-foot channel is strategically situated at the crossroads of the great east-west Columbia River waterway and the north-south Willamette-Puget trough. Thus the city has opportunity to serve the commerce of the world's oceans and the hinterlands of the Willamette Valley and the Inland Empire. The full potentialities of the locational advantages provided by the waterways have yet to be realized.

WATER PROBLEMS

Although the Northwest is favored with generous water supplies, several serious problems now exist and others are becoming serious. Floods and drainage problems have been apparent in the region since its earliest settlement. More recently, watershed deterioration is effecting quality and stability of water supplies; pollution is critical in some areas; on many streams water rights have been granted in excess of low-season flows. Conflicts for water use for recreation, irrigation, fish, transportation, and power are more and more in evidence. Many of these topics are covered in other chapters of this text.

Floods

Floods are a serious problem in some localities, particularly west of the Cascade Range. These fundamental processes of nature will continue to affect the region until streams are controlled by watershed protection and rehabilitation, storage reservoirs, and channel improvements.

Many of the valley floors of western Oregon and Washington are partially inundated every year, and because these floodplain areas contain productive agricultural land and have been intensively settled, floods are costly. The watersheds of these streams are generally small, but, owing to high precipitation, runoff is great with flows following the same cycle as precipitation. During the cool season when the rivers, greatly augmented with rain runoff, leave the highlands and emerge upon the flat floors of the valleys, their velocities are reduced and their crests rise. During the winter and spring of every year the discharges of the Willamette River and its major tributaries reach or exceed bank-full capacity at critical points. Except in unusually dry years about 100,000 acres are inundated annually, and frequently recurring floods cover from 150,000 to 270,000 acres. The average annual flood damage in the Willamette Basin, based on 1947 economic development and 1948 price, is estimated by the Corps of Engineers to be $8,560,000. Rivers tributary to the Puget Sound, such as the Skagit, Snohomish, Sammamish, Duwamish, Green, and Puyallup, annually inundate portions of their narrow, flat bottoms, totaling several thousand acres. Similar overflows are common along the coastal streams. Normally floods in these areas are flashy, of short duration, and flood flows are many times greater than the year-long average flow.

Floods within the Columbia River watershed, outside of the Willamette Valley, occur less frequently, but in some areas they have become serious menaces as economic development has progressed. The main stream through most of its course is entrenched within protecting walls which can withstand a large rise. The greatest damage occurs in the reach between 30 and 100 miles from the mouth. Lowlying lands along this area are frequently under water as a result of too rapid runoff in the early warm season. This condition also produces local floods in some of the tributary streams east of the Cascades, such as Kootenai, Flathead, Boise, Upper Snake, Yakima and Okanogan rivers.

Major floods have occurred along the Columbia River three times in the past 100 years: in 1876, 1894, and 1948. As economic development has progressed, damage caused by these, and even floods of moderate magnitude, has increased far out of proportion to the flood flow magnitude. Estimates indicate that the 1948 flood damages amounted to about $104,000,000. Approximately 582,000 acres were inundated, including the towns of Bonners Ferry, Idaho, and Woodland, Washington, and many others were partially under water; Vanport, Oregon, a war housing project with a population of about 18,000, adjoining Portland on the north, was destroyed. Throughout the basin 50 persons lost their lives, 120,000 were evacuated from their homes during the flood, and 38,000 lost their homes; 4200 acres of arable land were lost by stream bank erosion, and about 19,000 acres were severely damaged.

Flood-control developments in the region are carried out by the Corps of Engineers, who construct bank protections and make channel improvements as needs arise and appropriations are available. The U. S. Department of Agriculture has an active program of watershed management. The state of Washington has an active flood-control program under the supervision of the Department of Conservation and Development, giving aid in flood-control engineering and matching funds for financing construction of channel and bank improvements. Their work is coordinated with that of the Corps of Engineers, counties, flood-control districts, urban centers, diking districts, soil conservation districts, and irrigation districts.

Although some 20 million acre feet of storage regulation are available, this amount falls far short of solving all the flood problems of the region. However, the storage reservoirs that have been recommended for construction in the comprehensive plan for development of the Columbia River, together with a broad program of local protection work, will meet the most urgent needs.

Drainage

Too much water on the land can be as detrimental to agriculture as too little. Drainage conditions restrict the adaptability of several hundred thousand acres in the Northwest. The major portion is found on the valley floors west of the Cascades where prolonged cool season precipitation and low gradient maintain soils in a thoroughly saturated condition and cause local ponding in areas with restricted outlets. The heavier soils are slow to drain in the spring but become dry and hard during the summer if not properly cultivated.

The largest single body of poorly drained land is found in the Willamette Basin.[9] Only about one-quarter of the total arable land of the valley floor has sufficient gradient and stream outlet to produce normally adequate drainage. About 30 per cent of the arable land on the valley floor, 480,000 acres, is subject to adverse drainage conditions, only one-third of which has direct outlets to stream channels. The remaining outlying areas are seriously affected by ponding and waterlogging because of flat topography and heavy soils. The adaptability of such land is restricted. The majority of field crops are either seriously damaged or killed when inundated longer than 5 days. When such ponding occurs, it becomes necessary to replant the land, usually to less valuable crops. When inundation may be expected frequently, land must be planted to late, fast-maturing crops, which often results in low income. Improvement of drainage facilities could increase the adaptability of at least one-third of the total cropland on the Willamette Valley floor.

Similar conditions exist on a lesser scale in the Puget Sound Basin and other areas of western Oregon and Washington.

A drainage problem of a different nature exists in some portions of the irrigated areas east of the Cascade Mountains. In many of the

[9] See Appendix J, Corps of Engineers, 308 Report, *The Willamette River Basin.*

low-lying lands accumulations of soluble salts and alkali occurred during the latter stages in the evolution of present landforms and drainage patterns. Inadequate drainage facilities in these areas cause waterlogging and greater concentrations of salts and alkali at the surface. This results in more limited adaptability and, in some cases, actual abandonment of farming. Many such areas can be reclaimed with establishment of proper drainage and farming techniques.

Various public agencies are working on drainage problems and practices in the Northwest, and their guidance is available to farmers. These include the State College Extension Services, which help organize drainage districts and aid in farm drainage design; the U. S. Corps of Engineers, who work with major drainage channels; the Soil Conservation Service, which works through soil conservation districts, makes surveys, and gives technical advice; and the U. S. Production and Marketing Administration, which makes incentive payments for approved improvements that are in line with good farming and the public interest.

Pollution

Accompanying the development of urban centers and industries in the Pacific Northwest has been the growth of pollution of surface waters. This problem has not reached the magnitude found in the regions of concentrated cities and industries of eastern United States, but it is of sufficient importance to cause concern. The Public Health Service has issued a summary report, *Water Pollution in Pacific Northwest Drainage Basins,* and is engaged in detailed study in the various sub-basins.[10]

The Public Health Service's findings indicate that 434 municipalities with about 2½ million people and 824 industrial plants discharge sewage and industrial wastes directly into streams. It has been determined that 400 municipalities and 211 industries discharge an organic pollution load having a population equivalent of approximately 16 million. These 211 industries account for about 82 per cent of the total known organic wastes discharged into streams. Inorganic wastes are discharged by 117 or more industrial plants.

Although the organic load carried by many streams is great, steep gradients and large volumes of flow induce rapid natural stream recovery during most of the year. Nevertheless, most of the areas of

[10] See *Water Pollution Series,* No. 6, Public Health Service, Federal Security Agency.

concentrated population and industry have polluted waters. Probably the greatest stream pollution is found in northeastern portions of the region, resulting from mining and mineral processing. The Willamette River Basin has become a serious pollution area with a discharge into streams of organic wastes equivalent to the refuse of 4 million people. The major sources are urban centers, food-processing plants, and pulp and paper mills, as well as silt, logs, bark, and other debris entering the streams from eroding agricultural land and cut-over forest lands. Similarly, serious pollution damage is found in the Puget Sound Basin of Washington. The populous Yakima Valley and the Central and Upper Snake River valleys have notable pollution problems. As a result of these conditions the full development of surface waters in several areas has been seriously impaired; fishing potentials and recreational values have been destroyed, water-front value lessened, and public health endangered. Moreover, the cost for treatment of water supplies for expanding population and industries is increasing.

Projects and plans for pollution abatement are under way in many sectors of the region. For example, sewage-treatment plants have been constructed by 15 of the 17 sewered communities in the Yakima River Basin; the Oregon Sanitary Authority has a program for controlling pollution in the Willamette River, and most of the pulp and paper industries are working to reduce their waste problems. Concerted action between communities and industries will help assure clean water for the future.

PLANNING AND COMPROMISE FOR THE GREATEST GOOD

The economy of the Pacific Northwest is so closely linked together by dependency upon its great water resources for domestic and industrial supplies, irrigation, energy, fish, transportation, and recreation that development or misuses in one locality may affect all other parts. Unfortunately, immediate needs have regulated Northwest water development. Even the works of the Federal Government for navigation, flood control, hydro power, irrigation, and fisheries have, in a large measure, resulted from crises situations. The early dredging of the Columbia River to Portland appears to have resulted from the crisis brought about by the impending loss of maritime trade to Puget Sound ports. The catastrophe of Vanport in the spring of 1948 resulted in increased attention to the need for flood control on the Columbia. The depression of the 1930's gave the Northwest the Public Works Administration, Bonneville and Grand Coulee dams, and the Columbia Basin Irrigation Project. The Korean War and the ensuing defense program gave impetus to more hydro installations, and work on the McNary, Chief Joseph, and Hungry Horse was accelerated and appropriations for The Dalles Dam made. Non-Federal utilities have been stimulated to expand existing facilities and build new units. The results of this limited planning for the future finds the Northwest at the beginning of the second half of the twentieth century short of needs in power generation. Furthermore, floods annually inundate several hundred thousand acres; pollution is a serious problem in some areas; some streams are overappropriated for irrigation; and the important fishery problem on the Columbia River system has not been solved.

Existing Cooperative Efforts

The Corps of Engineers and the Bureau of Reclamation, in cooperation with other Federal and state resource agencies, have prepared a comprehensive plan for the development and management of the Columbia River system. The long-range plan includes a grand total of 405 potential projects, large and small, single-purpose, and multiple-purpose, for the development of irrigation (Fig. 25), power (Fig. 27), flood control, navigation, recreation, fisheries, and other beneficial uses. A restricted group of 93 projects, which will meet the earlier needs of the region, has been selected from this potential list by the Corps of Engineers and the Bureau of Reclamation, and these two agencies individually have recommended projects for Congressional approval in accordance with their respective responsibilities. The main dams recommended for early development are shown on Fig. 28. The aggregate benefits of these projects would include 217,386 acres of irrigated land and 90,390 acres of supplemental irrigation, 5,337,600 kilowatts of installed hydro capacity, and 21,663,800 acre feet of active storage capacity.[11]

A large number of Federal and state agencies are participating in, or contributing to, the management, development, and use of Northwest water and land resources. Each agency has its own authorized function, ranging from basic investigations and fact finding (as by the Geological Survey and agencies in the Department of Agriculture)

[11] See *Data on Projects in the Coordinated Comprehensive Plan of Development for the Columbia River Basin,* Department of Interior, Bureau of Reclamation, and Department of the Army, Corps of Engineers. Prepared in the Regional Office, Bureau of Reclamation, Boise, Idaho, December, 1949. Reissue November, 1951.

to the planning, construction, and operation of major resource-management works (as by the Crops of Engineers, Bureau of Reclamation, and Bonneville Power Administration). All have the common objective of strengthening the region's economy. In attempt to coordinate their activities, the Columbia Basin Inter-Agency Committee was formed in 1946.[12] This committee, made up of representatives of

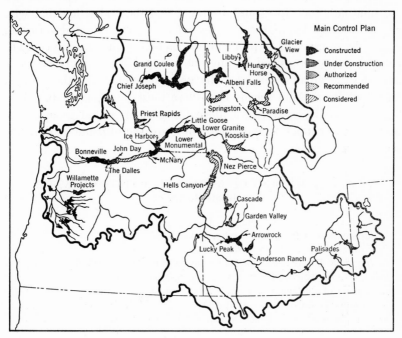

FIG. 28. Recommended dams for comprehensive development.

the individual resources agencies, works on a voluntary cooperative basis as a clearing house to coordinate resource programs so that benefits may be maximized and cost minimized.

Very substantial cooperation exists between the Federal and state agencies concerned. Some is of long standing, some is based on joint financing of common programs or on separate financing of mutually supporting programs, and some extends only to consultation in formulating programs which are executed independently. In the long run, however, ever more intimate cooperative effort must extend to all

[12] See the *Columbia Basin Inter-Agency Committee and the Northwest,* prepared by the state and Federal agencies represented on CBIAC.

agencies and interests, private and public, to assure the fullest development and the greatest benefits possible from this major water and land resource upon which much of the Northwest's future well-being depends.

Appraisal Needed Now

The region is the fortunate possessor of rich water resources, but the time has come for sound appraisal and the realization that wise use and orderly development of this key resource is essential to further economic progress. The problems of conflicting interests are complex and are not to be solved by any one group. The guiding principle must be the greatest good for the greatest number for the greatest length of time. This means that there must be planning based on authenticated facts, and to achieve the goal interested groups must be willing to cooperate and compromise for the ultimate good of the region.

—   PRINCIPAL SOURCES OF BASIC INFORMATION ON WATER
RESOURCES

U. S. Geological Survey, Washington, D. C.:
   Surface Waters of the United States, 1899–1948.
   Part 13, Snake River Basin, and Part 14.
   Pacific Slope Basins in Oregon and Lower Columbia River Basin.
   Water-Supply Papers 253, 369, 486, 579, 890, 774, and others.
U. S. Bureau of Reclamation, U. S. Department of the Interior:
   The Columbia River, 1947 (House Document No. 473).
   Project planning reports on Sequim, Canby, Goose Lake, Rogue, and other projects.
   Development reports on the Columbia River Project.
Bonneville Power Administration, U. S. Department of the Interior, Annual Report, 1950.
Corps of Engineers, U. S. Department of the Army, North Pacific Division, Portland, Oregon:
   Review Report No. 308, on Columbia River and Tributaries, and Appendixes A through S.
   The Corps of Engineers in Oregon, 1950.
Division of Water Pollution Control, Public Health Service, Federal Security Agency:
   Summary Report on Pollution.
   Pacific Northwest Drainage Basins (a cooperative state-Federal report), 1951.
   Sub-basin reports in preparation.
State College Extension Services, Bozeman, Montana, Corvallis, Oregon, Moscow, Idaho, and Pullman, Washington:

Published station bulletins and circulars dealing with water resources in the separate states.

Federal Power Commission:

Electric Power Statistics, 1950.

U. S. Department of Agriculture, including Soil Conservation Service, Pacific Northwest Range and Experiment Station, with regional offices in Portland.

CHAPTER

12

Forests of the
Pacific Northwest

STEPHEN N. WYCKOFF [1]

The history and settlement of the Pacific Northwest are inextricably linked with its forests and the uses to which they have been put; its future prosperity will be equally dependent upon our wisdom and foresight in using them.

Ever since the white man came to this region the forests have provided fuel, shelter, and a means of livelihood for much of the population. Simple logging and milling started with the first permanent settlement. Before long, lumber was shipped to California, the eastern states, and foreign countries, and lumber manufacture soon became the primary industry of the region. Other wood-using industries developed as time passed, and today forests contribute to the support of a major part of the population.

Forests of the region, in fact, are one of the greatest natural resources in the United States. The Pacific Northwest contains two-thirds of the old-growth saw timber remaining in the entire country—a vast storehouse of raw materials for industries that provide jobs in many sections of the nation. If managed wisely for continuous production, the region's forests will remain a great economic asset and a source of pleasure and welfare to the people. If not so managed, the forests can become an economic liability and a social burden.

Values of the Forest

Wood is the most familiar asset of the forest, and in the Pacific Northwest 75 out of every 100 forested acres grow merchantable tim-

[1] The author is indebted to the Pacific Northwest, Northern Rocky Mountain, and Intermountain Forest and Range Experiment Stations, U. S. Forest Service, for many of the data contained in this chapter.

TABLE 1

FORESTLANDS OF THE PACIFIC NORTHWEST, BY CHARACTER OF GROWTH AND
STATE, AS OF JANUARY 1, 1945

(thousands of acres)

State	Total Land Area	Total Forest-land	Commercial Forestland							Non-commercial Forest-land
			Total Commercial Forest-land	Mer-chantable Old-Growth Timber	Mer-chantable Young-Growth Timber	Pole Timber	Seed-ling and Sapling Timber	Poorly Stocked Seedling and Sapling and Deforested Area		
Washington	42,865	24,100	19,874	6,615	2,969	3,544	3,643	3103		4,226
Oregon	61,664	29,755	26,330	11,904	4,810	3,957	2,512	3147		3,425
Idaho	52,997	18,813	10,149	2,236	2,530	2,255	2,078	1050		8,664
Western Montana *	15,978	13,019	8,909	3,740 †			2,959	1,854	356	4,110
Total	173,504	85,687	65,262	24,495	10,309	12,715	10,087	7656		20,425

* 1949 data.
† Total area of merchantable timber; area by age class of timber not available.

ber products—sawlogs for lumber manufacture, plupwood, fuel wood,
poles and piling, and special grades of logs for plywood manufacture.
These are the commercial forestlands, where timber grows at a rea-
sonably rapid rate, the tree species have commercial value, and the
terrain is suitable for profitable removal of the raw products. On
other areas, called noncommercial forestlands, the growth rate is
slow, the cover consists of trees and shrubs without value for timber,
the ground is too inaccessible and rugged for logging, or the land has
been set aside for parks and preserves. In the West Coast Subregion,
merchantable timber grows on about 26 million acres of commercial
forestland; in the Intermountain Subregion, on about 20 million acres;
and in the Northern Rocky Mountain Subregion, on another 20 million
acres. Noncommercial forests grow on an additional 20 million acres
in the Pacific Northwest Region; more than four-fifths of this is in
the Intermountain and Northern Rocky Mountain subregions.

All forests, whether commercial or noncommercial, have other
values. Much of the water for homes, industries, irrigated farms, and
hydroelectric generators comes from forest watersheds. Forests pro-

tect the soil upon which they grow from erosion, keeping silt from streams, reservoirs, agricultural land, and river and harbor improvements. The melting of snow and runoff of rain are affected by the condition of the forest itself and by the porous, absorbent soil and litter of the forest floor. The plant cover and soil also affect the rate at which melted snow or rain will percolate into the soil. Thus, by favorable forest conditions, floods are prevented or at least lessened and stream flow is regulated, to the benefit of man in the valleys below.

Another extensive use to which the forests of the region are put is for grazing. Mountain meadows and open grasslands scattered through the forests furnish summer forage for livestock. East of the Cascades, the open character of many commercial forests permits the growth of grass, shrubs, and weeds that provide forage for great numbers of range cattle and sheep. Except for water yields, much noncommercial forestland is chiefly valuable for its forage crop.

The American people are turning in increasing numbers to the forests for recreation. Stream and lake shores are dotted with camps and picnic grounds. Various organizations and even towns and cities are establishing permanent forest camps for their members and citizens. Fishing and hunting bring in thousands at certain seasons. Winter sports are enjoyed in the higher mountains in scenes of forest beauty. Indeed, forest recreation is now increasing so rapidly that it is difficult to predict its future extent. The average person, bent upon an outing in the open, will most frequently state that he is going "to the mountains" or "to the hills." However, it is obvious that were the mountains denuded they would have little attraction for him. The forest is the magnet that draws the campers and tourists, bringing millions of dollars to the Pacific Northwest.

Closely associated with forest recreation is the value of the forest as a wildlife habitat. The crowds that daily watch the feeding of the bears in the national parks, the interest of most people in seeing a deer, elk, or cougar in its native haunts, the thrill of big-game or bird hunting or fishing, all testify to the importance of the forest in preserving these forms of life in their native environment.

The Nature of a Forest

Ostensibly a forest is an aggregation of trees. Actually it is a biological universe consisting of numerous kinds of plant and animal life, all forming a complex association. It contains trees, shrubs, annual plants, ferns, mosses, fungi, and a teeming world of microscopic plants. Similarly, it includes many forms of animal life—the larger animals, birds, reptiles, insects, and equally great numbers of microscopic forms. The trees, which man usually considers as forming the forest and which he prizes for their utility and beauty, are merely one element in this complex association. Each tree species and each individual lives, grows, reproduces itself, and dies only in relation to the other forms of life, the soil, and the climatic conditions about it.

Each organism within the forest possesses certain inherent characteristics which enable it to persist, grow, and reproduce itself. To do so, however, it must secure certain life necessities. A tree requires sunlight, soil moisture containing dissolved plant foods, and sufficient room in the soil to maintain a root system which will gather the food and moisture and anchor the tree firmly in place. It must escape by good fortune or defend itself by protective devices from attacks of many insect and fungous parasites. In this life struggle the tree must compete with many neighbors. The struggle between individuals is keen and merciless. Each bit of sunlight, water, food, or growing space gained by one tree must be won from its neighbors, both nearby trees and other surrounding organisms. The result is an extremely complex group of biotic forces reacting upon the individual tree. These biotic forces plus soil and climate constitute the forest environment within which the tree must survive or die. Soil and climate are more stable than the biotic factors. But the character of the forest soil may be affected for a considerable period by a severe forest fire. And fluctuations in precipitation and temperature, particularly when extended over many years, may profoundly affect the entire biotic complex, and thus the whole forest as well as each individual tree.

The ecological effect of these numerous environmental forces upon the forest as a whole and upon the tree in the forest is extremely subtle, but profound. Because of these forces the forest is maintained seemingly in a condition of static balance but in reality in a state of dynamic change, progressing toward but seldom attaining a climax, or nearly static condition. But because of their complexity and delicately balanced relationships, the environmental forces are particularly susceptible to disturbance by the introduction of artificial conditions.

Man's activities in harvesting the trees, the fires that too frequently accompany his presence, his use of the undergrowth or meadow for pasturing domestic livestock, and his very presence in great numbers have a powerful effect upon the environmental forces within the forest and thus upon the forest itself. In fact, man and his activities become one of these environmental forces. Forests being used by man for any purpose must continue to exist in an environment of which man is a part. Realization of his effect upon the forest, his power to preserve or to destroy it, will determine his success or failure in maintaining forests for both raw materials and the indirect values he prizes so highly.

Wise management of a forest consists of using the natural forces rather than replacing them with artificial conditions. Generally speaking, the most productive forest will be that in which the natural forces of growth are kept at an optimum. The system of management will be most successful that protects the forest from its enemies, subjects it to the minimum of disturbance, and favors by whatever means possible the tree species most valuable to man, growing in the most usable form.

Effect of Growing Conditions on Forests

The extent of the Pacific Northwest, from the Pacific Ocean to the Continental Divide in Montana, and from the Canadian boundary to the southern border of Idaho, gives rise to a great variety of growing conditions. The annual precipitation on the western, ocean-facing slopes of the Olympic Mountains and the Coast Range is the heaviest in the United States, in some localities averaging 120 inches. Precipitation is materially less in the trough between the Olympic Mountains-Coast Range system and the Cascade Range. Each of the Cascade Range precipitation decreases rapidly, until in the Intermountain Region semiarid conditions prevail, with annual precipitation of 10 inches or less. Farther to the east the Selkirk, Bitterroot, and Rocky mountains block the west winds from the ocean and wring from those air currents most of the moisture not lost over the mountains to the west. Thus, the northern Rocky Mountain Region with averages of 15 to 40 inches has a greater annual precipitation than the Intermountain Region. Similarly, as distance from the Pacific Ocean increases, seasonal variations in temperature increase. On the west slopes of the Olympic Mountains-Coast Range systems, monthly mean temperatures through the year vary between 60° and 30°. In contrast, those in the Intermountain and northern Rocky Mountain areas vary between 60° and 20°.

Other factors, often more local in nature, alter growing conditions and thereby affect the character and rate of growth of a forest. Daily, seasonal, and yearly ranges of temperature generally increase with altitude. Throughout the world the western sides of hills, mountains, and mountain ranges derive greater amounts of heat from the sun's rays than the eastern sides and are therefore warmer and as a general rule drier. In the northern hemisphere, the southern sides of mountains receive more solar heat than the northern sides and are thus similarly warmer and drier. These differences have a marked effect upon plant growth, except where other factors, such as proximity to cool, moisture-laden winds from the ocean, may outweigh them. This occurs in the West Coast Subregion where the west slopes receive greater precipitation from the ocean winds than the east slopes. Various types of soil may differ to a marked degree in depth, ability to retain moisture, and amounts of available plant food. By such means they affect the forests that grow upon them.

Forest Types

Because of these variations in environment, forests differ from place to place, and these differences are so marked that they serve as a basis for general classification into forest types. A forest type is an area of forest broadly uniform in character and composition.

The term "forest type," as commonly used, contains within its meaning several diverse elements which detract from its simplicity. The two principal elements are most easily described as the concepts of vegetative type and of economic type. If a forest type were considered solely as a vegetative type its recognition would be based only upon the tree species of which it was comprised, and it would probably be named for the most numerous one or two species. Such a type designation would be primarily descriptive of what the type contained. However, since mankind values certain tree species more highly than others, and since the most valuable species within a certain type may not be the most numerous, the economic element frequently enters into forest-type definition and designation. An excellent example is the western white pine type in northeastern Washington, northern Idaho, and northwestern Montana.

In parts of this type, western white pine may predominate; in other places it may be a relatively small part of the stand, either by number of trees or timber volume. This species, however, is far more valuable than any other species associated with it. Considered as a vegetative type, the forests growing western white pine would sometimes be named hemlock type, sometimes white fir type, because in various places each of these species predominates in number. But, because of the pre-eminent value of the western white pine, the type as a whole is given this name. The effect of this economic consideration is greater than merely assigning a name to the types. The aim of forest management by professional foresters and landowners is to increase the

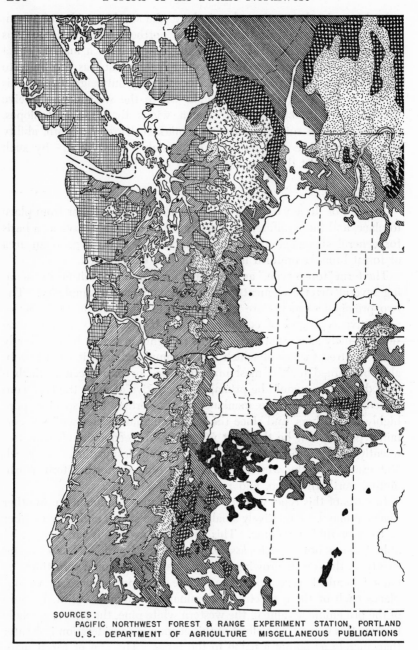

SOURCES:
PACIFIC NORTHWEST FOREST & RANGE EXPERIMENT STATION, PORTLAND
U. S. DEPARTMENT OF AGRICULTURE MISCELLANEOUS PUBLICATIONS

FIG. 29.   Forest types

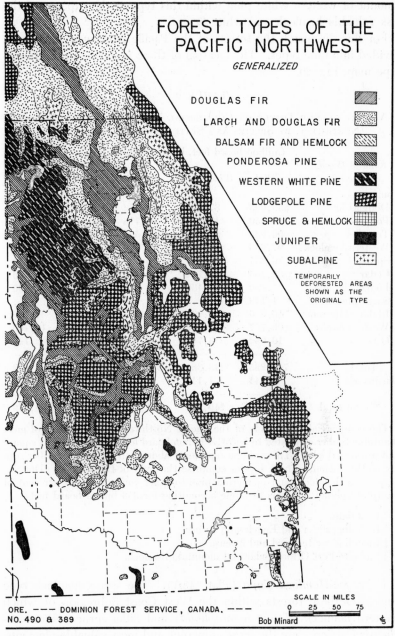

FOREST TYPES OF THE
PACIFIC NORTHWEST
GENERALIZED

DOUGLAS FIR

LARCH AND DOUGLAS FIR

BALSAM FIR AND HEMLOCK

PONDEROSA PINE

WESTERN WHITE PINE

LODGEPOLE PINE

SPRUCE & HEMLOCK

JUNIPER

SUBALPINE

TEMPORARILY
DEFORESTED AREAS
SHOWN AS THE
ORIGINAL TYPE

SCALE IN MILES
0   25   50   75

ORE. ——— DOMINION FOREST SERVICE, CANADA, ———
NO. 490 & 389

Bob Minard

of the Pacific Northwest.

amount of western white pine within this type at the expense of the less valuable hemlock and white fir.

For this discussion the forests of the Pacific Northwest have been divided into nine types. The location of these is shown on the forest-type map, Fig. 29.

TABLE 2

VOLUME OF SAW TIMBER ON COMMERCIAL FORESTLAND IN THE PACIFIC
NORTHWEST, BY SPECIES AND STATE, AS OF JANUARY 1, 1945

(million board feet, lumber tally)

Kind of Wood (Species)	Total	Washington	Oregon	Idaho	Western Montana *
Conifers					
Douglas fir	353,093	87,655	243,572	12,888	8,978
Ponderosa pine	100,150	17,420	62,778	10,624	9,328
True firs	66,933	35,296	22,558	8,333	746
Western hemlock	97,253	72,875	22,980	1,227	171
Spruce †	16,351	4,837	3,183	3,877	4,454
Cedar ‡	30,465	18,702	7,190	4,217	356
Lodgepole pine	5,489	460	711	1,822	2,496
Sugar pine	4,146	......	4,146	......	......
Idaho white pine	16,556	2,201	1,742	11,494	1,119
Western larch	26,767	5,172	3,555	6,280	11,760
Other conifers §	10,032	3,746	6,162	......	124
Total	727,235	248,364	378,577	60,762	39,532
Hardwoods	4,144	1,141	2,812	34	157
Grand total	731,379	249,505	381,389	60,796	39,689

The commercial forestlands of the Pacific Northwest bear a volume of merchantable timber estimated to be 731.4 billion board feet, lumber tally (1 square foot an inch thick). This volume represents about half of the saw timber supply of the nation. Three species comprise the bulk of the volume. Douglas fir, western hemlock, and ponderosa pine together comprise 75.26 per cent of the total volume, Douglas fir alone accounting for 353 billion board feet.

* 1949 data.
† Including Sitka and Engelmann spruce.
‡ Including western red and incense cedar.
§ Includes Port Orford cedar and mountain hemlock.

1. *Spruce-Hemlock Type* (Plate 15A). The spruce-hemlock type comprises those forests within the West Coast Subregion of which western hemlock (*Tsuga heterophylla*) and Sitka spruce (*Picea sitchensis* Carriere) are the most numerous and most valuable elements. It occurs in a narrow belt along the Pacific Ocean, west of the Coast

Range and Olympic Mountains, extending southward to a point about halfway down the Oregon coast. It is also found to a lesser extent at altitudes of 2500 to 4000 feet on the west slope of the Cascade Range of Washington, although spruce is frequently absent here. The species within this type are moisture loving and flourish under the conditions of heavy precipitation and moderate temperatures that prevail in the range of the type.

The principal species of the spruce-hemlock type are western hemlock, averaging about 60 per cent; Sitka spruce, about 11 per cent; and western red cedar (*Thuja plicata*), about 16 per cent. The remaining 13 per cent consists of Pacific silver fir (*Abies amabilis*), grand fir (*Abies grandis*), Douglas fir (*Pseudotsuga taxifolia*), and small amounts of red alder (*Alnus rubra*) and bigleaf maple (*Acer macrophyllum*). As in some other forest types, the species named first in the type designation is not the most numerous but is recognized in the name because of its relatively high economic value.

2. *Douglas Fir Type.* The Douglas fir type is that forest within the West Coast Subregion in which Douglas fir predominates. Over much of its extent, Douglas fir constitutes 90 per cent of the timber volume. Its principal associates are western hemlock, western red cedar, and grand fir, with Pacific silver fir at higher elevations. In smaller amounts it also contains Sitka spruce, noble fir (*Abies nobilis*), western white pine (*Pinus monticola*), red alder, and bigleaf maple. In southwestern Oregon, near the southern limit of the type, it also contains some ponderosa pine (*Pinus ponderosa*), sugar pine (*Pinus lambertiana*), California incense cedar (*Libocedurs decurrens*), and Port Orford white cedar (*Chamaecyparis lawsoniana*), a species of very limited distribution but of particularly high value.

The Douglas fir type covers the great sweep of area throughout the north and south length of the West Coast Subregion, from the margin of the coastal strip of spruce-hemlock type, across the Coast Range, Puget Trough, Willamette Valley, and Rogue River Valley, and into the Cascade Range, extending up their western slopes until changes in growing conditions give rise to other types. It occurs in areas where precipitation is ample for luxuriant tree growth but less in amount than where the spruce-hemlock type thrives, and where temperatures are moderate. In extent it far exceeds any other forest type in the West Coast Subregion, and in commercial value any other type in the entire Pacific Northwest.

3. *Balsam Fir-Hemlock Type.* As elevations increase on the western slopes of the Cascade Range, conditions are found that are less favor-

able to the principal species of the spruce-hemlock and Douglas fir types. Other species appear; and, although the species of the lower types still persist, they generally occur as a smaller proportion of the forest stand. Gradually the forest is altered to a different forest type, known as the balsam fir-hemlock type. It is characterized by a predominance of the balsam firs (the true firs in distinction to Douglas fir) and the hemlocks. The balsam firs—Pacific silver fir, noble fir, and alpine fir (*Abies lasiocarpa*)—generally constitute about 45 per cent of the forest volume, and the hemlocks—western hemlock and mountain hemlock (*Tsuga mertensiana*)—an equal part. In the southern part of the type, Shasta red fir (*Abies magnifica shastensis*) is quite frequent. The remaining 10 per cent consists of Douglas fir, western red cedar, Engelmann spruce (*Picea engelmanni*) and Alaska yellow cedar (*Chamaecyparis nootkatensis*).

The balsam fir-hemlock type occurs in a narrow, irregular belt on the upper slopes of the Cascade Range. It generally lies between 3500 to 5500 feet of elevation. Precipitation is usually ample for other types, but more severe temperatures favor the more hardy tree species appearing in this type.

4. *Subalpine Type.* Above the balsam fir-hemlock type and extending to timber line is the subalpine forest type. An area of ample precipitation but with heavy snows and severe temperatures in winter and thin soils, it is less favorable to tree growth than the lower elevations. Trees are uniformly smaller, poorly formed, and generally unmerchantable. At this altitude and under these conditions only the hardier species persist. These subalpine forests consist of alpine fir, noble fir, Pacific silver fir, Shasta red fir, mountain hemlock, Engelmann spruce, Alaska yellow cedar, western white pine, whitebark pine (*Pinus albicaulis*), lodgepole pine (*Pinus contorta latifolia*), and alpine larch (*Larix lyallii*).

The subalpine type extends as an irregular belt on the upper slopes, both east and west, of the Cascade Range, in the Olympic, Selkirk, Bitterroot, and Rocky mountains, and to a limited extent in the Blue Mountains. Unsuited to the growth of commercial forests, its importance lies in its scenic beauty and consequent use for forest recreation, its value for summer grazing, and its function as a storehouse of winter snows, later to melt and feed the streams used by man at lower altitudes.

5. *Ponderosa Pine Type* (Plate 15*B*). East of the high elevations of the Cascade Range, cut off from the mild, moisture-laden winds of the Pacific Ocean, lies the ponderosa pine forest type. This type ex-

tends from the Black Hills of South Dakota to the Cascade Range and the Sierra Nevada, and from eastern British Columbia to New Mexico and Arizona. It is widely distributed over the mountainous portions of the Pacific Northwest. Growing conditions are relatively severe, and the ponderosa pine type is incapable of attaining the tree size or growth rate of the forest types of the West Coast. Nevertheless, because of its extent and value, ponderosa pine is economically one of the most important forest types of the region.

The key species in this type is ponderosa pine; its most common associates are grand fir, western larch (*Larix occidentalis*), Douglas fir, and lodgepole pine, with California incense cedar and sugar pine in southern Oregon. Ponderosa pine frequently comprises 85 per cent of the total forest volume within the type.

In contrast to the heavy stands and dense, luxuriant undergrowth frequently encountered in the forest types of the West Coast, the ponderosa pine type is open, the trees are more widely spaced, and even the undergrowth is sparse. This condition gives rise to a park-like forest, relatively easy to traverse. The ground is often covered with grasses, annual plants, and shrubs valuable for forage. As a result, large areas of the ponderosa pine type are utilized for grazing as well as for timber production.

6. *Western White Pine Type* (Plate 16A). The western white pine type occurs only in the Northern Rocky Mountain Subregion, except for very limited areas in the southwestern part of Oregon. Clothing the middle to lower slopes of the Rocky, Bitterroot, and Selkirk mountains, but generally occurring at slightly higher altitudes than the ponderosa pine type, the western white pine type is a forest of dense growth of which western white pine is the most important species economically. Its most frequent associates are western hemlock, grand fir, western larch, western red cedar, and lodgepole pine. Rough terrain results in high logging costs; costs are high for protection from fire, white pine blister rust, and insects; and cheap water transportation to the large eastern markets is lacking. Consequently species other than western white pine and western red cedar can seldom be logged at a profit. Western white pine may often constitute a relatively small part of the forest stand within the type, either in number of trees or volume of timber, but nevertheless may represent the principal financial value. The proportion of species may vary over wide limits in the type. In local areas western white pine may comprise 60 to 80 per cent of the forest stand; in others, it may be as low as 15 to 20 per cent.

7. *Larch-Douglas Fir Type* (Plate 15A). The larch-Douglas fir forest type occurs in the Northern Rocky Mountain Subregion and in the Blue Mountains, Colville Mountains, and east slopes of the northern Cascade Range in the Intermountain Subregion. It is generally found at about the same altitude as the western white pine type. It is a type containing a number of species, varying in proportion in different localities. None of the principal species are outstanding in value in relation to the others. The principal components of the type are western larch, Douglas fir, grand fir, and lodgepole pine. Scattered throughout the type western red cedar is found, and in certain localities Engelmann spruce is numerous, these two species being the most valuable within the type.

8. *Lodgepole Pine Type.* At relatively high elevations in the Northern Rocky Mountain and Intermountain Subregions, and to a lesser extent in the West Coast Subregion, there occur extensive areas of lodgepole pine type. In some localities, particularly at lower elevations, the type is temporary in nature, owing to the fact that lodgepole pine may take possession of the ground after a forest fire, later to be replaced by other species. At higher altitudes, the type is more permanent. It frequently forms dense, almost pure, stands of lodgepole pine, extending almost unbroken over large areas.

9. *Juniper Type.* The juniper forest type occurs in the Intermountain Subregion, and to a limited extent in the Northern Rocky Mountain Subregion. Lying altitudinally below the other types of these subregions, it is the last outpost of forest growth where forest and semidesert meet. The type usually consists of very open stands of Sierra juniper (*Juniperus occidentalis*), the trees interspersed with mountain mahogany (*Cercocarpus* spp.), and the shrubby flora of the open semidesert.

REFERENCES

Andrews, H. J., and R. W. Cowlin, "Forest Resources of the Douglas-Fir Region," *U. S. Department of Agriculture Miscellaneous Publication* 389, 1940.

Cowlin, R. W., and F. L. Moravets, *Forest Resources of Washington,* Olympia, Wash., Division of Forestry, 1940.

Eliot, W. A., *Forest Trees of the Pacific Coast,* New York, Putnam, 1938.

Lord, Russell, Ed., *Forest Outings,* Government Printing Office, Washington, D. C., 1940.

Pacific Northwest Regional Planning Commission, *Forest Resources of the Pacific Northwest,* Government Printing Office, Washington, D. C., 1938.

Sudworth, G. B., *Forest Trees of the Pacific Slope,* Government Printing Office, Washington, D. C., 1908.

U. S. Forest Service, *Pacific Northwest Forest and Range Experiment Station. Forest Statistics*, Portland, Oregon, 1934–1940. Processed. (Published as separates for forested counties of Oregon and Washington.)

U. S. Forest Service, *Northern Rocky Mountain Forest and Range Experiment Station*, Forest Survey Releases 1–18, Missoula, Montana, 1936–1940. Processed.

U. S. Forest Service, *A National Plan for American Forestry*, Government Printing Office, Washington, D. C., 1933, 2 vols. (U. S. Cong. 73rd, 1st Sess., *Senate Document 12*).

U. S. Forest Service, *The Western Range*, Government Printing Office, Washington, D. C., 1936 (U. S. Cong. 74th, 1st Sess., *Senate Document 199*).

13

Forest Utilization in the Pacific Northwest

JAMES STEVENS

ᔥ The conversion of wood into merchantable products for national and world markets has been the largest single source of income for Oregon and Washington since 1849. Today Oregon is first among all the states in lumber manufacture, and Washington leads in production of woodpulp. In both states, forest and wood-conversion income exceeds the returns from agriculture and food processing. The forest industry is a close third to agriculture and mining in Idaho and western Montana. Since 1940, new techniques have greatly increased the efficiency of forest utilization so that expanding markets have been supplied without draining off the resource. Exports to these new markets are paying for forest-management practices that provide for more intensive utilization in woods and mills, for the growing of new tree crops, and for the steady reduction of losses from forest fires, insects, and disease. The end of timber mining is in sight. The treatment of timber as a crop prevails generally throughout the Pacific Northwest.

Foresters have a saying, "Forestry begins with the stump." Certainly all forms of wood utilization begin there, from the rugged mine prop that serves a thousand feet underground to the elegant office desk that serves a thousand feet up in a skyscraper, and from the roll of butcher's paper to the debutante's rayon dress. Each American home, in vital parts, begins with the shout of "Timber-r-r!" and the crash of a falling tree. This is the starting point of all forest utilization.

MODERN LUMBERING

Mechanized Operations

Almost complete mechanization has eliminated many time-honored practices. Timber operations today differ in numerous respects from the old familiar woods practices which moved west with the loggers from the white pine belt of the Lake States. On a sample timber watershed containing 135,000 acres of the Pacific Northwest's 65,232,-000 acres, a typical woods operation bears but slight resemblance to the methods of 1900 or even those of the 1920's.

Two men in metal safety hats stoop to swing a powered chain saw close to the root spread of an aged Douglas fir; they are typical of thousands on the same kind of job, with the same sort of tool, at this hour of a work day in the woods of Washington, Oregon, Idaho, Montana, and British Columbia. Called timber fallers,[1] one operates the power saw, the other, who grasps the handle end of the oval steel plate with a chain belt of saw teeth around its edge, is the head faller. A third man stands by, a pickax swinging from his heavily gloved hands. On one side of the handle is the narrow bit of a falling ax, on the other a short but sharp pick—a modern tool in the woods.

The head faller guides the saw, the operator speeding the motor at his end of the frame. The motor spits, snorts, and sends the chain belt whirring in a blur of sharp, spinning teeth of steel. Then the stooping men swing the power saw carefully against the shaggy bole of the old fir, the teeth of the whirling chain biting into bark and grain. In seconds the cut is deep; then the saw is swung out for a second slash a few inches above the first. The pickax man swings the ax bit, striking and pulling with the pick, slabbing out chunks to leave a gaping undercut. As he labors, the fallers shift to the other side of the tree. The cutting comes through to the mauling of wedges, the "Timber-r-r!" cry and the topple and crash of 200 feet of tree. The bucking of logs is also by chain saw. Modern falling is more like machine-shop operation than like the old-time chopping of the undercut and pulling on the "misery whip," i.e., the crosscut saw of the timber fallers who used muscle power alone.

Small stumps are made in the Douglas fir stand from the understory of Western red cedars and West Coast hemlocks which the prelogging crew fells, bucks, and removes with new types of light logging ma-

---

[1] Common usage has made "fellers" and "felling" obsolete in the Pacific Northwest.

chinery. Small tractors snake out the cedars for the pole market and the hemlock for pulpwood. Snags are felled and windfalls bucked to clear the way for the main logging and to add to the harvest.

On one side of the down timber a big tractor hauls several logs at a trip on a logging arch (Plate 16B), which, like the tractor itself, runs on crawler wheels. The ends of the logs are suspended by cable from drums on the rear of the tractor through the top of the arch frame. They are hauled to a loader, which is basically a power shovel with a set of tongs replacing the shovel dipper at the end of the digging arm. One man operates the machine, clamping the tongs on one of the logs left by the tractor, then lifting and swinging it to the trailer bunks of a logging truck. The converted power shovel is also mounted on crawler wheels.

On the upper side of the down-timber area an engine, set on huge log sleds like the steam donkey engine of the 1920's, yards logs downhill for 1500 feet or more. The big sticks are then picked up by a giant loader with a single boom, anchored with its house on a turntable and crawlers. The steel wire-rope lines run up to blocks that dangle 180 feet aloft on a trimmed, topped, and guyed Douglas fir— a spar tree. The high pull tends to lift the big logs over stumps and other obstacles on the haul to the landing.

Tree Topping

At the next setting the high rigger and his helpers make a new spar tree. The rigger harnesses himself in climbing irons, heavy leather life belt with its front attached to a steel-cored rope that encircles the tree, and with a double-bitted ax and light crosscut saw swinging from ropes behind. As the rigger climbs, limbs are chopped or sawed off, then 40 feet of top is cut. The next phase is a climb with light line and block to begin the tough and complex operation of rigging up the spar. A number of systems have been developed for machine skidding of logs by spar tree lifting haul. They divide broadly into skyline types with tail spar and the high lead with single-head spar.

Logging Trucks

From this main side of the large logging area, massive truck trailers on 18 huge timber-trade tires wheel down mountain grades into swift travel over private highways through second-growth timber country. The destination on one line is the head of an old logging railroad where in one swing an apparatus lifts a truckload of logs weighing 40 to 50 tons onto railroad logging cars. Other truck out-fits, some with cedar poles or hemlock logs from the prelogging, others piled with pulpwood logs from the true firs at 3000 to 4000 feet eleva-tion, roar away for dumping into tidewater booming grounds. One small truck with hemlock pulpwood rolls along from a re-logging job.

All through the woods the men are wearing metal safety hats, in compliance with state laws and regulations. Boxes of firefighting tools are stationed at working centers; power pumps and tank trucks are standard equipment. A new type of pump attached to the motor of a chain saw can force strong streams through twin nozzles. For instant action on wrecks, broken parts, injuries, or outbreaks of fire, a two-way radio system is part of each mobile unit. Bulldozing tractors and power shovels are making roads in the virgin timber, and farther on public and private forestry men are cruising and sur-veying for future road building and logging. Federal, state, munici-pal, and private ownerships are intermingled throughout the 135,000 acres. Good forest economics requires harvesting as a unit.

There is a logging camp, with repair and supply shops, a cookhouse, and 20 bunkhouses. By far the greater number of employees, how-ever, have families and homes and drive their own automobiles to the job. Like the spring log drive, the skidroad, and bullteam, the traditional bunkhouse camp of the woods has all but disappeared in the Douglas fir subregion since World War II.

Pine Logging and Farm Woods

Logging in the pine subregions has likewise come far from the horse-drawn high wheels which were as characteristic of the open pine stands on gentle slopes as were the yokes of oxen on winding skidroads in the mountain lands of the Douglas fir. The two big wheels that would be backed over a bunch of pine logs for hauling were the forerunners of the logging arch that trails the modern tractor. The lodgepole pine, formerly a weed tree with the West Coast hem-lock, is now in demand and presents special problems. A light logging arch on rubber tires will bear a dozen of the slender logs at a trip on a tractor hitch. A logging crane can put nine long lodgepoles at a time between truck stakes. Similar mass handling permits profitable utilization of the small logs at the mill.

The power saw, the light tractor with hydraulic mechanism for a small bulldozer blade or for a lift in front, the market truck, and other modern farm machines have revolutionized farm woodland manage-ment throughout the Pacific Northwest. Farm timber harvesting and trucking are now possible with a minimum of labor. Expanding markets, particularly in the pulp and paper industry of western Washington, have added new values to trees on the farm. The salvage logging of old cedar stumps and windfalls in farm woodlands and of Douglas fir snags left by loggers as long as 50 years ago has put many young growth stands into better shape while increasing farm income.

MILL OPERATIONS

Logs in the Water

The long train of log cars is anchored on the unloading ramp above the tidewater booming grounds. On a parallel track behind the train the steam-powered unloading machine and its crew tackle the first car, which holds 40 tons of timber: Douglas fir, West Coast hemlock, and Western red cedar. A boom slants up from the loader and over the logs. The kicker arm and power beam are attached to the unloading engine. With a single kick, one car of logs at a time is dumped over the brow of the ramp into the water. As the machine moves on its track for another place kick, the logs dive, and splashes rise like waterspouts.

A log herding tug and a crew of boom men with long pikepoles follow the dumpings. Out in the water from the ramp the piling of sorting booms tower above the backwater as the crew works the sorted logs into separate pockets. The firs of highest grade, "peeler" logs, are boomed for rafting to plywood plants. The cedars are sorted for sawmills or shingle mills. The finest hemlock is put in rafts for the making of finish and other highest grades of lumber, with the lower grades pocketed for towing to pulp mills. The true firs and Sitka spruce are similarly sorted. Around each assortment the tugboat pulls a string of four long boomsticks, the ends chained together to form the corral of a standard raft for towing. Most of these logs are towed 50 miles to a large center of lumber, pulp, and plywood production.

Logs are stored and sorted in the rivers of the Douglas fir subregion. In the pine subregions log-packed lakes above sawmill dams are common. With the coming of the tractor and the motor truck, however, transportation of logs on rivers and lakes has dwindled. Typical in all subregions is the log slip, or jackladder, that arches up from millpond to log deck, with big logs crawling upward on the chain conveyor to the saws.

Through a century of sawmilling in the Pacific Northwest the log started its journey through the saws with its bark, while at the end of the line a large amount of sound wood went up in smoke. For 50 years the towering refuse burner was a feature of the night scene. By 1950 the burners were gone from the larger operations and in some areas the smaller sawmills were shipping lumber leftovers of pulpwood quality to chip production plants. The value of chips without bark caused hydraulic barkers to be added to sawmills as well as to pulp mills. This has resulted in the marketing of a variety of bark products, leaving only wet bark as fuel for mill power plants.[2]

Barking and Sawing

The logs that are graded for the sawmill deck stop on the log slip to enter a metal sheathed room where each log is caught in a machine for quick turning. It is turned at will and moved ahead under a nozzle that pours forth a stream of water with pressure of 1400 pounds per square inch. In seconds the bark is torn from the log and washed away. The operator watches through a bulletproof window as he handles controls for moving the log and the nozzle, sending bits of bark and slivers flying like shrapnel with slashing spray.

With bark washed to the fuel bins, the skinned logs hit the deck to await turns on the log carriages of two headsaw rigs. One is a vertical bandsaw with teeth on each side which makes cuts as the carriage rolls ahead and again as it returns on its track. The other is a larger single-cut bandsaw that cuts the big logs into thick cants, or oblong blocks, for further sawing by other machines. The slick slabs, first cuts from the log, are routed for the chipper.

Sorting by grade is intensified by the head sawyer at the start of each log through manufacture. The absence of bark, revealing knots, pitch pockets, and other characteristics, enables the sawyer to guess the grades at a glance. Clear wood of dense grain, circling the log between the outside rings of sapwood and the coarse grained and knotted heartwood, is highest in value.

The cants (blocks) from the headsaws are routed to the gangsaw, a machine with a battery of vertical saw blades which are pumped up and down through one or more blocks at a time, cutting boards 1 or 2 inches thick.

[2] In Mason County, Washington, an advanced center of forest industry integration, any wood that might be burned could be utilized more profitably in manufacture of fiberboard and woodpulp. As a result, a new logging camp 30 miles up in a wilderness forest was equipped with oil-burning heating and cooking stoves, and all grades of fuel wood were shipped down to the mills for conversion into standard market products.

Other cuts from the headsaws roll to the edger, where adjustable circular saws take away rough edges of sapwood and slice the remainder in widths according to grade. Further along the production line, vertical and horizontal resaws make new cuttings. The main trimmer has 21 saws in its line. Saws dart down, trimming pieces of varying grades from each single length.

Marking and Sorting

Out from the sawmill and over the sorting table the rough lumber moves. Graders scan each piece for its individual characteristics and the use it fits best. The grade is marked on each piece. The best grades are conveyed to a stacker that mechanizes the work of preparing cars of lumber for the dry kilns. Other lumber, with such mill products as railroad ties and structural timbers, is trucked away to yard storage, cars, or cargo docks, by motorized lumber carriers called "straddlebugs."

Drying, Planing, and Shipping

The kiln-dried grades are set moving on conveyor chains through the planing mill. There the best lumber is not only dressed and shaped but is graded again, racked by grade, size, and species, then tied in unit packages for retail markets. The higher grades are loaded into boxcars by hand, and the common and economy grades and timbers are stacked in the yards by traveling cranes.

Meanwhile, the bark from the logs has been used in the fires that heated the boilers for the generation of power while bark-free edgings and trimmings race through the chipper of the sawmill and pour into a barge bound for a pulp mill.

TABLE 1

LUMBER PRODUCTION IN PACIFIC NORTHWEST, 1945–1949

(thousand board feet, lumber tally)

State	1945	1946	1947	1948	1949
Washington	3,257,995	3,422,289	3,705,401	3,659,523	3,442,058
Oregon	5,003,547	6,328,317	7,102,410	7,842,402	7,185,042
Idaho	780,453	863,964	950,791	1,103,649	926,496
Total	9,041,995	10,614,570	11,758,602	12,605,574	11,553,596

Statistics for western Montana not available.
Source: Pacific Northwest Forest and Range Experiment Station.

The Pine Lumber Industry

The pineries of the Pacific Northwest are but a corner of the larger western pine lumber region that extends to the Black Hills of South Dakota and southward through vast operations in California to Arizona and New Mexico. The queen tree of the entire region is the ponderosa pine; but white pine, sugar pine, Douglas fir, the true firs (grouped under the trade name of white fir), larch, and lodgepole pine also yield important wood products. In logging, the first distinction between the pine country and the Douglas fir coastal country of British Columbia, Washington, Oregon, and northwestern California, is the ease of operation in the open pine stands.[3] In contrast to the fir timberland, the pine region is called "the short-log country." Tree selection is common in the pines, in contrast to area selection in fir. State laws specify the various provisions for reforestation.

In the pine sawmill, the short logs, usually 16 feet in length, are sliced into shop, box, and building lumber grades and sizes.

Although the pulp and paper industry is in its infancy in the pine woods, the refinement of lumber manufacture is unsurpassed. For example, knotty pine paneling was long used as common lumber; but fine manufacturing, with sales promotion and advertising, raised it to a quality item of high returns. Similar techniques have extended the use of pine products in the manufacture of furniture, toys, and endless specialties. Another major use is in the template shops of industrial steel fabricators.

Pine Box Lumber

Box shook is the outstanding product of the pine lumber industry; parts of the log that are too low in grade or unsuited in size for shop or building uses go into shook mill and box factory.

The shook side of one typical pine sawmill has in storage thousands of blocks and boards salvaged from utility lumber grades. A cutoff saw whips each piece of material into short lengths, followed by a

---

[3] The broad problems and processes of logging and lumbering in the Douglas fir and the pine subregions of the Pacific Northwest are intrinsically the same throughout. The differences in details, particularly those of thousands of uses, grades, and items among the principal species, are a jumble of technicalities. Literature on all phases of the Pacific Northwest forest industries is available at school and public libraries and from the West Coast Lumbermen's Association, 1410 S.W. Morrison St., Portland, Oregon; the Western Pine Association, Yeon Bldg., Portland, Oregon; the Douglas Fir Plywood Association, Tacoma, Washington; and the Red Cedar Shingle Bureau, White Building, Seattle, Washington.

battery of bandsaws that slashes blocks into sheets. Conveyor belts and rolls lead to shook fabrication machines, including a nailing rig that nails shooks to form the familiar end patterns of fruit and vegetable crates. Cleating and wiring machines complete the process, with bundles of shooks for shipment to fruit and produce packers.[4]

Shingle Weaving

Throughout the region's history, the western red cedar shingle industry has held a strong place in the economy of western British Columbia, Washington, and, to a lesser extent, Oregon. At present 90 per cent of the wood shakes and shingles used in the United States are from the Pacific Northwest.

A new Oregon shingle mill is typical of the modern industry in Washington and British Columbia. Here the logs are cut into 16-inch bolts by an 86-inch circular saw, each cut moving on by chain conveyor. Workable blocks, or bolts, for shingle-making travel on gravity rolls to four sawing units. At each machine the shingle weaver presses the bolt to and fro, slicing the shingles from the bolt. Each shingle is tossed into one of the four chutes for the four standard grades. The chutes slope to the packing department on the floor below. Sawdust and shavings are baled as industrial "cedar tow." Narrow shingles are salvaged by stapling matched pairs into V shapes for hip and ridge shingling on roofs.

FOREST PRODUCTS

Pulp and Paper

The raw material for pulp and paper manufacture, pulpwood logs in the booms as well as the loads of chips from sawmill leftovers, must be free from bark and other impurities. Bark removal in Northwest mills has gone through successive phases of sawmill slabbing, shaving the log with revolving disc knives, and rubbing it clean with revolving drums. Hydraulic barking, however, saves from 12 to 15 per cent more of the log.[5] The pulp mill's own cut of logs into chips has been augmented by a steady supply from sawmill leftovers.

---

[4] In the small pine sawmills that have no shook departments, box grades of lumber are shipped to factory centers, even as rough, air-dried building lumber is consigned to large planing mills.

[5] The Crown Zellerbach Corporation states: "At 12 per cent saving (through hydraulic barking) of the Camas paper mill's annual cut of 200 million board feet per year, the practical effect is that 600 acres of timber a year are reserved

Pulpmaking Techniques

The five common processes for extracting fibers from wood and working them into paper and other woodpulp products are widely used in the Pacific Northwest. (1) The groundwood process is the pressing of wood against spinning grindstones to tear the fibers apart and pulp them while retaining as much of their structure and strength as possible. Between 80 and 90 per cent of newsprint, and various other economy grades of paper, are made from groundwood. (2) The sulfite process employs an acid calcium bisulfite solution for cooking the cellulose fibers that make up about 50 per cent of pulpwood's content and removing the lignin, which is nature's binding agent for forming cellulose into solid wood. This chemical cooking is the first stage in making the better grades of paper. (3) The soda process produces white pulp from short-fiber hardwoods. (4) The kraft or sulfate process adds sodium sulfide to caustic soda for cooking pulp and works well with Douglas fir pulpwood; the product is of superior strength, but it is dark and difficult to bleach. Kraft pulp production has soared in the region because of its general utility value for heavy-use paper. (5) In the semichemical process chemicals are applied merely to soften the wood, then mechanical operation separates the

TABLE 2

NUMBER AND AGGREGATE CAPACITY, IN TONS PER 24 HOURS, OF PULP MILLS
IN PACIFIC NORTHWEST BY STATE AS OF JANUARY 1, 1952

Note: Where a plant manufactures more than one type of pulp each process is listed as separate mill.

State	Pulp Mills													
	Total		Sulfite		Sulfate		Soda		Semichemical		Mechanical		Miscellaneous	
	No.	Capacity	No.	Capacity	No.	Capacity	No.	Capacity	No.	Capacity	No.	Capacity	No.	Capacity
Oregon	13	1891	6	650	2	430			1	145	2	571	2	95
Washington	28	5942	13	3122	5	1823	1	70			8	797	1	130
Idaho	1	160			1	160								
Total	42	7993	19	3772	8	2413	1	70	1	145	10	1368	3	225

No pulp mills in western Montana.

for cutting." Such success has encouraged continued experiments with portable wood chippers, and chemical and other small-scale log-barking devices, to serve small operations and farm woodland owners.

fibers. Corrugated and other filler types of paper are the principal products.

In the process of chemical and semichemical pulpmaking, the wood chips from the logs, together with bargeloads and carloads from the sawmills and many cores of plywood peeler bolts, are run over moving screens. Small chips are sieved through to storage in bins above the digesters. A digester (a big-scale pressure cooker) holds up to 55 cords of chipped wood. The process of cooking with chemicals dissolves the lignin, sugars, resins, and mineral salts, leaving the cellulose. Screening, washing, beating, and storage in tanks completes the making of pulp; some of it is destined for woodpulp-products plants elsewhere, some for local paper manufacture.

In papermaking the pulp is first mixed into a mass that is 90 per cent or more water, then streamed through cleaning and screening machines and spread on the wet end of a Fourdrinier sheet-forming machine. Series of press and felt rolls carry the pulp on from the first screen to rolls for shaping sheets of moist pulp, the sheets speeding up and down a double deck of steamheated drying rolls, and then out as paper through the pressing and smoothing rolls to the winder.

New Uses for Douglas Fir

In terms of forest utilization in the Pacific Northwest, kraft container board is a product of high promise. Its basic paper can be made from Douglas fir chips, although, of all the species available in large quantities, West Coast hemlock, with some Sitka spruce, is still the essential wood for highest-quality woodpulp products. Container board paper comes from the pulp mill in rolls that look like heavy brown wrapping paper, which are bound with steel straps for shipment to container manufacturers. One type has 21,000 feet of paper, 70 inches wide, in a roll weighing 3300 pounds. In producing the board, three plies of paper are commonly used, a corrugated filler with smooth sheets outside and inside. The grocery carton is an everyday example, for which demand has grown enormously since World War II.

The "Peeler" Log

Cream of the Douglas fir harvest, the "peeler" log is cut into "blocks," from 8 to 16 feet in length. The logs move from mechanical or hydraulic barker to the peeling lathe which, in effect, unrolls the growth layers of wood in veneer sheets that vary from $\frac{1}{10}$ to $\frac{3}{16}$ of an inch in thickness, each sheet being handled as though it were a sheet from a roll of paper, sliding into trays 150 feet long. The next stage is the clippers and the cutting into widths for assembly in panels.

At the clippers, skilled "graders" work to slice out defects and send on as many clear, high-grade veneers as possible. Drying in 100-foot ovens reduces the moisture content to less than 5 per cent, and selected sheets are then run through glue-spreading machines. Carrying glue on each side, one of these sheets is sandwiched between dry sheets, to form standard panels of three, five, seven, or nine plies. The plies of wood are next subjected to pressures close to 200 pounds per square inch and steam heat of 260° to 285°, for 4- to 10-minute periods. There is also a cold-pressure process for setting the adhesives. Grading, sanding, and trimming convert fir veneers into marketable materials for essential uses.

Hardboard

Chipping machines have become standard installations of the Douglas fir plywood industry. From peeler block cores and other leftovers of plywood production, material for more than 1000 tons of woodpulp is salvaged daily in the Douglas fir subregion. Chips are also used in the manufacture of hardboard, a smooth, dense material that is formed from felted wood, through heat and pressure, into boards ¼ inch or ⅛ inch thick. The Plywood Research Foundation has brought out a new product that combines standard plywood and hardboard for the building industry.

Minor Forest Products

Minor forest products are an expanding feature of the farm economy. A familiar example is the Christmas tree from the young Douglas fir forest. An item new in its rising commercial importance is huckleberry brush, valued by the floral industry for sprays and blossom backgrounds. Salal is another floral spray product that commonly goes to market with huckleberry brush and sword fern. Cascara bark brings woodland income from the drug industry. Madrona and bigleaf maple burls are always marketable. Small wild fruits, such as blackberries, blue and red huckleberries, Oregon grapes, blackcap berries, salal berries, salmonberries, and blue elderberries, are gathered for local use.

Minor forest products provide seasonal income for thousands of dwellers on stump ranches and in forest communities. The managers of large commercial forest properties, both public and private, have had to cope with trespass and added fire hazards as greens pickers grew into armies and buyers multiplied. Forest protection organizations employ planes to fly over areas where people swarm to pick berries in summer during fire weather, broadcasting appeals to be careful with fire. Industrial tree farm companies throughout the region are developing programs of cooperation with greens pickers and Christmas tree cutters, allocating specific areas to families or groups and relying upon them to keep guard against trespassers. Such measures, related to the growing cooperative programs with sportsmen's organizations and with scenic conservation groups, are carrying forest education to the most remote areas.

Various research agencies all have programs of farm woodland management and marketing in which minor forest products are given special attention. Christmas tree culture is a means of utilizing the commercial forest resource and at the same time improving the young tree crop. This is of great concern to the region's 100,000 owners of farm and other types of small commercial forest holdings, comprising more than 5 million acres. Other items of value include car stakes, corral poles, hop poles, garden stakes, fuel wood, cedar shakes, oyster-bed stakes, pussy willow, and leaf mold.

MAJOR FOREST PROBLEMS

Forest Fires

All issues and distinctions in management fade away under the menace of fire. Public agencies and private companies combine for forest-fire prevention. "Protection" is the authority that closes down log production for long stretches in the season of the best logging weather, the driest weeks of summer. "Cold decks" of logs are built up, and long booms of logs are stored to supply plants during fire closures. In planning for a new tree crop on a harvested area, fire is the hazard of first consideration.

Fire Fighting. The record of a typical big-scale battle serves to illustrate the integrated place of modern forest-fire fighting. The following is a digest of official reports.

> The temperature was above 90°, the relative humidity between 14 and 16 per cent, and fuel moisture 4 per cent. At 11:50 A.M. a mountain lookout noted a wisp of smoke from the barnyard of a rancher. Through his radio transmitter he called the state dispatcher, but during the seconds required to make the call the fire had burst into a smoke column. In 1 hour the fire was over the ridge of a timbered mountain 2 miles away, its peak at an elevation of 3900 feet. The fire was carried on a

strong wind from the east, away from the National Forest where the U. S. Forest Service stood guard, spreading over lands under state and industry protection.

From the center of a two-way radio network, the state forester enlisted fire crews from ten counties. Every call was made, not simply to bring on men, but to build an organized, mechanized, and well-equipped force for the big-scale battle. In the first hours effective control was impossible. The fire was "spotting," leaping into the tops of great trees and throwing embers long distances ahead. It raged on through the night unimpeded, spot fires merging into a solid front of driving flames.

By morning 20 tractors were in battle array, and the fire was attacked at dawn along head and flanks. There were now 200 rugged, seasoned firefighters from the nearest logging operation, and contractors brought crews and machines in the early morning. Tank trucks, kept ready for emergency use on logging operations, with four-wheel drives carried 2000 gallons and more of water, with powerful pumps and other equipment. They wheeled over the trail roads that the tractors were bulldozing for the fire. Soon 40 industry and state pump trucks, the smallest carrying 500 gallons at a load, were in action. Experienced power-saw operators and their machines were trucked up, to swarm ahead of the fire, falling thousands of snags. At his headquarters the state forester took numberless calls from his fire bosses on the lines, while urging the counties to send more tractors, tank trucks, chain saws, and men. His wardens scouted by wire for "low boys," types of trailer beds on which tractors might be rolled to the fire.

Work went on, bringing tough problems by the minute. The wind became shifting and erratic. Each change called for shifts in the battle plan, including men and machines. After 5 days and nights, the blaze was surrounded and extinguished, but the losses were estimated in millions of dollars. It had killed the trees on 1200 acres of virgin timberland, 2000 acres of thriving young commercial forest growth had been blackened, and seedlings on 2200 acres of recent cutovers were in ashes. Modern methods, machines, and forest radio communications had held this fire, under fearful conditions of drought, to a relatively small circle of destruction. A similar fire that "got away" killed trees containing 500 million board feet.

FOREST-FIRE PREVENTION. Most forest fires are man-caused, and 90 per cent of them result from use of forest lands by the public. However, in the northern Rocky Mountains many fires are caused by lightning. In the Kaniksu National Forest of Washington and Idaho several hundred fires have been started in one day by a series of "dry" thunderstorms. In 1940 cooperative programs of public education on fire prevention were started on the theme of "Keep Washington and Oregon Green." Next "Keep Idaho Green" and "Keep Montana Green" were organized as state movements. In British Columbia a Junior Forest Warden program for educating people on the needs for forest-fire prevention has been growing since 1933. The "Keep Green" movement is now nation-wide, with 34 state organizations. With it, the Joint Advertising Council and the U. S. Forest Service have made similar progress with a joint national program, employing an animal symbol, the famous "Smokey Bear," for its appeal to the public on forest protection.

Parasites and Diseases

The spruce budworm, the bark beetles of the pines and Douglas firs, the hemlock looper, the white-pine blister rust, and various other parasitical enemies and diseases now kill more trees than fire. The spruce budworm, a migrant moth species from Eastern Canada, is highly destructive. This defoliator alone compelled the spraying by plane of 2,128,000 acres in Washington and Oregon, during 1949, 1950, and 1951. The cost, $1.10 per acre, was financed jointly by private owners, the two states, and the United States government. Checks disclosed a mortality of 98.6 per cent from applications of DDT.

Light infestations remain in unsprayed forest areas. Close watch is kept for outbreaks, and the airplane and modern insecticides are powerful controls. The beetles, thriving in fire-killed and wind-thrown trees, are harder to reach. The salvaging of infected dead timber is the only certain defense against bark beetles. Spraying has halted past hemlock looper epidemics. The destruction of the wild currant bushes which are the transmitters of blister rust from tree to tree is the defense against this disease.

Forest protection from fire, parasites, and disease calls for the cooperation of all ownerships and agencies concerned, as the enemies of trees know no boundary lines. This is also true of problems of rodent control, of the damage done to trees by porcupines and bears. Storms sometimes blow down whole sections of a forest. Ice and snow may break down many trees.

TREE FARMS

Industrial Forestry in Timber Utilization

The tree-farm movement, with industry and agriculture as working partners, began in the Pacific Northwest in 1941 and in a decade grew into a program of private forest management on 26 million acres in 35 states.[6]

[6] The latest survey showed approximately 7 million acres of certified tree farms in the Pacific Northwest, in several large and many small ownerships. Certifying

The true nature of the tree-farm program is most clearly outlined from a stump's-eye view. It is from this vantage point that the industrial forester projects his tree-farm survey on a large watershed or a tributary area. The standing snags, or rather the lack of them, among the stumps are a measure of defense against forest fires. The living trees left by the loggers as seed sources proclaim the promise, or the lack of it, for continuing tree life, growth, and future harvests.

The tree farm is today's progressive phase of industrial forestry on private, taxpaying lands. It corresponds to the similar utilization areas of the national forests and other productively managed forest ownerships of the Pacific Northwest, including the Crown lands of British Columbia. Farm woodland owners present a similar progress picture in both pine and fir regions, with increasing numbers of small certified tree farms.

Problems and Issues in Forest Management

In the years since World War II, the tree-farm movement has become progressively constructive and integrated in forms of cooperation. Competitive interests eventually find common ground for working compromises and peaceful progress.

There are, however, irrepressible conflicts that have gravely affected and will continue to affect forest utilization. British Columbia log and lumber exports to the United States, and the Federal program of forestland acquisition and regulation of private-industry operations on privately owned forests, are two major examples. Logging trucks on the public highways are a familiar problem to every motorist in the region. Taxation enters the logging and lumbering picture in a thousand ways, and has always been the main obstacle to retention of cutover lands for growing long-time crops of trees by private owners. So-called yield tax laws passed by Oregon and Washington state legislatures in 1929 have all but failed to win cooperation from private owners, largely because of the multiplicity of reports and inspections required for the most minor cutting operation on any acreage under the plan.

agencies for the region are the Industrial Forestry Association and the Western Pine Association, both of Portland, Oregon. To qualify for tree-farm certification, a forest property must be privately owned, taxpaying, approved by a professional forester for its permanent management plan (measures in effect for protection, harvesting, and restocking), and finally be accepted by the directors of an official certifying organization. The applicant must also agree to periodic inspections. Tree-farm certificates in the Pacific Northwest are frequently revoked on both large and small properties.

TABLE 3

OWNERSHIP OF COMMERCIAL FORESTLAND IN PACIFIC NORTHWEST, BY STATE,
AS OF JANUARY 1, 1945

(thousands of acres)

State	Total	Federally Owned or Managed			State, County, and Municipal	Private
		Total	National Forest	Other *		
Washington	19,874	7,761	5,811	1950	2334	9,779
Oregon	26,330	15,251	11,530	3721	1101	9,978
Idaho	10,149	6,436	5,838	598	925	2,788
Western Montana †	8,909	5,625	5,068	557	485	2,799
Total	65,262	35,073	28,247	6826	4845	25,344

* Includes forestland owned by Indians but managed by Federal Indian Service.
† 1949 data.

TABLE 4

OWNERSHIP OF SAW-TIMBER VOLUME ON COMMERCIAL FORESTLAND IN PACIFIC
NORTHWEST BY STATE, AS OF JANUARY 1, 1945

(million board feet, lumber tally)

State	Total	Federally Owned or Managed			State, County, and Municipal	Private
		Total	National Forest	Other		
Washington	249,505	114,949	99,465	15,484	31,758	102,798
Oregon	381,389	243,552	179,096	64,456	7,452	130,385
Idaho	60,796	32,821	30,601	2,220	7,721	20,254
Western Montana *	39,689	24,087	21,655	2,432	2,511	13,091
Total	731,379	415,409	330,817	84,592	49,442	266,528

* 1949 data.

Vital Areas of Cooperation

Railroad relations form a long chapter of the region's forest history, from the Federal land grants for railroad building in the period 1860–90 to the boxcar shortages of the present. Ships and timber were basic to the pioneer commerce, and today 60 per cent of the tonnage shipped from Pacific Northwest ports is forest products. The influence of certain Federal forest laws, such as the Clarke-McNary Act, which provides for matching of Federal funds with state and private funds for forest protection, is a constructive force in the regional economy.

Technology and Research

The ways of life and work in the timber, from tree falling to carloading, are in rapid evolution through the test tube of the chemist and the drawing board of the engineer. There is even talk of shooting logs by rocket from stump to mill pond, as modern camp tales of the new Paul Bunyan [7] are told by forestry and logging engineer graduates of Pacific Northwest forestry schools.

Research in forest utilization offers the best example of cooperative relationships between government, industry, and agriculture. Chemical and market research have each played a part. Ingenious farmwoodland owners are also making their contributions. Many a farmer has his own portable sawmill and planer.[8]

Modern Portable Sawmills

An efficient type of portable sawmill that has increased pine operations is mounted on heavy airplane wheels, with an edger unit. The mill can be knocked down, moved 5 miles, and be sawing again within 5 hours. It provides outlets for young pine crops owned by ranchers. Another type of mill that is moved from small setting to small setting on rubber tires is 32 feet long, weighs 2 tons, and is mounted on a two-wheeled trailer. The frame can be partly folded for the road. On a good highway the mill can safely be trailed along at 45 miles per hour, by a standard 1½-ton truck. Built-in jacks on a tubular steel frame permit quick setting-up on a farm woodlot or on any cutover area for relogging. Four men can produce 1000 board feet per hour from ordinary small pine or fir logs.

[7] Folklorists call Paul Bunyan America's greatest original myth. In stories told by the Lake States' lumberjacks of the 1880's, Paul Bunyan was a boss logger who operated a camp so big that four-horse teams and wagons were employed to fill the sugar bowls and salt and pepper shakers in the cookhouse. It was told that the littlest runt in camp broke his leg one winter—3 feet below the knee. A modern story is that Paul Bunyan, cruising into new country, picked up a strange piece of rock and bit it hard in his sampling. It was uranium, and the bite split the atom. The explosion blew out one of the teeth that Paul Bunyan had used in pulling all the stumps in North Dakota to clear the land for King Pete the First of Sweden. Paul's lost tooth, the story goes, became known as Chimney Rock, a landmark on the Oregon Trail.

[8] One farmer in Washington's Puyallup Valley built a large and handsome dairy barn from lumber cut in his own home-made mill from his own 35-year-old Douglas fir trees.

A motor truck with light loading rig is in growing use for log gleaning and farm-woodland operations by the new portable sawmills. Called cherry picker, it takes away the jags of lumber. Rubber-tired log cars are lightweight versions of the big tractor arches on large logging operations. Another illustration of the research trend is the portable chipper and a portable type of power log splitter. Still in the experimental stage, such machines hold promise for the utilization of logging leftovers or the residue of timber harvesting, which as yet cannot be economically transported to mills, manufactured, shipped, and marketed.[9]

Radio Telephones in the Timber

Two-way radio systems were first used in forest-fire control. The larger logging companies next adopted two-way radio for communication between all operations, including mobile installations on logging trucks. The success of industrial forestry radio in the Pacific Northwest has led to its adoption in 25 timber states.

Cooperation and Integration in Research

Research ranges from experimentation in the field to the chemical laboratories in forest industry plants and to the universities of the region. There is also growing cooperation and integration in forest research between the United States and British Columbia, a source of many contributions.[10]

Engineering research moves forward with developments in timber prefabrication designs, glued-up laminations, end and edge gluing of lumber, wood preserving, and related projects. Future planning is in terms of an integrated group of wood-using plants on the mill site,

---

[9] Studies by the Washington State Institute of Forest Products show that in 1948 an average of 2800 board feet per acre remained on recent cutovers as logging residuals. Before 1940 the average was more than 10,000 board feet per acre. The leftovers have been reduced by new markets for pulpwood logs and for utility grades of lumber that were largely unmarketable. A national advertising campaign by the West Coast lumber industry, carried on since 1945, is outstanding as an example of market research and development in improving forest utilization. Promoting popular acceptance of utility lumber, the campaign had powerful effect in transforming cull logs into market logs.

[10] Sources of publications in the large and ever-changing modern library of Pacific Northwest forest research are University of Idaho, Moscow; Oregon State College, Corvallis; University of Washington, Seattle 5; Washington State College, Pullman; the University of Montana, Missoula; the University of British Columbia, Vancouver; state and provincial forestry departments; the larger lumber and pulp companies; and the U. S. Forest Service, Portland, Oregon.

which would include not only lumber, plywood, and pulp manufacture but also a fiberboard factory and bark products plant as well, and eventually distillation units for production of wood yeasts, proteins, sugars, molasses, alcohol, oils, and resins.[11]

Pattern of Progressive Forest Utilization

Sample plots are variously thinned and pruned to determine the right ways to increase the yields of wood while improving the stand that is kept growing for the main harvest. Patterns of seed selection are being formed, to develop hardier seedlings for planting by hand. Other studies deal with the multiple menace of fire, insects, disease, rodents, wind throw, bear, deer and rabbit damage, trespass, preservation of roadside trees, the establishment of public camp grounds, and many more problems of industrial forest management. One project seeks to reverse the ancient and still prevailing method of falling big trees "down the hill," in the way they lean, and to bring them down in an uphill fall by power haul on a line that a climber has attached high up in the individual tree. On other plots, selected trees are bound with steel to force seed production. Soil and weather studies are another important item.

Bark Products

A Douglas fir log scaling 2000 board feet will shed about 1000 pounds of bark. A program of making a market for so much bulk and weight on sawlog, pulp log, and peeler log began with laboratory reduction of Douglas fir bark to its separate constituents. Pilot-plant production was based on the laboratory results. This led to a detailed investment proposal to management. A full production plant was approved. Field market researchers then went to work with dozens of widely diverse industries to prepare for sales promotion of the new bark products: a compound for oil drilling, soil mulches, and insulating material.

An amazing use of great value to the oil industry was discovered in a related development of market research for new wood-chip products. A pulp production project brought forth a new type of cooking liquor

[11] Synthetic rubber production requirements for ethyl alcohol in World War II caused the government to build a plant at Springfield, Oregon, for conversion of sawdust through a process of hydrolysis into wood sugars, and another at Bellingham, Washington, for utilization of sulfite pulp production residuals for the same purpose. The peacetime product remains in a poor competitive position, with cane molasses alcohol in the free market.

that can be burned after use to generate power and for recovery of its chemicals to use again. This process greatly reduces stream and air pollution. The process cannot be adapted to most pulp plants, but it is a step forward.

The grouping of a variety of wood-conversion plants for efficiency and the utmost in forest utilization is feasible for small industry units. The way has been shown in centralized lumber remanufacturing and wood-chipper operations for groups of small mills. The tree-farm program is suitable for farm-woodland owners and others with small timber holdings who have permanent management plans in effect. The new types of portable sawmills, wood chippers, light logging equipment, and lumber trucks can make the rounds in serving groups of small timber owners, all on the old-time pattern of the neighborhood threshing machine in grain-growing districts.

Summary of Conditions and Problems

The Pacific Northwest has 65,262,000 acres of commercial forest-land; more than half of it is owned and managed by the Federal government. More than half of the commercial saw-timber reserves are under Federal ownership. Privately owned and managed wood-using industries, however, are the region's largest single source of income and provide an increasingly important market for 100,000 small forest owners, mostly farmers. A probable 40 per cent of the region's timber harvest is from young growth on cutovers and burns. In areas of early settlement, as much as 60 per cent of the log harvest is from young growth. The continuing rapid growth of the woodpulp industry and the widespread adoption of light, fast machines for utilization of the small trees of young stands are a significant influence on the forest future.

Wildlife and Its Conservation in the Northwest

HARRY H. CALDWELL

Wildlife in the broadest sense signifies all living plants and animals except those that have become domesticated. In the narrower sense, the word "wildlife" has often connoted only game, fur-bearing and predatory species. Here, wildlife will include the wild vertebrate animals, principally mammals, birds, and fishes.

Conservation of wildlife can be expressed simply as the proper use of this resource, but three distinct ideas are inherent. They are (1) preservation of the present supply, (2) restoration of what can and should be restored, and (3) management to produce the largest number of beneficial living animals, consistent with their own good, with the primary uses of lands and waters, and with the needs of man.

In wildlife management there are many complex problems. One of these results from the fact that wildlife legally belongs to the public and not to the landowner. Consequently, management practices must reconcile the proper concept of wildlife with the rights of the landowner and the right of citizens to have access to public property. With few exceptions, wildlife controls are exercised by the state, though much of the land may be under Federal ownership. Another major problem concerns the relative inaccessibility of wildlife. This has forced management programs to be concerned with the environment rather than with the animals themselves.

Biotic Provinces and Life Belts

The distribution of wildlife can be correlated with biotic provinces, which are differentiated by the character of the habitats. Dice [1] de-

[1] Lee R. Dice, *The Biotic Provinces of North America*, University of Michigan Press, Ann Arbor, Michigan, 1943.

259

fines *biotic province* as a large, contiguous geographic area characterized by the occurrence of one or more important ecologic associations
that differ from the associations of adjacent provinces. In general
the biotic provinces are characterized by peculiarities of vegetation
type, ecological climax, fauna, flora, climate, and soil. In practice
there is overlapping of life forms in adjoining biotic provinces, and
boundaries are seldom sharply defined.

Life belts are vertical subdivisions of biotic provinces and they are
extremely important in the mountains. Frequently life belts or zones
are not continuous and thus a life belt may, for example, recur under
proper conditions of altitude and slope exposure on widely separated
mountains within one biotic province. It seems best to think of each
life belt as limited to a single province, because each province is more
or less distinct in its environmental factors and also in its flora and
fauna.[2]

As the population of this nation has increased, land and water resources have been used more intensively for agricultural, industrial,
and commercial purposes. This has resulted in the fencing and plowing of prairies and valleys, the cutting of forests, and the damming
of rivers. These changes have had an effect on all wildlife species.
Moreover, as the country developed, an increasing number of people
hunted the birds and mammals and angled for the fish, which further
affected the various wildlife species. Even with its increasing population, the Pacific Northwest still has great wilderness areas in the
Cascades, Rocky Mountains, and Coast Ranges. Birds and mammals
have inhabited these areas for thousands of years, and through the
ages various species have become closely adjusted to their environments. The conservation of native wildlife is directly related to the
maintenance of these natural habitats, which in turn are benefited
by the conservation of forests, grasslands, and water resources.

It is the general opinion that in the early days, fish, birds, and mammals were very abundant throughout the Pacific Northwest. There
is reason to believe that the increase of population pressure and the
killing by fishermen and sportsmen have reduced wildlife numbers,
but it is also true that, in certain places, game birds, mammals, and
fish were not found in earlier days and have actually become more
numerous since the advent of man.

[2] *Ibid.*, p. 3.

Fresh-Water Fish

The Pacific Northwest has several distinctive and valuable kinds of game fish, which include a large variety of both warm- and cold-water species. The larger cold streams that extend to tidewater have favored the establishment of the wonderful steelhead and rainbow trout. The rainbow is a beautiful, gamy fish that lives throughout the year in the upper stretches of many mountain rivers and lakes. The steelhead is a sea-run rainbow that, for some ancestral reason, migrates to the sea and develops up to 10 or more pounds before it returns to fresh water to spawn.

The Clark trout, commonly called cutthroat, is also widespread in this region. It was first described by Captain William Clark of the Lewis and Clark Expedition. This, like the rainbow, has a divided family, a part migrating to the sea and returning and the other staying in fresh water all the year. The lamprey, another migratory species, somewhat resembles an eel in its habits but is not a game fish and may be destructive to other fish. The Dolly Varden is also a species found in northwestern waters, but, as it has the predatory habit of living on other fish, it is rarely propagated in hatcheries and little effort has been made to increase its numbers. The introduced Mackinaw trout also feeds on other fish and has been destructive to them.

Other fresh-water game varieties in the Pacific Northwest are whitefish and grayling. Huge sturgeon weighing several hundred pounds occur in the Columbia and Snake rivers. Like trout, several kinds of bass, and other warm-water, spiny-ray species have also been introduced. The Kamloop trout, a variety of giant rainbow native to British Columbia, was planted in Lake Pend Oreille and has been widely promoted because of its large size.

In accordance with their natural requirements, certain species like the cutthroat and the rainbow inhabit streams and lakes because the food and water conditions are favorable. For this reason, every effort should be made to protect and hold the balance of fish in such waters. In too many cases fish wardens have lacked the necessary scientific training for successful game-fish propagation with the result that exotic species from other regions have been liberated in northwestern waters without prior knowledge concerning the possible survival of the introduced species, or whether they would interfere with the native fish. Certain streams adapted to cold-water species have been stocked with warm-water species such as bass, crappies, or perch. The reverse has also occurred. As a result many species have failed to survive. Carp were introduced, although they are much inferior in eating quality to many species of native fish that were crowded out by them.

Another important aspect of the inland water fish population is the increasing problem of water pollution from domestic and industrial wastes and from increased silting of streams and lakes, coincident with increased cultivation of land and the cutting of timber. Further pollution has come from the disposal of mine and mill wastes and use of dredges on many important fishing streams. Other causes for injury to fish habitats include the filling of stream beds with fallen timber during logging operations, forest fires, and soil erosion.

The great dam-building program here in the Northwest has had two major effects on fish: (1) they prevent or hinder the passage of anadromous fish (those that live part of their lives in the ocean or bays and must go up the rivers to spawn), and (2) they change the character of the streams in such a way as to discourage cold-water forms and encourage warm-water species. The water is warmed up, and the gravelly spawning sites are covered by still water.

The four major approaches to fish conservation are (1) artificial propagation, (2) introduction of exotic species, (3) legal restrictions, and (4) habitat improvement. Of these approaches the first two have met with only limited success. The survival rate of planted fingerlings remains low, and the cost of planting large fish becomes uneconomical. In many instances where exotic species have been introduced, the anticipated fishing did not materialize; yet planting of fish in many lakes and streams does provide sport for fishermen in water where otherwise game fish would be lacking.

According to the Washington State Game Commission, the number of game fish planted in 1951 by the state of Washington in inland lakes and streams was 44,470,714, distributed among five species of trout. The trout were raised in state hatcheries and about half were legal size when liberated. Oregon and Idaho also liberate many millions of fish annually from state hatcheries.

Legal restrictions have produced both good and bad results that varied with particular species under different ecologic conditions. The Black Bass Act of 1926 made it a Federal offense to transport bass across state lines for the purposes of sale. The law was amended in 1947 to include all game species.

Another noteworthy piece of Federal legislation is the Dingell-Johnson Bill of 1950, which provides that the Federal tax on fishing tackle be returned to the states for use in research and management of the

TABLE 1

TROUT PLANTED IN NORTHWEST STATES

	Washington 1951	Idaho 1951	Oregon 1948–50
Cutthroat	2,301,620	10,378,289	5,381,589
Eastern Brook	2,283,668	765,641	7,570,386
German Brown		107,085	
Rainbow	12,304,484	6,532,345	26,781,290
Silvers (Kokanee)	25,506,060	1,356,790	2,007,795
Steelhead	1,074,882	89,420	
Kamloop		564,837	2,029,398
Others		16,590	1,031,432
Total	44,470,714	19,810,997	44,801,990

sport species. Each state was apportioned in accord with its area and the number of fishing licenses sold. In the resultant management projects, the Federal government pays 75 per cent of the cost and the state contributes the remaining 25 per cent.

Of these four approaches to fish conservation, habitat rehabilitation offers the greatest hope for fisheries improvement though it may be costly to initiate.

Waterfowl and Upland Birds

Originally the Northwest possessed considerable areas of swamps and lakes suitable as nesting and resting places for migratory waterfowl (Plate 17A). One of the main migration routes for birds from the far north summer breeding grounds to the California and Mexican winter feeding areas passed over the Pacific Northwest, some of the flocks going east and some west of the Cascades. Many of the feeding grounds of waterfowl have been drained and otherwise destroyed. The ill-advised drainage of lower Klamath Lake is a case in point, where part of the former lake bed and marshes that were the resort of myriads of waterfowl has become an alkali waste. In northern Idaho, stream and lake pollution by mine-waste waters has taken a toll of migratory waterfowl. Any damage to the breeding places lessens the stock, thereby decreasing the number of birds available for hunting.

For many years it was virtually impossible to induce the various states to pass effective laws for migratory waterfowl protection. One of the first important steps was the Migratory Bird Treaty made between Great Britain and the United States and ratified December 7, 1916. The necessary Enabling Act was passed July 3, 1918, thereby ending the wholesale shooting of ducks and geese and making the sale of wild fowl illegal in the United States.

Even though the killing of migratory waterfowl was controlled, these birds still declined in numbers because of the change in breeding and feeding conditions. Many of the nesting places were destroyed, and birds, like the canvasback and the redhead ducks, greatly decreased in the Pacific Northwest. During the past few years, more efforts have been made to restore breeding areas. The stoppage of spring shooting, forbidding the baiting of ducks where they are hunted, and the shortening of seasons and bag limits have helped restore the numbers of certain species.

The Federal Aid to Wildlife Restoration Act was passed in 1937. This act is of vital importance, because it enables the Fish and Wildlife Service of the Department of the Interior to cooperate with different states in scientific research and in the establishment of reservations for wildlife protection. Under this law many migratory bird refuges have been established. Already there has been a definite increase in various kinds of waterfowl, such as mallards, pintails, and widgeons, the most abundant species in the Pacific Northwest. Red Rock Lakes Migratory Waterfowl Refuge in southwestern Montana protects the trumpeter swans in one of their few remaining breeding grounds.

In this widely varied Northwest there are many types of upland and forest game birds that were introduced or evolved (Plate 17B). Of the upland species, some are regarded as forest dwellers, whereas others prefer the peripheral zone around cultivated fields and are known as farm game birds. The commonly found forest game birds of the Northwest are the blue grouse, Franklin grouse, and ruffed grouse, all of which are essentially nonmigratory. Seasonal movements take place, although they are usually altitudinal, illustrating the life-belt concept. Movements from one type of cover to another and diurnal movements that correspond to microclimatic changes have also been noted. The most abundant bird through the extensive wooded country was the blue or sooty grouse, which inhabited the fir forests from California to Alaska. This grouse, dark or sooty blue, is similar to the Richardson grouse east of the Cascade Range, where climatic conditions produce feathered coats lighter in color.

The ruffed grouse is also characteristic of this area. It is dressed in rich red-brown, which is replaced by a distinctive gray coat in the higher and drier areas. On logged-off land and in the wild crabapple and ash thickets, these were once abundant. The elongated black feathers on the sides of the neck, forming a ruff, identify the cock.

The Franklin grouse is more distinctive than the ruffed grouse. For some reason it is utterly indifferent to the approach of man and will scarcely move out of the trail. It is also called "fool hen."

The white-tailed ptarmigan or "snow grouse" is best adapted to higher latitudes or altitudes. Most remarkable is its change of coats with the seasons, a well-known example of adaptive or protective coloration. A dress mottled with black and brown for the summer or breeding period is shed and replaced by one of pure white when the snowy period arrives. Although a former resident of snow-capped peaks in Oregon, this bird has disappeared there but still survives on the slopes of Mt. St. Helens, Mt. Adams, and Mt. Rainier in Washington.

In eastern Oregon and Washington sportsmen formerly were accustomed to flush a flock of pale-brown grouse from the meadowlands. These would have been Columbian sharp-tailed grouse, which, like the prairie chickens farther east, were birds of more open country.

Every section of the Pacific Northwest, varying in its ecologic association, is the home of a particular species of grouse. Perhaps the most distinctive of all are the open sagebrush stretches where the pines and even the junipers are replaced by wide reaches of sand and gray sage. Here nature has created the largest and most stately grouse of America, commonly called sage hen. The weight of a sage cock may be anywhere from 5 to 8 pounds. His tail is long with narrow, pointed feathers. In the spring he struts somewhat like a turkey gobbler, with fan-shaped tail spread and air sacs inflated, giving his breast a balloon-like appearance. As if nature had not been lavish enough in its supply of upland game in the Pacific Northwest, she also furnished several species of quail. The mountain or plumed quail were quite common in the wooded areas of western Oregon and Washington. A second species, called the California, little blue, or valley quail, was a native of southern Oregon, but is now common in other parts of Oregon and Washington.

The bobwhite quail, a bird of the East, has been introduced into many other parts of the country. It is now abundant in the fields of the Pacific Northwest. It does not, like the mountain quail, live so much in the wilder sections but is found in farming areas, where it holds its own like the California quail. Quail not only provide sport to the hunter but also, along with songbirds, help the farmer by devouring insects and weed seeds.

The ring-necked or Chinese pheasant was introduced into Oregon in 1881. It multiplied so rapidly in the Willamette Valley that later thousands of them were killed each season. Then after about 30 years conditions changed and the birds began to decrease in number in the Willamette Valley. They were introduced in many other parts of the Pacific Northwest, and they are scarcely more abundant in eastern Oregon and the Palouse regions of Washington and Idaho than in the western parts of Oregon and Washington. Because these birds seem to be more available for sportsmen, the game commissions have spent large amounts of money in game farms. Here, thousands are raised and released each year, thus furnishing game for the sportsmen when the season is closed in many places on grouse and quail. For example, in 1951, 117,500 birds, mostly Chinese pheasants, were liberated from state game farms in Washington. Hundreds of thousands of dollars have been spent to propagate these pheasants, European or Hungarian partridges, chuker partridge, and other foreign birds. Artificial propagation of game birds must be coincident with habitat improvement to make the increase in numbers lasting. Pheasants, quail, and partridges are essentially farm game birds, and their numbers are closely related to farming practices.

The current decline in the number of farm game birds has been associated with the advent of power farm machinery, which brought in the era of "clean farming." When fields were cultivated up to property fences, and bramble thickets were removed by plowing or herbicides, the vital winter and nesting cover was destroyed. Many states and sportsmen groups are now trying to restore the needed habitat cover through programs of shrub plantings. In addition to providing cover, such shrubs as multiflora rose and wild grape also provide food and protection against predators, heavy snow, and wind.

Forest Fur Bearers

Pursuit of the beaver in the 1820's was one of the stimulants to northwestern exploration under the financial backing of the fur trading companies. Beaver, muskrat, mink, otter, and marten are the principal forest fur bearers. Muskrats are also found in nonforested areas. Of these varieties, the beaver is more important because of his hide and "engineering" abilities. Beaver numbers, once thinned out in a period of excessive slaughter, are gradually being restored through protection, stocking, and transplanting.

Big Game

Three kinds of deer inhabit the region (Plate 18A). The Columbian blacktail, found west of the Cascade Range, is more a resident of the forested areas, where it has abundant summer and winter food supplies. The deer browses largely on the leaves of lower limbs and bushes.

The western white-tailed deer was formerly common in Oregon, but with the increase of population it disappeared entirely from the Willamette Valley foothills. A few have been reported in Douglas County on the west side of the Cascades and in the Davis Lake region of Crook County on the east slope. In northeastern Washington and northern Idaho, the white-tail deer are still present in sizeable numbers. In 1951, the white-tail deer population of northern Idaho was estimated at 22,500.

A larger species, the mule deer, begins to appear east of the Cascades and generally south of the white-tail deer areas in Idaho. There has been a marked increase in these animals during more recent decades, frequently after forest fires. They have spread out and now occupy areas where they were not formerly found. Their number in Idaho was estimated at 120,000 for the year 1951. Years ago in Oregon most deer hunting was west of the Cascades, but today it is largely east of the mountains. Because of the increasing number of hunters, it was thought the deer would decrease more and more, but instead they have been increasing. Perhaps one partial reason for the increase of deer in the east has been the killing of predatory animals, such as the coyote, bobcat, and mountain lion. The summer food supply is usually abundant, but the increase in number of deer depends greatly upon winter food supply and cover.

In regard to the elk that inhabit the Pacific Northwest, the Roosevelt elk ranges from the Olympics south along the coast line of southern Oregon. In the Olympics they have increased in numbers, also in Clatsop County, Oregon. In the 1920's there were comparatively few elk in eastern Oregon and Washington. A few were introduced from the Jackson Hole country, careful protection was provided, and their numbers increased. But in each instance the elk herd was only able to increase because of a satisfactory habitat. In the Clearwater National Forest, a series of large fires in 1910, 1919, and 1934 denuded large portions of the forest. In the burned areas the brush growth that followed the fires has favored great elk herds in the Selway-Lochsa drainage. These herds could not attain such size before the fires and are already starting to shrink as the new stands of trees replace and crowd out the open bush vegetation. The extensive burned-over lands of north-central Idaho are now populated with over 20,000 head of elk. This is the same area where the starving Lewis and Clark Expedition was forced to eat its horses because of game scarcity a century and a half ago. Today, it contains about one-half of the state's elk population.

Contrary to widely held opinions, forest game animals have increased in numbers most rapidly where man has cut timber. This has been especially true of the mixed-habitat species like cotton-tail rabbits, ruffed grouse, and white-tail deer.

In regard to the antelope or pronghorns, the largest number was formerly in southern Oregon and southern Idaho. None were found in Washington, but some have since been introduced. Because of the gradual increase since the 1930's, an open season has been established in Oregon and Idaho. Hundreds are killed each season, but even so the numbers seem to keep up fairly well. A large Federal refuge has been established in the Hart Mountains in southern Oregon for the protection of antelope, mule deer, and sage grouse.

The American bison or buffalo was formerly abundant in southeastern Oregon and from the plains of the Columbia River, east, but seems to have disappeared before the arrival of white men. Buffalo can be now seen in Yellowstone National Park, and on the National Bison Range in Lake and Sanders counties, Montana.

The Shiras moose also has a very limited range in Idaho, Wyoming, and Montana, but the numbers have been steadily increasing in Yellowstone Park.

Bighorn or mountain sheep are scarce in the Northwest. Those that formerly ranged in southeastern Oregon have been exterminated. A small number still range in the extreme northeastern part of Oregon and some in Washington, also farther east in Idaho, Montana, and a few in Yellowstone Park. There has been a decrease in some areas and a slight increase in others. Some mountain sheep have been introduced in the Hart Mountain Refuge of southern Oregon.

Mountain goats were formerly reported in the Oregon Cascades, but they have now disappeared. They are still found, however, in the Cascades in Washington, and especially in Mt. Rainier National Park, above Lake Chelan, and farther north. A few range in Idaho and Montana and are quite abundant in Glacier National Park.

As the population of the Pacific Northwest has increased and the livestock range is enlarged, some big-game species have held their own but others have been crowded out and have gradually disappeared. It should be remembered that the taking of a reasonable proportion of existing game is a harvest that furnishes both food and sport. If sensible conservation methods are followed, a good harvest of game should continue indefinitely.

The business of catering to sportsmen in the Pacific Northwest is large, and residents of some communities receive much of their income from hunters, campers, and fishermen. The exact value of wildlife to an area is always difficult to assess. By knowing the number of fish and game caught each year and placing a value on each by species, one reaches some conclusion relative to the dollar value of this food. Likewise, by tabulating the number of hunting and fishing licenses sold (over 250,000 in Washington and over 175,000 in Idaho annually) and the average annual per capita expenditure per sporting venture, totals of several additional million dollars can be obtained. However, no satisfactory method has yet been devised to assess the value of the personal pleasure that one gets in hunting, fishing, or merely watching or photographing the wide variety of fish and game animals of the Pacific Northwest.

REFERENCES

Bailey, Vernon, "The Mammals and Life Zones of Oregon," *North American Fauna*, No. 55, U. S. Department of Agriculture, Bureau of Biological Survey, 1936.

Bailey, Vernon, *Animal Life of Yellowstone National Park*, Charles C Thomas, Springfield, Illinois, and Baltimore, Maryland, 1930.

Bailey, Vernon, and Florence Bailey, *Wild Animals of Glacier National Park*, Department of the Interior, National Park Service, Government Printing Office, 1918.

Bennitt, Rudolph, "Wildlife Conservation and Geography," *Journal of Geography*, Vol. 39, pp. 217–225, September, 1940.

Biennial Reports of the Fish and Game Department of the State of Idaho.

Dahlquest, Walter W., *Mammals of Washington*, University of Kansas, Lawrence, 1948.

Davis, William B., *Mammals of Idaho*, Caxton Printers, Caldwell, Idaho, 1939.

Dawson, William L., and John H. Bowles, *The Birds of Washington*, Occidental Publishing Co., Seattle, 1909.

Dice, Lee R., *The Biotic Provinces of North America*, University of Michigan Press, Ann Arbor, 1943.

Gabrielson, Ira N., *Wildlife Conservation*, The Macmillan Co., New York, 1941.

Gabrielson, Ira N., and Stanley G. Jewett, *Birds of Oregon*, Oregon State College Cooperative Association, Corvallis, 1940.

Taylor, Walter P., and William T. Shaw, *Mammals and Birds of Mount Rainier National Park*, Department of the Interior, National Park Service, Government Printing Office, Washington, D. C., 1927.

Washington State Game Commission, Olympia, Washington, numerous publications.

Recreation and Tourism

JOSEPH T. HAZARD

In pioneer days leisure was hard earned and its hours were fleeting. The lure of those few leisure hours was toward the settlements and towns, not away from them. The tour had not arrived, for journeys were events of necessity rather than vacations.

Now, there is a daily exodus from home and office, from mart and plant, from loft, factory, and farm, in the search for some kind of recreational release. The weekend trip and the longer tour have been born of the strong desire for more complete rest and relaxation, a difference in activities, or for new and changing scenes. Recreation as a recognized part of the American way of life has been made easier by a number of modern developments.

1. An average of 370 leisure and vacation hours a year above the usual hours of labor.

2. Improved transport media.

3. Income above subsistence needs.

4. The general acceptance of the vacation idea.

5. Systematic development of recreation as a major industry.

Mountains as Background for Outdoor Life

The Pacific Northwest has developed a broadly regional identity in national recreation (Plate 18B). No single factor is more important than the mountains with their meadows and parklands, their high bench lakes, waterfalls, and milky torrents, their summer snowfields and winter playfields, and their ranges and summits. From the Grand Tetons west to the Olympics and from Crater Lake, Oregon, north to Mt. Baker and the Canadian Selkirks, three distinct types of recreational use have developed.

1. The smooth highway, the graded trail, and the comfortable highland resort are now available to the average man.

2. The elusive fastness, the exacting snow finger or rock face, and the isolated pinnacle or peak tempt the hardy and adventurous.

3. The winter ski resort, tucked away beside the mountain highway, nestled within the high valley pocket, or set still higher against steep slopes of the mountain, serves three types of skiers: (a) the novice and dilettante demanding lifts, hot and cold water, and a cuisine; (b) the cross-country runner, who makes the resort merely a starting point from which he ventures ever deeper into untamed snows, with meager food and camp on his back; (c) the contest skier, defiant of the laws of gravity, whose records and achievements are followed by tens of thousands.

Among the inviting ski locales are some that have become internationally known. Competition in meets, open to the world, have been held in Sun Valley, Mt. Spokane State Park, Mt. Hood, Mt. Rainier, Snoqualmie Pass, and Stevens Pass.

The Climatic Factor, Winter and Summer

Climatic variations in the Pacific Northwest have their distinct influence on both summer and winter recreations.

Western Montana has two main regions for recreation, based upon summer and winter influences of climate: (1) The wind-swept eastern Rockies, embattled by polar air masses in winter, are climatically severe for winter sport but attractive for summer trails and camps. Glacier Park lies within this region. (2) Within and behind the Rockies the severities of Montana's continental climate are tamed by the modifying influences of protecting mountains. Missoula and Kalispell, at the confluence of mountain valleys, have good conditions for winter recreation. Cool summer trails lead to a complexity of higher valleys well served by private resorts and forest camps.

Idaho has two distinct climates and a zone of transition: (1) Northern and central Idaho have a continental climate modified by protective mountains. Central Idaho is mainly inaccessible except in summer, when its deep canyons, high forests, rugged ranges, clear lakes, and rushing rivers appeal to the exploring and adventuring type of men. The deep canyons of the Snake and the Salmon rivers offer possibilities for future recreational development in sections where large game flourishes almost undisturbed. (2) The mountains of south-central Idaho lie between the modified continental climate and the steppes to the south. Here are Sun Valley, Payette Lakes, and other winter and summer resorts. The arid steppes, south, blend into the watered mountains; long northern reaches of plateau and range temper the cold from the northern continent; southern and northern exposures present variety and recreation is emphasized both in summer and in winter. (3) Southern Idaho with its steppes climate is generally unfavorable to outdoor recreation except in local resorts near cities.

Western Washington and Oregon are essentially similar in climatic adjustments. West of the Cascades the climate is temperate marine, except where modified by relief features. Recreation is affected by the variable weather conditions, and the thousands of local weather pockets add spice and variety to year-round outdoor activity.

Eastern Washington and Oregon, east of the Cascades, has a special type of steppe climate that is greatly modified by altitude and its position relative to the surrounding mountains. Lake and mountain resorts are favorites for summer vacations. Winter sports are carried on in the Blue Mountains, and along the Yakima and Columbia rivers out from the larger cities.

Another recreational asset made attractive by both topography and climate is found in the lakes and streams throughout the Pacific Northwest. Blocked drainage, the aftermath of glaciation, has left thousands of lakes both great and small from near sea level to the slopes of high mountains. In western Montana, Idaho, Oregon, and Washington, rivers sweep down the valleys and loiter through the lowlands, while mountain rills plunge down slope in white foam or cascade over cliffs and mountain walls. These are recreational, or may be made so.

Shoreline Recreation

In its shoreline features and accessible salt waters, the Pacific Northwest possesses outstanding opportunities for boating, swimming, picnicking, fishing, and clam digging. The irregular coastline on the Pacific and the many islands and elongated peninsulas of Puget Sound provide Washington with a length of shoreline exceeded only by Florida among the forty-eight states. The beaches, bays, and bold headlands of the Oregon coast provide facilities that attract thousands of tourists. The scenery of the British Columbia coast and the Inside Passage to Alaska set among towering mountains rising steeply from sea level rivals that of the fiords of Norway. Thousands of small pleasure craft ply the protected coastal waters, and hotels and thousands of summer cottages shelter owners and visitors to the beaches and harbors. Hundreds of thousands of summer residents and tourists utilize these facilities. Improvements along the coastlines are expanding every year, so that the many opportunities for recreation become increasingly appreciated. Continued development of shoreline facilities is certain because of increasing population, construction of access roads, and increasing desire for recreation.

Protected salt-water sounds and bays abound along the North Pacific littoral, especially north of Columbia River. Willapa Bay, Grays Harbor, the Strait of Juan de Fuca, Haro Strait, Puget Sound, Georgia Strait, and the Alaskan Inland Passage provide thousands of square miles of inland salt waters with more than 10,000 miles of beaches. South of the Columbia are the carved cliffs and the bold headlands of the Oregon Coast.

Fishing, either quietly individual or competitive and publicized in numerous "salmon derbies," attracts many thousands of devotees. Both fresh and salt water, and the approaches to mountains and mountain passes, are increasingly rimmed with summer cottages, often used during the entire year, where families relax and entertain their friends. Their heyday is during the long and sunny Northwest summers.

Wildlife, Fish, and Game

The prevalence of rugged mountains, the wide spread of forest cover, the intricate and isolated salt- and fresh-water nooks and lanes, and the lush grasses of meadow and parklands have combined to favor large piscatorial and wild-animal populations. These multiply the attractiveness of the Pacific Northwest to fishermen, hunters, camera fans, and visitors in general.

Since breaks in the wildlife barrens of dense and matted virgin timber have come with forest industries, both birds and wild animals in western Washington have increased. Counts prove that wildlife now exceeds that of the days of Lewis and Clark. Bear, deer, and other types of wildlife are a vital part of the background attracting visitors to the parks and forests. Salmon in the salt waters and trout in the annually stocked lakes and streams lure additional thousands.

Forests are probably the greatest single recreational asset of the Pacific Northwest. In fact, the Society of American Foresters has a division of recreation, and the United States Forest Service, in each regional headquarters, has its supervisor of recreation. Many individual national forests have trained personnel working helpfully under the special "Division of Recreation and Lands."

Visitors in Northwest National Forests

In the year 1917 there were 3 million visitors to the national forests. In 1950 the annual forest visitors had passed the 100 million mark. In Region Six, the U. S. Forest Service, which includes the seven national forests of Washington and the thirteen of Oregon, this recreational use was tabulated for the year 1952 under nine classifications, each bearing special gifts for human happiness, as shown in Table 1.

TABLE 1

1952 CLASSIFICATION OF U. S. FOREST VISITORS, REGION SIX

	Washington	Oregon
Campgrounds	474,200	512,375
Picnics	478,355	479,194
Winter sports	166,050	227,900
Organization camps (Scouts, etc.)	43,694	24,780
Hotels and resorts	123,411	531,765
Recreational residences	52,017	35,547
Wilderness areas	7,942	15,220
Other special areas	297,395	449,243
Highways and water routes	6,489,646	8,112,630
Totals	8,132,710	10,388,654

Selected Areas for Recreational Concentration

Throughout the national-forest areas of the Pacific Northwest are hundreds of special sites, permanently dedicated to personal and public use. Three types are most permanent and important: (1) Forest homes (summer-home permits for one approved building): average $20 a year ground rent, with larger rentals for homes occupied 9 or more months a year. (2) Clubs and organizations (larger sites and rentals): more than one building allowed upon approval by Forest Service. (3) Campgrounds, picnic areas, wholly or partly equipped. In the 152 national forests, with more than 179 millions of acres of reserved public domain, there are 4500 odd sites "specially selected and improved" for campers and picnickers. Of these, listed and more or less improved, Idaho has 356 in 13 U. S. Forests; Montana has 220 in 11 U. S. Forests; Oregon has 297 in 13 U. S. Forests; Washington has 221 in 7 U. S. Forests.

Sports Invade Winter's "Snowbound Isolation"

A fourth type of selected areas within national forests for this recreational concentration is relatively new. But by December, 1950, the

Forest Service was able to announce officially that "The national forests have 240 developed winter sports areas with a capacity of 285,000 skiers at one time." In the Pacific Northwest the more important ones are as follows.

Idaho. Bogus Basin in the Boise National Forest and Sun Valley in the Sawtooth National Forest.

Montana. Big Mountain in the Flathead National Forest and Lookout Pass in the Coeur d'Alene National Forest.

Oregon. Timberline in the Mt. Hood National Forest; Hoodo Bowl in the Willamette National Forest; and Spout Springs in the Umatilla National Forest.

Washington. Heather Meadows in the Mt. Baker National Forest; Snoqualmie Pass in the Snoqualmie National Forest; and Stevens Pass in the Wenatchee National Forest.

With all this stress of recreation within national forests the Federal financial interests are well served. The Snoqualmie National Forest of Washington will prove the fact. In the year 1951 the Snoqualmie Forest, managed for the maximal multiple use, returned more than a million dollars to the United States Treasury, above all the expense of maintenance and development.

Preservation of "Primitive America"

Another public service, associated with recreation, has developed within national forests. To National Parks has been delegated the duty of safeguarding and developing certain feature areas of the nation. In addition to the national parks' selected areas, much true wilderness has been set aside and designated for restricted use. Recognized classes are:

Wilderness areas. At least 100,000 acres (no building) at least ½ mile from motorized transportation.

Wild areas. Wilderness (at least 5000 acres) near population.

Roadless areas. Economic values too great for exclusion (temporary utilization roads only).

Virgin areas. Natural vegetation undisturbed (under 5000 acres).

Natural areas. Special botanical or biological values (too small for a virgin area).

Montana Forest Service now administers a typical wilderness area. The regional forester has joined three primitive areas, the Pentagon, the South Fork (Flathead River), and the Sun River, forming a great wilderness along the central Continental Divide. Maps show trails, camp sites with horse feed, a dozen "regions of special interest." The resorts and dude ranches hug the boundaries but do not enter. Feeder roads connect the encirclement of Kalispell, Glacier Park, and Shelby, north; Great Falls and Helena east; Missoula south; and Polson west.

Many other primitive areas, including wildlife refuges, are found in the national forests of the Pacific Northwest, from the ocean, across diverse mountain ranges, and down and into the Great Plains. These areas are highly selective and are given permanency by proclamation. Change is at the dictates of scientific research, always with appraisal of the truest and most lasting values.

Trails in the National Forest

Inviting trails wind through lowlands and uplands of the vast reaches of northwestern national forests. The Cascade Crest Trail, now roughly completed, clings to the rugged divide of the Cascade Ranges from Canada to Oregon. It continues as the Oregon Skyline Trail from the Columbia River to California. Every mile of this "Crest Trail" is within one of the north-south U. S. National Forests that cross the two states connecting Canada and California with a recreational paradise of living green.

This lofty trail, the acme of scenic grandeur, continues south through California, welding the High Sierra crests and the desert heights into a continuous whole. These high trails of the three Pacific Coast states are unified for recreation in the Pacific Crest Trail System, combining more recreational variety and greater distances than any other world trail system.

National Parks and National Park Service

The Pacific Northwest now possesses six national parks, each established because of unrivaled, distinctive features (see Table 2). These six national parks within the region are a most important factor in stimulating Northwest tourism.[1] The government has provided free nature-guide service by range naturalists, who explain to the visitors the origin of the scenic features and tell about the trees, flowers, birds, and animals of the parks. Paved and oiled highways, hotels, cabins, shelters, and public camps have been provided to play host to millions of recreationists. More than 3 million visitors yearly enter the various national parks of the region (Fig. 30).

[1] For descriptions of Yellowstone (Plate 24B), Glacier, and Grand Teton National Parks and Craters of the Moon National Monument, see Section 3, Chapter 5. Crater Lake, Mt. Rainier, and Olympic National Park are mentioned in Section 1, Chapter 5.

TABLE 2

NORTHWEST NATIONAL PARKS

Name and Acreage	Estab- lished	1952 Visitors	Features
Yellowstone Federal: 2,313,100	1872	1,330,387	Volcanic, with 3000 geysers and hot springs; grand canyon lakes and waterfalls; wild-animal life
Mt. Rainier Federal: 241,571	1899	877,388	Largest single-peak glacier system in United States; great forests and flower meadows
Crater Lake Federal: 160,290	1902	302,132	Deep-blue lake in crater of volcano; colored lava walls 500 to 2000 feet high
Glacier Federal: 998,416	1910	630,949	Mountains, glaciers, lakes, Indians
Grand Teton Federal: 310,000 approx.	1929	795,475	Sharp-peaked Teton Mts.; home of "Mountain Men"
Olympic Federal: 840,838	1939	431,866	Loop highway, hot springs, Lake Crescent, dense forest

State Parks

The four Northwest states vary greatly in the administration and the scope of their state parks and state recreational areas. State preserves are many, increasing yearly in number and magnitude in Oregon and Washington, while definite geographic factors in Idaho and Montana favor national forest and park emphasis. In 1950 the four state administration and acreage of state preserves were as follows.

Oregon had 145 areas, with 57,882 acres, over half-developed by administration under the State Department of Highways.

Washington had 56 areas, with 55,864 acres, 40 developed parks, 8 parks soon to be developed, with the rest of the areas dormant; their administration is by a State Parks and Recreation Commission. The visitors in 1952 numbered over 2.6 million.

Idaho was limited to 4 areas with 8189 acres. One state park, the Heyburn, a former Indian tract of 7838 acres, is developed. It lies at the south end of Lake Coeur d'Alene; it has summer cottages, camping, picnicking, swimming, boating, and fishing.

Montana had 13 areas held for recreation, 18,265 acres, with one only developed as a state park. It is Morrison Cave, formerly the Lewis and Clark National Monument. This marvelous cavern is now reopened to the general public *guarded from vandalism!*

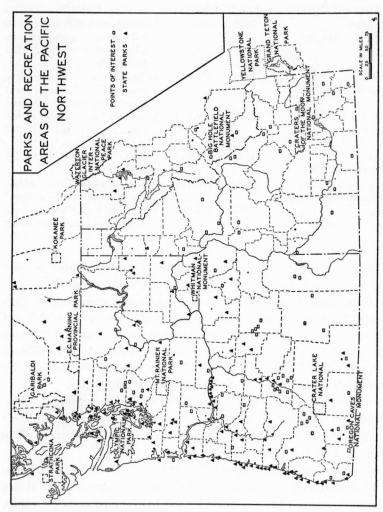

Fig. 30.   Parks and recreation areas of the Pacific Northwest.

Oregon with forward-looking jurisdiction from the state highway commission took an early lead in state park and recreational area development. As a natural result Oregon has achieved more advancement in public recreation than elsewhere in the Northwest. However, with more funds and more scientifically sound personnel, Washington has made real progress. The program has become complex, with attention of the commission to all outdoor interests (see Table 3). Two state parks will illustrate this variety of interests.

TABLE 3

NATIONAL FORESTS OF PACIFIC NORTHWEST

Idaho: 13 national forests, with 356 public forest campgrounds; 17 winter sports areas; resorts; hotels; cabins; and dude ranches; hot springs; packers; guides; horses; boats; and other facilities.

Montana: 11 national forests with 190 public forest campgrounds; 17 winter sports areas; resorts; cabins; dude ranches; adjacent hot springs with hotels; and packers and guides near forests available for long or short trips within forests.

Oregon: 13 national forests with 287 public forest campgrounds; 9 winter sports areas; commercial cabin camps and dude ranches in or near forests; pack-trip outfitters; and lake and stream fishing.

Washington: 7 national forests with 287 public forest campgrounds; 5 winter sports areas; commercial cabins and dude ranches; nearby commercial hotels and resorts; hundreds of fishing lakes and streams; massive primitive forests with a complex of high trunk and feeder trails; and the mountain goat "capital" of the United States!

Camano Island State Park, established in 1947, has 53 acres of timber with about a mile of bold cliffs over ideal salt-water beach. On one Sunday of 1952, 600 visitors dug 12,000 pounds of clams, under a limit of 25 pounds per person.

Sun Lakes State Park, 2400 acres, established 1945, is an oasis for recreation near Grand Coulee Dam, surrounded by semidesert.

Canadian Recreation

Tens of thousands of Pacific Northwest recreationists each year visit "Canada's mountain playgrounds," for Pacific Northwest tourism is indeed international. For years, mountain clubs have made annual treks to Garibaldi Park (Provincial, British Columbia), to upper Columbia Ice Fields, to Glacier Park (Canadian), to Mt. Robson and Jasper parks, to the Banff National Park districts, to Waterton-Glacier International Park, or to lesser-developed mountain playgrounds across

the border. Or individual members of outdoors clubs have joined
Canadian clubs on similar ventures.

British Columbia is a true part of the Pacific Northwest, and each
year it becomes an increasingly vital part of Northwest recreation,
with international boundary no hindrance to easy access.

The Growing Complex of Recreational Interests

With shorter working hours and increased family income, the programs for recreation have expanded. State parks and national monuments feature natural attractions and historical shrines. Besides 48
developed parks, Washington's "Commission" offers the public 6 natural forest areas, 6 tideland areas, 3 geological-exhibit areas, and 13
historical-site areas. The Oregon Caves, unique and beautiful, Idaho's
Craters of the Moon, which are so recently volcanic, are national
monuments, luring visitors. The protected islands of the San Juans
and British Columbia now attract hordes of vacationers. Dude
ranches from Montana to Oregon afford a maximum of riding and
outdoor life for those who like an equal maximum of comfort even
to luxury. Those who take their sports vicariously but with a full
measure of roughness follow the "roundups," like those of Pendleton,
Oregon, and Ellensburg, Washington. Golf is now "a sport of the
people," whereas, in older days, it was the luxury pastime of the privi-
leged few. Washington has more than 50 golf courses, 18 near Seattle
alone, with even more near Portland. To golf may be added outdoor
badminton, bowling-on-the-green, archery, and a succession of fishing
derbies.

Festivals in season lead tens of thousands outdoors. There are
Portland's Rose Festival, Salem's Cherry Blossom Show, Wenatchee's
Apple Blossoms Annual, and Puyallup's, earliest, Daffodils.

The Columbia River Highway, the Cariboo Trail Highway, Highway 99, The Olympic Loop, and the Oregon Coastal Route of scenic
Highway 101, the Mt. Hood and the Mt. Rainier Loop highways, all
lead the motorist to and through some of the best of the Northwest.
Trips to the Rogue River Gorge, Hell's Canyon of the Snake River,
are still in the class of exploration, daring trips well off the beaten
paths. Boat trips up Lake Chelan and Alaska's Inland Passage are
well within the reach of the most leisurely.

The access program for future recreation is increasing in magnitude.
Road building in the Pacific Northwest is opening new areas. Fortunately, nearly all the trunk highways projected and the farm-and-
mine-to-market networks reach new recreational meccas. Oregon is

showing the way. The most spectacular drive of the Northwest along the Oregon Coast was the beginning, making the Oregon Coast more accessible and better known than the Washington Coast, although both have great gifts for recreationists. The year 1951 added the newly constructed trunk highway through White Pass. It leads from Mt. Rainier National Park to the Yakima River country, adding superior new areas for camping, fishing, and hiking, with another access to the Cascade Crest Trail. The North Cascades Highway, now authorized and being located under the authority of the Washington Legislature, will soon be added. This will open the loftiest and the broadest scenic terrain of the whole Cascade Range.

It should be noted, as an interpretation of modern trends, that the legislators now consider well both the commercial necessity and the access to scenic attractions in planning new roads and highways.

In the Northwest, a Retained Frontier

The Pacific Northwest is indeed fortunate in its wealth of recreational opportunity, much of it under virtual frontier conditions which have not yet vanished. The wilderness isolation that Daniel Boone knew in the Appalachians of 1775–1800 can still be discovered in much of the Northwest, often within sight of a modern transmontane highway. The unspoiled lakes and waterways, the maelstrom of canyons, peaks, and ranges, the far-flung tangle of forests, and the salt-water beaches and waterways are a recreational heritage that few residents of the Northwest would care to see dissipated.

In the proper enjoyment of this heritage there is ample room for the Northwesterner himself, as well as for thousands, perhaps for increasing millions, of visitors from parts of America where the frontier has become a thing of the past. Guests within our gates, sympathetic toward nature and trained in the art of outdoor living, are more than welcome. But the Northwest is resolutely determined to safeguard its recreational assets. Fortunately, the careless camper, the reckless hunter, the despoiler of natural scenery, are being educated to better outdoor manners. Properly managed and conserved, this frontier playground can be preserved in perpetuity as a source of national health and individual happiness.

Agriculture

Agriculture is the fundamental base for the support of over a million people in the Pacific Northwest. From nearly 200,000 farms come annually products worth about 2 billion dollars. Chapter 16 describes the many types and systems of farming used, and each of the following chapters, 17–23, is devoted to a major agricultural industry and its particular problems. The reclamation of aridlands and the development of methods for soil conservation have been previously described. Such improvements will add to the number of farmers and the value of agricultural production in future years.

CHAPTER 16

Farming Types and Systems

OTIS W. FREEMAN

The choice of the type of farming carried on in any particular section depends upon both natural and human factors. The natural factors include water supply, climate, topography, soil, prevalence of pests, plant or animal diseases, location, distance to market, etc. Among the human variables are price, both of land and crops, ownership and tenure of the operator, marketing facilities, distribution and shifting of population, laws, taxes, freight rates, etc. It should be noted that cause-and-effect relationships between types of farming and the associated factors are not always easily recognized. Generally, the results come from a combination of factors rather than one only, and some of the relationships may be difficult to determine. For example, factors like character of soil, relief, amount of water used for irrigation, and presence or absence of drainage may determine whether certain fields are impregnated with alkali, are so wet that they find use for pasture only, or may be used for various crops. The success factor or factors may be difficult to determine. Or, insect pests like the beet leaf hopper may spoil a sugar-beet region, as has happened in several parts of the Snake River Valley. Certain counties have had similar difficulties with the alfalfa weevil. The control of pests like the codling moth may add so much to the expense of growing apples that it becomes one factor in causing growers to cut down their trees and turn to some other crop. Morning-glory vines, tarweed, fanweed, and other injurious weeds sometimes become such pests that the economy of a district may be impaired. Increases in taxes and freight rates may force a change in crops grown; the same thing may result from collapse of prices, or competition with growers closer to markets. Laws that compel the washing of spray residue from apples or that penalize eggs and dairy products shipped into distant markets

285

also affect crop systems and compel changes by the farmers in order to secure economic safety.

Gradually, as the result of trial and error, farmers gained the needed experience and knowledge and learned the best crops and farming

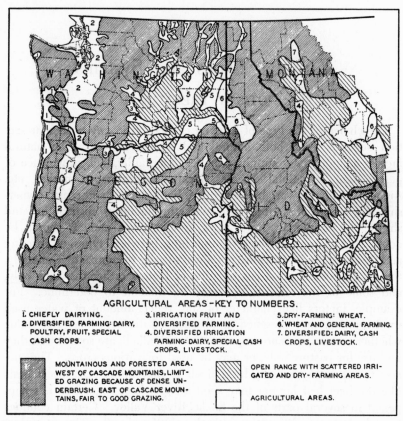

AGRICULTURAL AREAS – KEY TO NUMBERS.

1. CHIEFLY DAIRYING.
2. DIVERSIFIED FARMING: DAIRY, POULTRY, FRUIT, SPECIAL CASH CROPS.

3. IRRIGATION FRUIT AND DIVERSIFIED FARMING.
4. DIVERSIFIED IRRIGATION FARMING: DAIRY, SPECIAL CASH CROPS, LIVESTOCK.

5. DRY-FARMING: WHEAT.
6. WHEAT AND GENERAL FARMING.
7. DIVERSIFIED: DAIRY, CASH CROPS, LIVESTOCK.

MOUNTAINOUS AND FORESTED AREA. WEST OF CASCADE MOUNTAINS, LIMITED GRAZING BECAUSE OF DENSE UNDERBRUSH. EAST OF CASCADE MOUNTAINS, FAIR TO GOOD GRAZING.

OPEN RANGE WITH SCATTERED IRRIGATED AND DRY-FARMING AREAS.

AGRICULTURAL AREAS.

FIG. 31. Pacific Northwest types of farming. (*Pacific Northwest Regional Planning Commission.*)

systems adapted to the Northwest. Not infrequently the best results were obtained after careful experimentation, and plant and animal breeding, or by the introduction of new species from elsewhere. Cooperative marketing, the agricultural colleges and experiment stations, and regulations that helped insure quality produce are other factors that had effects on Northwest farm systems.

After discussing briefly the types of farming and farm systems in vogue in the Northwest, we shall describe the leading agricultural products, wheat, fruit, dairying, livestock, etc., in detail in later chapters. The charts showing farm-work schedules, Figs. 32A and 32B, drawn by Harold H. Rhodes, will be found highly instructive to study in connection with the various types of farming. In Chapter 11 there are also specific data on irrigated lands of the Northwest.

General Farming

General, or diversified, farming, as it is also called, is characterized by a combination of several crop and livestock enterprises. A survey in Idaho showed that 40 per cent of the income on general farms came from crops and 46 per cent from livestock and livestock products. This diversification is a sounder economy for most farmers than specialization on one product, since crop failure or low prices may bring financial disaster. General farms are quite widely distributed in the Northwest states. They are common in the Willamette Valley, where a single farm may grow wheat, oats, clover, and keep dairy cows, hogs, and poultry, and have an acre in small fruits or a small orchard of filberts or walnuts, and produce a few beef animals for sale each year. The general farm produces most of the food consumed by the operators, who also have the advantage of a variety of sources of income, since there is always something that can be sold to meet expenses. Many diversified farms have a wood lot to supply needed fuel and fence posts. A dairy enterprise is especially suitable, since it provides a regular cash income, and furnishes an outlet for farm-grown hay and grain, utilizes available pasture, furnishes manures to help maintain soil fertility, and distributes farm labor more evenly throughout the year.

Success of general farming depends greatly upon management, the owner making a more substantial income as operator than he could attain by leasing on shares or for cash rent to tenants. From 80 to 90 per cent of general farms in the Northwest are operated by owners or part owners.

In Washington general farming is most common in the northeast mountain valleys of Pend Oreille, Stevens, and Ferry counties, where farms average a quarter to a half section in size. In the irrigated sections of eastern Washington they are much smaller, 20 to 50 acres on the average. In western Washington small farms are the rule. Those farms devoted to general farming are also between 20 and 50 acres nearer the larger consuming centers, but are two or three times this size in more remote locations. This type of farming, well adapted

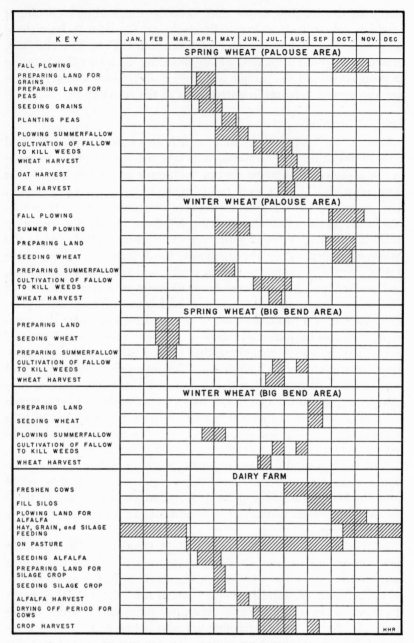

Fig. 32A.   Farm-work schedules.   Part I.

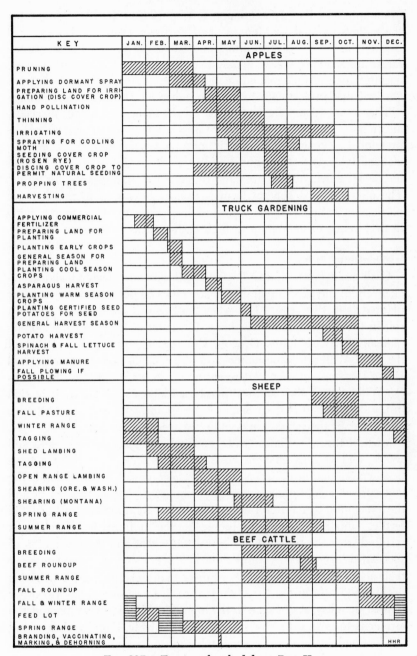

KEY	JAN.	FEB.	MAR.	APR.	MAY	JUN.	JUL.	AUG.	SEP.	OCT.	NOV.	DEC.
APPLES												
PRUNING												
APPLYING DORMANT SPRAY												
PREPARING LAND FOR IRRI- GATION (DISC COVER CROP)												
HAND POLLINATION												
THINNING												
IRRIGATING												
SPRAYING FOR CODLING MOTH												
SEEDING COVER CROP (ROSEN RYE)												
DISCING COVER CROP TO PERMIT NATURAL SEEDING												
PROPPING TREES												
HARVESTING												
TRUCK GARDENING												
APPLYING COMMERCIAL FERTILIZER												
PREPARING LAND FOR PLANTING												
PLANTING EARLY CROPS												
GENERAL SEASON FOR PREPARING LAND												
PLANTING COOL SEASON CROPS												
ASPARAGUS HARVEST												
PLANTING WARM SEASON CROPS												
PLANTING CERTIFIED SEED POTATOES FOR SEED												
GENERAL HARVEST SEASON												
POTATO HARVEST												
SPINACH & FALL LETTUCE HARVEST												
APPLYING MANURE												
FALL PLOWING IF POSSIBLE												
SHEEP												
BREEDING												
FALL PASTURE												
WINTER RANGE												
TAGGING												
SHED LAMBING												
TAGGING												
OPEN RANGE LAMBING												
SHEARING (ORE. & WASH.)												
SHEARING (MONTANA)												
SPRING RANGE												
SUMMER RANGE												
BEEF CATTLE												
BREEDING												
BEEF ROUNDUP												
SUMMER RANGE												
FALL ROUNDUP												
FALL & WINTER RANGE												
FEED LOT												
SPRING RANGE												
BRANDING, VACCINATING, MARKING, & DEHORNING												HHR

FIG. 32B.   Farm-work schedules.   Part II.

to mountain valleys, is a common system used in the Blue Mountains, the valleys of western Montana and northern Idaho, and on part of the irrigated land of the intermountain country. In Idaho general farms are found scattered widely over the state. The homestead laws account for the fact that most of them are 160 or 320 acres in size. On irrigated projects 40- to 80-acre general farms are prevalent.

The actual types of crops raised on diversified farms are markedly affected by the more specialized farms adjoining. In periods of depression the generalized farm is more self-sufficient than more specialized types and its greater number of enterprises permits emphasis on those which appear to offer the greatest opportunity for profit. The operator of a general farm is usually interested in possessing a permanent home with the expectation of a secure and modest living in preference to gambling on high cash returns from some specialty.

Cash-Grain Farms

Cash-grain farms of the Pacific Northwest are devoted almost exclusively to the production of wheat. Over 80 per cent of the acreage planted is in this crop. The wheatland consists of some of the best soil in the Northwest and includes the Palouse Hills and the sloping plateaus in Washington, Oregon, and Idaho, north and northeast of the Blue-Wallowa Mountains, and portions of the Waterville and Horse Heaven plateaus. There is some cash grain raised in the northern Willamette Valley and southeastern Idaho, especially by irrigation in the central and eastern Snake River Plains. Wheat farms also are important in the Clark Fork Valley of western Montana.

Most of the wheatland was taken for homesteads in the 1880's and 1890's, and various changes have occurred since then. There have been consolidation of farms, abandonment of submarginal land, the widespread substitution of power machinery for horses and men, and the recognition of erosion as a factor that requires control. In the fertile, subhumid Palouse the consolidation of farms into large units resulted from the profits made by raising wheat and the inclination of successful farmers to pyramid their holdings using profits to augment their acreage. In sections that are drier than the Palouse, wheat yields decline and a farm must contain two to five sections of land in order to provide adequate income to the operator. Here the problem of the farmer is to farm extensively and not intensively, thereby cheapening production by the use of power machinery so that a profit can be made on yields of wheat of eight to twelve bushels per acre.

Cash-grain farms have a comparatively simple organization which makes them readily adaptable to a system of tenant farming. Nearly half of the wheat farms in many sections are operated by tenants. Sometimes cash rent is paid, but most frequently a third of the crop is delivered to the owner. Experience shows that the share system better divides the risk between owner and tenant.

Livestock is usually a minor adjunct to a wheat farm, many of them having no horses, cows, or even poultry. Some farmers do not even bother with a garden or any crop except wheat. These men must purchase all their food, fuel for their machinery, and everything else they consume, paying for them from their one crop. A safer system of farming is to practice diversification, which progressive operators frequently do.

Some successful farmers keep livestock, but usually a wheat farmer keeps a cow or two, a pig, and a flock of poultry for his own use only. However, other men have found that a flock of a few score sheep can feed on the weeds in the summer fallow and on the wheat stubble, and pigs and turkeys can be fattened on the grain wasted by the combine in the fields. Even a few beef cattle or milch cows can be maintained on pastures that will utilize eroded land or other parts of farms unsuited to wheat. The fact that livestock can be raised as a by-product at small expense is becoming generally recognized by wheat farmers, and in the future it seems likely that they will practice much more diversification than they do at present. When that time comes, it is probable that farms will be reduced in size as the land will then be used more intensively.

A cash-grain section such as the Palouse, viewed from the air, presents a curious picture of bare fields of summer fallow, interspersed with green or yellow fields of grain, depending upon the time of year. Contour plowing and rearrangement of fields are beginning, but on the whole the divisions are at right angles, disregarding the hills which dominate the landscape. The highways, however, twist through the hills, with long straight stretches a comparative rarity. Farmsteads have generally good buildings, especially the houses in the better wheat sections. Barns are a minor feature, except where animal diversification is practiced. Usually there are sheds for the storage of machinery, but sometimes expensive tractors and combines are left exposed to the weather. Where rainfall declines, buildings tend to deteriorate; trading towns are also much more widely spaced than in the prosperous regions.

Crop-Specialty Farms

A crop-specialty farm is one from which 40 per cent or more of the value of all farm products is obtained from sugar beets, field peas, beans, hay, potatoes, hops, and other minor field crops. In Oregon specialty farms are numerous in the Willamette Valley; for example, there are 22,000 acres of hops, over half of the American total and equal to 18 per cent of the world's hop acreage. The hop yards near Moxee in Yakima County are an example of great concentration. The localities specializing on certain crops are mentioned in Chapter 20.

In Idaho and eastern Washington specialty farms most frequently occur in the irrigated sections. The average farm of this sort is characterized by the use of almost all the farmland for crop production with relatively small amounts in pasture or waste. Land values are relatively high, and in the irrigated sections crop-specialty farms average from 40 to 160 acres. Three-fourths of these farms in the Yakima Valley are 20 to 100 acres in size. Kittitas crop-specialty farms and those on dryland are somewhat larger. In northern Idaho and the Palouse dry-farming region, larger farms are the rule. Those in the eastern Palouse are mainly devoted to the raising of peas for seed. The large acreage devoted to alfalfa in the Snake River Valley and the Yakima Valley largely results from the demand for hay by the sheep raisers. During years of high returns from cash crops, the acreage in alfalfa tends to decrease. Some hay farms are found in the Puget Lowland, especially in Clark, Whatcom, and Skagit counties. In Idaho less than a third of the crop-specialty farms keep swine, but those usually have the offspring of two or three sows to market each year as a side line.

To succeed in crop-specialty farming the management should be in the hands of the owner. Where farms are leased they are devoted largely to annual crops that more readily lend themselves to tenant farming. Hops, a perennial, are almost invariably produced by owners.

Some specialty crops leave their own cultural features. For example, the alfalfa farms have numerous haystacks or enormous piles of baled hay, the latter protected by rude sheds or covering of boards and canvas. A characteristic of a potato district is the huge storage cellars, many of which are owned by cooperative associations. The hop yards have their wire trellises running from post to post to support the vines and homely shedlike kilns in which the hops are dried. During the season hundreds of pickers live in temporary and often nondescript camps, which once seen form a never-to-be-forgotten feature of the area.

Fruit Farms

The fruit farms can be divided conveniently into the orchard fruits and the small fruits. The location of these fruit regions is discussed in Chapter 18 on orchard fruits and in Chapter 19 on small fruits. Fruit farms are generally small. In the Wenatchee Valley the apple orchards average 15 acres. About 70 per cent of the fruit farms in the Yakima Valley are 10 to 50 acres in size. Of course, not all of a farm is necessarily in fruit. In the Yakima Valley diversification is more common than in the Wenatchee Valley. Berry farms for the most part are small. In western Washington they usually are 3 to 20 acres in size, with many of the farms under 3 acres. The large amount of intensive hand labor, high value of the producing land, high taxes and water charges, and other expenses all favor small acreages for both tree fruits and berry farms. Orchard management needs both personal interest and experience, and this constant attention and careful handling are best given by an owner, tenants rarely proving satisfactory. However, some large apple properties are successfully handled by managers.

Both orchard and berry farms are small, resulting in a compact population pattern, with trading centers every few miles. Most homes in the towns have a family orchard and small fruits. Outside the city limits, the fruit orchards are larger and the houses somewhat more scattered, but otherwise there is often little to show where the town leaves off and the country begins. Neat houses with all modern improvements, flowers, and yards are characteristic. Unfortunately in many orchard districts garages are preferred to poultry houses or cow sheds. In fact, many fruit farms produce nothing but one or several types of fruits and have no cows or chickens and often no garden. In times of low fruit prices or other handicaps, it may prove impossible for a man raising nothing but fruit to meet his expenses, whereas the operator who diversifies and devotes only a part of his acreage to fruit may not make so much money in boom times but is in a much sounder economic position. A fair degree of diversification is practiced in parts of the Yakima Valley and the Willamette Valley, resulting in comparatively less debt and a sounder base for the community than if there were excessive specialization. In Washington during the depression of the 1930's several thousand acres of mature bearing apple trees were pulled out on the marginal lands where expenses could not be met during times of low prices. Valuations of fruitland are high compared with that devoted to most other crops; and considerable investment is required to own such a place and much capital is required to finance the crops. Since transportation is vital for the marketing of fruit, the only land that is used for its commercial production is provided with such facilities.

Truck Farming

Although small areas devoted to truck farming are found adjacent to every large city in the Northwest, there are certain districts where truck gardening ranks high among the farm systems. In Walla Walla and Franklin counties in Washington truck farms constitute 10 per cent of all farms within the county. In Walla Walla County over three-fourths of the truck farms are 3 to 19 acres in size; in Franklin County the majority are 20 to 40 acres. Onions rank first as a truck crop in Walla Walla County; melons, lettuce, and asparagus in Franklin County. Other sections important for truck gardens are the Puyallup Valley and the Sumner and Kent districts, the latter famous for its lettuce. The area tributary to Portland contains more truck farms than any other district of Oregon. Commercial vegetable production requires large amounts of hand labor, and, although the land yields crops of large value, considerable expense is needed to make it so produce. The work is hard, and oftentimes Oriental and recent immigrant labor is employed. The homes of the hired workers are usually little better than shacks, even the owner may not occupy a first-class dwelling, but the land is always beautifully maintained, a new crop being planted almost before the first is harvested.

Dairying

Dairy farms are widely distributed in the Northwest, and the income from dairying makes this industry the leading one in many sections. Dairying is carried on in a variety of situations. Among them are (1) neighborhood of all cities and towns where demand for fresh milk exists; (2) the green pastures along the Pacific Coast, where soil and climate are ideal for dairying and unsuited for most other farming; (3) irrigated land in the dry interior sections of the Northwest, based both on irrigated pastures and alfalfa; and (4) mountain valleys and other nonirrigated meadows and pastures unsuited for money crops but available for pasture and hay.

The predominant dairy-producing region of the Northwest is in western Washington and Oregon in a belt of rainfall which has 40 to

80 inches per year. The mountain land may still be in forests but the lowlands have been cleared; the long growing season gives pastures a carrying capacity much greater than nonirrigated ones east of the mountains. Summer precipitation is low, but pastures along the river bottom lands receive seepage from upland areas, providing sufficient moisture for sustained plant growth. In average production of milk per cow, the Pacific Coast area ranks first among the dairy regions of the Union. Holstein cows are preferred because of their heavy milk production, although herds of Jerseys, Guernseys, Ayrshires, and other breeds are also kept. Much milk is sold to the urban population, which totals 1.5 million people in Washington, Oregon, and British Columbia. In addition, large condenseries and butter and cheese factories utilize the surplus. A comparatively small amount of concentrates and hay for winter feeding makes the cost of producing milk comparatively low. Most of the dairy farms in the Puget Sound district have 20 to 100 acres. In Oregon, in addition to a widespread dairy industry in the Willamette Valley, the coastal lowlands valleys, especially at Tillamook, are of great importance. Along the Pacific the dairy industry takes precedence over all other forms of farming put together.

Dairying on irrigated land is important in the Yakima, Kittitas, and Walla Walla valleys in Washington, the Deschutes Valley and the Umatilla district in Oregon, in the central and western portions of the Snake River Valley and the Bear Lake district in southeastern Idaho. Usually in irrigated districts, some land receives seepage from adjoining irrigated tracts, making it too wet for crop purposes but available for pasture. In addition, some natural and planted pastures are both irrigated for the dairy cows. On some farms devoted to growing alfalfa, the stall feeding of cows is practiced the year around. Irrigated dairy farms are comparatively small in size, half of those of Walla Walla County running between 20 and 100 acres; three-fourths of those in Benton County are 10 to 49 acres in size. The dairy farm is usually characterized by a large and well-built barn for shelter and storage of fodder, a milk shed, and other buildings, but silos are relatively unimportant if compared with the Middle West farms.

The broad mountain valleys of northeastern Washington and northern Idaho, the scablands and hilly tracts near Spokane, the valleys and high benchlands in the Blue Mountain section, and hilly foothill farms in all the states find in dairying a logical source of income. Terrace areas usually have sufficient rainfall for pasturage the majority of the year, with some bottom land or other moderately level fields on which permanent hay or grain hay can be raised. When cream is shipped, the distance to market is not so important as for fresh milk, and shipments made every few days may take care of the product adequately. The skim milk is available for pig, poultry, and calf feed; pork, veal, eggs, chickens, and other fowl are sold to supplement the income from the cream. An occasional baby beef may also be matured. The carrying capacity of these farms depends upon the amount of hay that can be produced for winter use. Most of the farms do not raise enough grain and have to purchase concentrated feed, but there would be no profit in producing the milk if the hay had to be purchased. The smaller farms still practice hand milking. Only the larger places commonly have milking machines.

Dairy farms require labor throughout the year, with the peak for labor coming during the haying season. A steady income is earned by the dairymen, but the work is monotonous and vacations are difficult to arrange as cows require milking twice daily. The unirrigated dairy farms in the interior are naturally larger than those in irrigated sections or on the more humid west side. The common size for the dairy farms mentioned is 160 to 320 acres. Like dairy farms elsewhere, the barn is generally larger than the house, as befits the requirements. Usually several other buildings to house the calves, pigs, and poultry are in evidence. Gardens and small home orchards are common adjuncts. The work is confining but gives a greater degree of security than most other forms of agriculture.

Animal-Specialty Farms

An animal-specialty farm differs from a stock ranch in that the stock are produced primarily by farm feeding on the specialty farm and by grazing methods on the stock ranch. The cattle, sheep, and hogs on animal-specialty farms are generally maintained and fattened on farm-raised feed and farm pastures, although concentrated feed may be purchased by some feeders. In Idaho nearly 80 per cent of all animal-specialty farms are irrigated. In Washington most of those in Yakima County are irrigated, but in the Okanogan Highlands such farms are commonly nonirrigated. Ferry County has the highest percentage of farms of this type in Washington, the average size being a quarter to a half section. Since the management of such a farm is an important consideration, 85 per cent or more of the animal-specialty farms are operated by owners or part owners. Investments in machinery and the employment of machines are relatively small on the   animal-specialty farms, but there are naturally numerous buildings for the shelter of livestock. In southern Idaho sheep rank with beef cattle and hogs on animal-specialty farms, but in other parts of the Northwest beef cattle and hogs are the more important animals. Numerous farms in the Willamette Valley and in northeastern Oregon are of the animal-specialty type. The keeping of pigs there is quite closely associated with dairying. An animal-specialty farm resembles general farming except in the relative value of the animal products. Milk produced is 40 per cent or more of the income on the farm, whereas in general farming the income from the crops and animal products including milk is about equally divided. Animal-specialty farms may grade into cash-grain and dairy places as well as general farms.

A particular type of animal-specialty farm is devoted to raising foxes or other fur producers. Domestic production of furs is a comparatively new enterprise and one adapted to land of no value for agriculture. The food for the animals can be fish, inferior meat, and cereals, and the shelters can be constructed on any sort of land. Fur farms are found scattered over the entire Northwest but are most frequently located near towns and cities in Oregon around Portland, Eugene, Astoria, and Coos Bay. Northwestern Montana, northern Idaho, the Spokane region, and the northern Puget Sound are other sections having numerous fur farms. It is a common industry too in British Columbia and Alaska. In the latter territory off-shore islands where the foxes and mink live in semicaptivity are favored situations.

Stock Ranches

Stock ranches in general are of large size, comparatively few having less than 500 acres, with a section as large as 5000 acres being more common. Some very large ranches exist in the Northwest, and, whereas the acreage is large, their actual number in any one state is comparatively few. The largest stock ranch in Washington is between Sprague and Lamont and includes about 110,000 acres, not all in one continuous block of land but stretching along for a distance of nearly 30 miles. Stock ranches of more than 10,000 acres include only 2 or 3 per cent of the total number in Idaho. Large ranches are fairly common in eastern Oregon especially in the semidesert areas. In Washington they are of significance in Okanogan, Ferry, Kittitas, and Yakima counties. A favorite location is near to range in the national forest for summer feeding, with available winter feed in the irrigated valleys that have comparatively mild temperatures during the winter. The sheep ranches in the Columbia Plateau, southern Idaho, and southeastern Oregon use the desert browse for spring feed during the lambing season. When the browse and other herbage become dry and brown in the hot summer and would be nearly worthless, herds of the animals are enjoying grazing in the high mountain forest. They return to the lowland pastures and hay fields for the winter.

The value of the stock ranch is very low per acre. The requirements for grazing per animal are high, often between 40 and 100 acres per animal unit (interpreted as 1 cow or 4 sheep). Some of the stock ranches are merely winter feeding grounds and lambing quarters for sheep, with most of the grazing being secured on national forests and other pastures. Most of the cultivated land, a considerable proportion of which is irrigated, is devoted to hay. Remoteness from railroads is unimportant as the livestock can be driven long distances to shipping points. The scablands and other rough land in southeastern Washington, and the canyon slopes and dry rolling plateau areas of Oregon, useless for other purposes, are available for stock ranches. In the early days these were frequently built to their present size by the cow hands taking up homesteads adjacent to the home ranch and later selling the land to their employers. In deserts the control of water was a primary objective in the land ownership. Large stock ranches are seldom homogeneous but rather are scattered over a considerable area, with each holding controlling water supply. By this means, control over large areas of the public domain could be exercised.

The organization of grazing districts under the Taylor Grazing Act now enables the government to exercise control over the range industry. Grazing districts cover all southeastern and much of central Oregon, and one exists just south of the Columbia River in the extreme north-central part of the state. There are also grazing districts in the southern half of Idaho and western Montana, where large enough areas of public domain exist to make it worth while. None have yet been organized in Washington.

Low prices and other bad economic conditions have compelled the liquidation of some old-time stock ranches, but still the range industry in Idaho, Oregon, and Montana is more important than is sometimes recognized because most of the activity occurs in the more remote sections and apart from the better-known agricultural regions of the Pacific Northwest. Machinery, aside from that used in making hay, is not much required on a stock ranch. More than 80 per cent of the ranches are managed by owners or part owners. The buildings may sprawl over a considerable area and include numerous corrals and low sheds, the home ranch usually having the largest area of hayland the place possesses. Trading centers are few and widely scattered. Stock ranches frequently are located 100 miles or more from shipping points and main supply centers.

Poultry Farms

A poultry farm offers a striking contrast to the huge stock ranch inasmuch as most of the farms devoted to this industry cover only a few acres. In Washington the more important poultry sections are those of the Puget Sound Basin, including the island counties. A common size for these farms is 10 to 40 or 50 acres, but in King, Pierce, and Snohomish counties half of the farms are 9 acres or less in size. Even on the larger places only a few acres would be actually devoted to the chicken business. In general, the main poultry-producing centers of Washington share much the same area as do the dairy farms. Favorable climatic conditions, rather low price for land, cooperative marketing, and the fact that little capital is required to start in the poultry industry have resulted in a phenomenal growth since 1920.

Poultry raisers often come from among persons who have retired or been displaced in commercial or industrial life of the coast cities. A very strong cooperative association has greatly assisted in the marketing of the produce, and its substantial branches are prominent among the commercial buildings of cities in the poultry districts. The poultry houses and the flocks of active white Leghorn hens are prominent features of the districts. The dwellings are usually modest. Poultry raisers commonly have a garden and perhaps a fruit orchard and a cow but seldom are able to raise much of the feed for their flocks, which provide all the cash income. The outlay for feed is usually the largest expense. Yakima and Spokane valleys in eastern Washington are active in the poultry business but not nearly so important as the western area. In Oregon the Willamette Valley is the leader, where many farms, mostly small, are devoted to this industry. Commercial egg production ordinarily brings in about 8 per cent of the gross agricultural income of Oregon. Poultry farms, including turkeys, are locally important in Idaho, and a minor industry in western Montana. They are also of general occurrence in the vicinity of cities everywhere in the Northwest. It is probably needless to say that most poultry farms are operated by owners.

Self-Sufficing Farms

Self-sufficing farms are those on which half or more of the total value of all farm products is used by the operator's family. These self-sufficing farms are found in greatest numbers in the timbered or cutover areas of the Northwest, as the Puget Sound Lowland, and mountain valleys tributary to the north Idaho panhandle and western Montana. They also occur on the cutover land of the coast region of Oregon and in the foothills about the Willamette Valley. Where physical conditions permit, it is possible by planting a variety of crops and keeping several kinds of animals to make a farm nearly self-sufficient. High land values, mortgage payments, and taxes which require substantial cash payments make it difficult for a farmer to live on a self-sufficing farm. Hence, in general, this type of farm is located beyond the immediate neighborhood of cities and is seldom found within the areas of established substantial agriculture. The personal factor is also important, and in general the operators of self-sufficient farms, who are also nearly always the owners, are those who are either willing or forced by necessity to live a "simple life." They must be contented with a somewhat lower standard of living than is found in those types of farming that provide a larger cash income. The quarter-section farm is the more common, but many are of smaller size, especially where purchased from logging companies or other corporations.

Most of the self-sufficing farms are nonirrigated, and where irrigation is practiced it is generally a local affair with water taken from some mountain stream or spring. The value per acre is low. The farm may include much rough land and be inaccessible because of distance from towns and poor roads. The buildings are often of home construction and represent only a small investment. Livestock is seldom more than enough to supply family needs; 2 or 3 horses, a cow or two, a pig, and a small flock of poultry are about all, the number of animals being limited by the comparatively small amount of hay and grain produced and by the disinclination or inability of the owner-operator to go into the business on an extensive scale. Hand methods of clearing are commonly used because funds are lacking for hiring or for purchase of power and machinery. The clearing of land and preparation for crops therefore proceed slowly. Those living on self-sufficing farms are frequently men who have saved a limited amount of capital from logging or industrial occupations and, through age, sickness, or unemployment, have decided to seek independence on a small farm. Another type may be called "residual," and consists of those left behind by a shifting industry like logging. With a few cows, pigs, chickens, some hayland, a large garden, small family orchard, and a wood lot from which some cord wood may be produced for sale, it is possible to provide a fair standard of living with a very small cash outlay.

Part-Time Farms

The part-time farm is one on which the operator spends 150 days or more off the farm in other than farmwork. Part-time farms are of greatest significance near large cities and highly developed industries, where men live who like to live in the country while employed in factories or service occupations in the city. Altogether, thousands of families live on part-time farms. Even in Idaho, where urban population is small, a survey showed 2570 part-time farms in the state, representing 6 per cent of the total. In western Washington and the Willamette Valley this number is greatly exceeded. The income derived from part-time farms is not adequate to support a family, but that is generally unimportant as the homeowner expects to earn much of his expenses elsewhere. Some part-time farms are associated with the logging industry, and then the farm, in size and general organization, resembles the self-sufficient farms in the area. But near the cities the part-time farms seldom exceed more than a few acres in size. Oftentimes the buildings have been wholly or partially built by the owner. The garden, poultry, a cow, and berry patch supply much of the food for the family and may furnish a surplus for sale. This is a fluctuating farm class and may shift to self-sufficient if business is bad.

Summary

From the combined effects of numerous factors, eleven well-defined types or separate systems of farm enterprises have developed in the Pacific Northwest: (1) general, (2) cash-grain, (3) crop-specialty, (4) orchard and small fruits, (5) truck, (6) dairy, (7) animal-specialty, (8) stock ranch, (9) poultry, (10) self-sufficing, and (11) part-time.

REFERENCES

"Agricultural Resources and Factors Affecting Their Use," *Idaho Agricultural Experiment Station Bulletin* 207, Moscow.

Baker, O. E., "Agricultural Regions of North America," *Economic Geography*, Vol. 7, pp. 109–153, 325–364; Vol. 8, pp. 325–377.

"Graphic Summary of Agriculture and Land Use in Oregon," *Agricultural Experiment Station Circular* 114, O. S. C., Corvallis, 1935.

Johnson, Neil W., and M. H. Saunderson, "Types of Farming in Montana," *Montana Agricultural Station Bulletin* 328, Bozeman, 1936.

"Nature and Distribution of Types of Farming in Washington," *Washington Agricultural Experiment Station Bulletin* 301, Pullman, 1934.

Physical and Economic Geography of Oregon, Oregon State System of Higher Education, pp. 146–208, 1940.

"Present Land Uses—Washington," *Washington Agricultural Experiment Station Bulletin* 288, Pullman, 1933.

"Trends in Agriculture in Washington, 1900–1930," *Washington Agricultural Experiment Station Bulletin* 300, Pullman, 1934.

"Types of Farming in Idaho," *Idaho Agricultural Experiment Station Bulletin* 208, Moscow, 1934.

CHAPTER

17

Wheat and the Minor Cereals

WALLACE T. BUCKLEY

The production of small grains, wheat, oats, barley, and rye, constitutes an important segment of the agricultural economy of the Pacific Northwest. As a source of farm income, and in terms of acreage, this group of cereals holds first rank among the field crops. Of the group, wheat is by far the most important in both respects. About two-thirds of the small-grain acreage is cropped to wheat, and its annual value is normally five times the combined value of barley, oats, and rye.

The pre-eminent position held by wheat is the resultant of variable economic factors, operating over the years in a more or less static environmental framework. The pioneers of a century ago brought with them crops and cultural practices from the homeland, and custom played an important part in early crop selection. But, in a region of considerable diversity in soil, climate, and topography, the force of previous experience and training gave way to new enterprises or combinations of enterprises on the farms. As the frontier of settlement moved across the semiarid grasslands of the Columbia Plateau, the farmer, faced with the problem of selecting a crop or combination of crops, reacted to the basic principle of "comparative advantage" [1] in order to maximize his income from the factors of production under his control. Except in the very beginning of tillage of the Columbia Basin when subsistence farming was necessary, the "dry-land" farmers have found that wheat provides the best economic returns. Although

---

[1] This is "that an area tends to specialize in the products in which its ratio of advantage is highest, or its ratio of disadvantage is least, exchanging these for those from other areas which have an advantage in other products." Walter W. Wilcox and Williard W. Cochrane, *Economics of American Agriculture*, p. 5, Prentice-Hall, 1951.

"comparative advantage" is a variable phenomenon, neither economic nor physical changes since the occupation of the land has materially altered this condition. No such advantage as that enjoyed by wheat prevailed for the other small grains and they have had but limited development, generally as subsidiary crops.

Conditions of soil, climate, and surface favorable for wheat culture were found in the Columbia Basin of eastern Washington, eastern Oregon, northern Idaho, and in the Snake River Plain of southern Idaho. Here is the "wheat country," characterized by large farms, the use of machinery for virtually all operations, a low ratio of labor per unit of land, and a tendency, particularly in the drier areas, toward a "one-crop" farming system.

The Rise of Wheat Production

Wheat growing began with the occupation of the Willamette in the 1840's. It developed rapidly from a local subsistence crop to a commodity that entered into both regional and interregional trade. The growing towns in the Willamette Valley, the boom prices in numerous mining camps of the interior that flourished for a time, and the California market were the principal outlets for the pioneers. The rapidity and ease with which a crop could be matured, its relative nonperishability, and its ready disposal for cash were all significant for the development of wheat.

Commercial wheat farming on a larger scale came when the center of production shifted to the Columbia Basin. The ratification of the Indian treaties in 1859 opened the interior for settlement, but for a number of years, open-range stock raising dominated the grasslands of the interior.

Farming, other than for subsistence, was severely handicapped by slow and costly overland transportation. Measures to improve the accessibility of the interior were undertaken as early as 1851, when a portage tramway was built around the Columbia River Cascades. In 1863, the Celilo-Dalles portage railroad was completed and the Baker Railroad from Walla Walla to the Columbia River was in operation by 1875. Large-scale commercial wheat growing on the interior grasslands came with the completion of the transcontinental railroads which made both regional and interregional markets more accessible. The Northern Pacific was completed to the Coast in 1883, the Union Pacific, via the Oregon Short Line, in 1884, and the Great Northern reached Puget Sound in 1893. Branch-line construction soon provided haulage facilities to most parts of the interior.

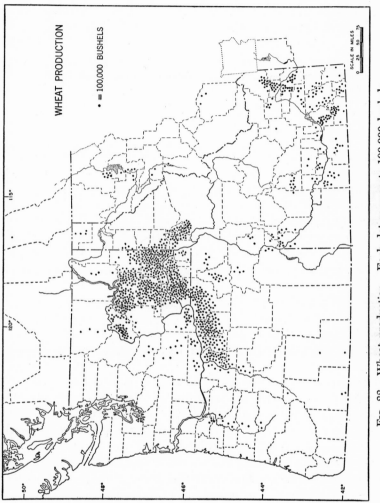

FIG. 33. Wheat production. Each dot represents 100,000 bushels.

The Willamette Valley led in early wheat growing; followed by expansion into Eastern Oregon and Washington after 1870. Oregon's leadership was maintained until 1894 when Washington forged into first place, a condition that continues to the present, increasing until about 1920, but Oregon's wheat lands have become stabilized at approximately 1 million acres (Fig. 34).

In contrast to Oregon, Washington wheat, with unimportant exceptions, has always been associated with the so-called Columbia

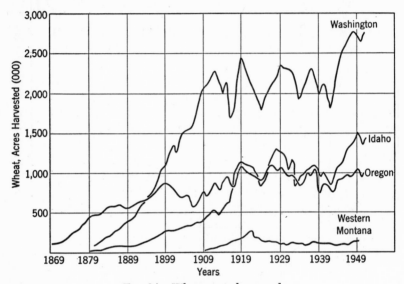

FIG. 34. Wheat acres harvested.

Plateau. From less than 200,000 acres in 1880, Washington's area in wheat increased tenfold in 30 years. Between 1910 and 1940, the harvested acreage averaged about 2.1 million acres. During and since the second World War, the trend in acreage has been upward, with an all-time high in 1951 when 2,744,000 acres of wheat were harvested.

Wheat acreage in Idaho expanded at a fairly uniform rate until a total of 600,000 acres was reached in 1916. Stimulated by high war prices, Idaho wheat acreage doubled by 1919. After 1920, as in Washington and Oregon, wheat acreage stabilized at about 1 million acres. Demands associated with World War II and the postwar years brought a second period of rapid increase to a record high of about 1.5 million acres.

Wheat acreage in the 14 counties of Western Montana reached a peak in 1921, when 285,000 acres were harvested. In subsequent years, the cropped land leveled off at 100,000 acres.

The heart of the wheat country, with some 80 per cent of the crop, covers the eastern portion of the Columbia Basin (Fig. 33). On the west the limits of wheat culture are set, generally, by the 10-inch isohyet—a crescentic boundary extending northwestward into Douglas County, Washington, and southwestward to include the Horse Heaven district of south-central Washington and the John-Day-Deschutes section of north-central Oregon. A secondary center is found on the Snake River Plain. In the counties comprising the wheat country, wheat occupies more than 50 per cent of the cropland. In some of these counties, a virtual one-crop farm economy has been achieved with more than 95 per cent of the cultivated acreage in wheat (Fig. 35).

Minor areas tilled in the same fashion are found in intermontane basins and valleys of northern Idaho, western Montana, and the Blue Mountains of Oregon.

The average annual wheat crop, over the 10-year period 1941–50, was 122 million bushels harvested from some 4.8 million acres (Table 1). These figures represent about 10 per cent of the nation's crop

TABLE 1

AVERAGE ANNUAL WHEAT PRODUCTION AND HARVESTED ACREAGE
1941–50

State	Acres Harvested	Bushels	Peak Production Bushels	Year
Washington	2,407,000	63,905,000	79,268,000	1948
Idaho	1,363,000	32,000,000	38,106,000	1949
Oregon	900,000	23,125,000	27,818,000	1949
Western Montana *	110,000	2,600,000	....	....

* Estimated for 14 western counties.

from but 7 per cent of the wheatlands, a reflection of the excellence of the physical base for wheat farming and the efficiency of the techniques practiced in the Pacific Northwest.[2]

[2] The average annual yield per acre of wheat for the 20-year period 1931–50 for the United States was 15 bushels; for the Pacific Northwest, 23 bushels.

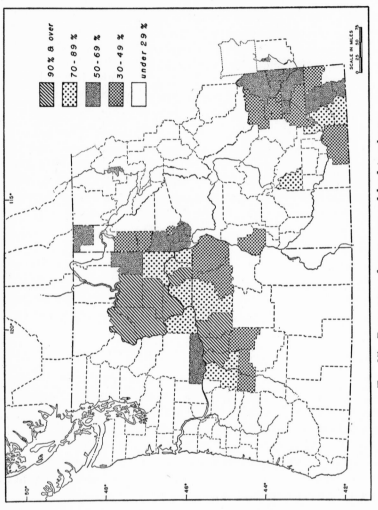

FIG. 35. Percentage of gross cropped land in wheat.

Areas for Wheat

The commercial wheat region of the Columbia Basin may be divided into two zones, on the basis of differences in annual precipitation. The eastern, subhumid zone includes the wheatlands of the Palouse and those immediately south of the canyons of the Clearwater and Snake rivers in Idaho, southeastern Washington, and the Pendleton district of northeastern Oregon. This zone has an average annual precipitation of 15 inches on its western margin and 20 inches or more on the east and south. Where typically developed, it is a maturely dissected hill country with the local relief generally less than 400 feet. Some of the cultivated slopes in this steeply rolling area are in excess of 50 per cent. Annual cropping is common in the subhumid zone, with this system most prevalent on the wetter, eastern margin.

The western, semiarid zone extends from the Big Bend district in north-central Washington southward to include the Horse Heaven area of south-central Washington and the wheatlands of north-central Oregon. There the average annual precipitation ranges from 15 inches on the east to 10 inches on the west. The topography varies from nearly level to gently rolling and hilly. The wheat-fallow system is typical of the semiarid zone.

The wheat region of southern Idaho is included in the semiarid zone as the precipitation here averages less than 15 inches. On its broad benches and plains, the wheat-fallow system is practiced, but dry-farming is supplemented by irrigation of wheat which accounts for almost one-half of the southern Idaho crop.

Farm Size

Evidence of the farm-settlement pattern resulting from the homestead influence persists today in the "wheat country." Commercial farms are generally multiples of the original 160-acre homestead unit. Farm sizes in the subhumid zone varied from 100 to more than 2000 crop acres, with a tendency for units of 160, 320, 480, and 640 acres.[3] The average farm size increased from 360 crop acres in 1935 to about 440 acres in 1950. This was accompanied by a decrease in 16 years of about 20 per cent in the number of farms. The decrease occurred chiefly through consolidation of small and medium-sized farms. Larger farms have remained more or less constant in size since 1935. The

[3] E. B. Hurd and O. L. Brough, Jr., "Farm Size and Land Use in the Wheat-Pea Area of Washington and Idaho, 1935–50," *Station Circular* 169, September, 1951, State College of Washington, Agricultural Experiment Station, Pullman.

shift away from the smaller farm units resulted from the use of more machinery but less labor as the farm size increased.

Consolidation of farm units has been carried farther in the semiarid than in the subhumid zone. In Whitman County, Washington, the core of the Palouse region, the average farm is 670 acres. In Adams County, adjoining Whitman County on the west, and in the semiarid zone, the average farm is 1834 acres. Maximum size is found in Morrow and Gilliam counties of north-central Oregon, where the average farm unit is 2195 and 3165 acres, respectively. Optimum operating economies become more effective on larger farms in the wheat-fallow area than in the continuous-cropping districts of the subhumid zone.[4]

Cropping Systems

The most desirable lands, those taken first by the homesteaders in the interior, were those of the grass covered Palouse hills. Cultivation began in the valley flats, but soon fields were extended up the steeper slopes. After the subhumid lands came into private ownership, the frontier of settlement moved into the semiarid lands. Over the years the dry edge of the wheat country has expanded and contracted with variations in rainfall and in wheat prices. This alternately caused both settlement and abandonment of marginal wheatlands. The desert periphery is in sharp contrast to the permanence of the economy of the more humid portions of the wheat country.

The first "breaking" of the grasslands was generally preceded by a burning-off of the surface accumulation of grassy material to make the initial turning of the sod less difficult. Different types of walking plows were used. The peg-tooth drag harrow was used to prepare a smooth, finely pulverized seedbed, but some seeding was done in unharrowed sod. From one to several such operations generally followed the plowing and preceded the cropping of the land.[5] Annual cropping with wheat, typical of the pioneer farming system, left problems. Weeds became increasingly troublesome and yields decreased. As the wheat farmers became aware of the merits and techniques of summer fallowing, the practice was incorporated in the farming system and afforded a solution to declining yields and weed infestation.

---

[4] What is probably the largest wheat farm in the Pacific Northwest is located in the Horse Heaven district of south-central Washington, where 100,000 acres are operated under one management.

[5] W. A. Rockie, "Man's Effect on the Palouse," *Geographical Review*, January, 1939, p. 38.

According to Rockie,[6] in the first decade of occupation, an empire of grass became an empire of wheat, but the second decade saw the empire of wheat changed into a checkerboard of wheat and fallow. The technique of summer fallowing included the cultivation of the idle fields during the summer months for the purpose of weed control and to maintain a dust mulch that conserved the soil moisture by retarding evaporation. Crop residue, stubble and straw, which interfered with the attainment of a smooth, dusty field surface was disposed of by turning the fields in the autumn following harvest.

Repeated pulverization of the soils under the wheat-fallow system has resulted in new problems for the dry-land farmer. Most serious has been the depletion of the organic content of the soil. From this has come a nitrogen deficiency and a compaction of the soil which, because of reduced moisture absorption capacity, has increased susceptibility to erosion.

The gradual decline in soil fertility and destruction of the soil itself through erosion have been more or less concealed by the fact that during the 58-year period (1879 to 1937) the per acre wheat yields for the Pacific Northwest increased from 18.9 to 19.9 bushels.[7] The increase in per acre yields has been achieved by a variety of factors: improved methods of cultivation; new types of machinery, the tractor, which permits better timing of farm operations; and improved varieties of wheat.

There has been an increasing awareness of the destructive nature of the wheat-fallow and continuous cropping systems. Extensive research by Federal and state agencies has developed a conservation program designed to restore or increase, if possible, the organic content of the soil, and to reduce to a minimum the loss of soil from erosion. Although acceptance of the conservation principle is general, its effective application is not universal.

Expert opinion is divided as to the effect of applied conservation on the net income of wheat farmers. Conclusive proof that conservation practices would show a more or less immediate increase, or at best no decrease, in net farm income would probably cause a revolution in wheat tillage methods.

THE USE OF NITROGEN FERTILIZER. The cropping systems of the wheat country, wheat-fallow in the semiarid zone and various com-

[6] Rockie, op. cit., p. 39.

[7] Ben H. Pubols and Carl P. Heisig, "Historical and Geographic Aspects of Wheat Yields in Washington," Bulletin 355, December, 1937, p. 12, State College of Washington, Agricultural Experiment Station.

binations of wheat-fallow, wheat-pea, or annual cropping in the sub-humid zone, have resulted in a general depletion of the soil organic matter. This depletion lessened the supply of nitrogen to a point where the productive capacity of the soil has been impaired. Where soil-building legumes, principally alfalfa and sweet clover, are included in a crop rotation the nitrogen depletion can be checked; this practice is not general. More common is the plowing under of stubble and straw for the purpose of increasing the supply of organic matter and nitrogen. The incorporation of these residues may result in a decline in yield of the following crop as the available nitrogen is reduced temporarily during the period of decay of the plant material in the soil. The possibility of correcting nitrogen deficiencies by the application of fertilizer has been the subject of study. From preliminary experiments, it appears that applications of nitrogen combined with plowing under of crop residues are profitable, but few farmers as yet follow this practice.

Winter and Spring Wheat

Both spring and winter wheat are planted in the wheat country, but no distinctive regions may be delineated as the acreage seeded to each type and its location varies greatly from year to year. Winter wheat is generally preferred as it usually out-yields the spring-sown varieties. In years when fall moisture is favorable, winter wheat is sown. If moisture conditions are unfavorable, seeding is deferred until spring. Another factor that causes great variations in the ratio of winter to spring wheat is the practice of reseeding to spring wheat those fields of winter wheat that have been damaged by winter killing or other causes.

Unfavorable moisture conditions and winter damage may happen anywhere in the wheat country, but the hazards tend to occur most frequently in the semiarid zone; hence, it is here that spring wheat tends to reach its greatest importance.

VARIETIES. Of the hundred known varieties, eleven accounted for almost all the Pacific Northwest wheat seeded in 1950. The winter varieties and their percentage of total production were: Elgin, 28.27; Turkey, 20.25; Rex, 11; Golden, 9.5; and Hymar, 6.4. The spring wheats and their related positions were: Federation, 6.2; Baart, 5.6; and Idaed, 2.1.

Preference in varieties tends to change. New varieties better adapted to regional differences in climatic and soil conditions have been developed by the State Colleges and the U. S. Department of

Agriculture or have been introduced from abroad. The continuing research is directed toward finding or developing new wheats that will better meet the requirements of producers and processors. Improvements sought are those having to do with growth habits, disease resistance, harvesting characteristics, and milling and baking qualities.[8]

Wheat Enemies

Numerous insects and diseases prey upon the growing wheat. Vagaries of weather also affect growth and yields. Some years show small damage; in other years the injury is great.

Winter killing of fall-sown grain results from several causes, including lack of snow cover, drying winds, and extreme diurnal range of temperatures, especially in early spring. Drought, wind and water erosion, late spring frosts, lodging of the stalks from strong winds and heavy rains, and occasional hail storms are other injurious effects of the weather. Hot, dry winds when the wheat heads are soft and green may cause shrinkage in yields of many bushels per acre.

Cutworms, locusts, grasshoppers, wireworms, and the Hessian fly are among the insect enemies. Cutworms and grasshoppers are controlled by the use of poisoned bran. Sometimes rodents destroy much grain.

Smut, rust, and certain mildews are among the diseases of wheat, but the development of smut- and rust-resistant varieties has greatly reduced damage. For example, in 1920, 50 per cent of all wheat shipments from the Pacific Northwest were graded smutty. New varieties and seed treatment methods reduced the smutty wheat to 2 per cent in 1942.[9] By 1948 the percentage of samples graded smutty was 14; in 1950, 30.6; and in 1951, 24.7.

Wheat Culture

Before 1914, tillage practices were simple. Horses or mules were used in plowing, cultivating, seeding, and harvesting operations. The machinery covered narrow strips of ground compared to the present big units, and it took longer to complete the work. It was difficult to

[8] "Recommended Pacific Northwest Wheat Varieties," *Pacific Northwest Bulletin* 4, Agricultural Experiment Stations, University of Idaho, Oregon State College, the State College of Washington, Pullman.

[9] "Controlling Wheat Smut," *Pacific Northwest Bulletin* 1, July, 1950, Agricultural Experiment Stations, University of Idaho, Oregon State College, the State College of Washington.

complete plowing seeding and harvesting during the time when conditions were the most favorable. During World War I, tractors were introduced but were inefficient and costly to operate, especially on the hills. With improvement, these machines increased in number

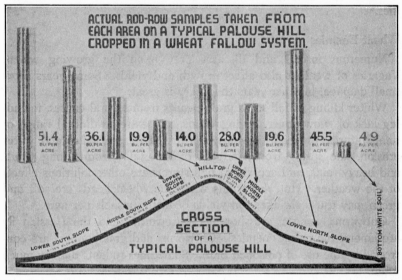

Fig. 36. Cross section of a typical Palouse Hill, showing comparative yields of wheat. Sample soil columns from the same sections showed the following results:

Section	Depth of top soil
Lower south slope	44 inches
Middle south slope	18 inches
Upper south slope	10 inches
Hilltop	none
Upper north slope	20 inches
Middle north slope	24 inches
Lower north slope	42 inches

and in consequence, horses became less numerous. Less land was needed for forage and more acreage could be devoted to wheat.

Today nearly all wheat is raised by using large machinery. With a big tractor and gang plows, a farmer can plow from 40 to 80 acres per day. With three to five cultivators or rod weeders, he can till from 320 to 640 acres of fallow ground in a long day. To seed 160 acres or more daily using three drills or more pulled by a caterpillar tractor is common. Obviously the wheat farmer can now handle several times the area possible at the turn of the century. Results from this mechanization include: less hours of labor required per acre; less employment of hired labor; increase in size of farms; and farm operations performed quickly when conditions are favorable, permitting increased yields at less cost.

Repeated crops exhaust the mineral and organic fertilizers. This combined with erosion and the soil structure by the tillage methods employed has caused serious deterioration in soils, especially on the hilltops (Fig. 36). Moreover, erosion of the upper slopes threatens the more productive lands below. Some farmers have taken hilltops, steep slopes, and gulleys out of cultivation and have seeded such areas to grass. Such areas then are available for pasture. Dairy cows and other livestock can be added to most wheat farms to advantage. There may be less land in wheat in the future, but the resulting changes in the cultural landscape, as in the Palouse, would be all for the better.

Harvesting

The wheat harvest normally begins in the first week of July and is completed in mid-August, an over-all season of some 6 or 7 weeks (Plate 19A). There are regional differences in the time of harvest from year to year because of variations in the growing season and differences in maturing.

An evolution of the harvesting methods has taken place over the years. Power machinery and bulk handling have reduced labor requirements. The man-hours per acre of wheat between 1910 and 1914 were 15.2. For the 1945–48 period the rate had been reduced to 6.1 man-hours per acre. One hundred bushels of wheat in the 1910–14 period required 106 man-hours; for the years 1945–48, the labor requirement had been reduced to 34 man-hours.[10] This economy in use of labor, although most general, has been most notable in the harvesting operation.

Horse-drawn headers and binders were used in the early days. Threshing was done by steam-powered machines owned by custom threshers who, accompanied by their crews and equipment, moved through the countryside during the harvest season. A large number of horses was required for the cutting operation and for movement of the wheat from the fields to the threshing machine. Labor requirements were also high. The local labor supply was augmented by an

[10] "Gains in Productivity of Farm Labor," U. S. Department of Agriculture, *Technical Bulletin* 1020, 1951.

influx of harvest hands from the cities of the Pacific Northwest and by migratory laborers who followed the harvest.

The combined harvester, or combine, made its appearance before World War I. The heavy, cumbersome, horse-drawn machines were best adapted to the flatter wheat lands. With improvement in design, the combine became increasingly adaptable to rough topography and its economies in harvesting gave it wide acceptance. Furthermore, the threshing machine, seldom owned by the farmer, was replaced by the farmer-owned combine and the harvest-season labor requirements were sharply reduced.

An even more profound change in wheat culture came with the development of the farm tractor. Before World War I, a few farmers were experimenting with this new type of motive power, but because of fuel and maintenance costs and the unwieldiness of the machines they were not particularly successful. When improved types appeared on the market, they found ready acceptance. The lighter, flexible crawler types of tractors, powered by diesel fuel instead of gasoline, accomplished the virtual end of horse-drawn implements in wheat farming. The rising tide of power farming is illustrated in Table 2.

TABLE 2

HORSE POPULATION AND NUMBER OF TRACTORS ON FARMS IN FIVE REPRESENTATIVE COUNTIES * IN EASTERN WASHINGTON

Year	Horses	Tractors
1925	84,000	518
1930	65,000	1,074
1940	20,296	3,216
1945	11,704	4,385
1950	6,343	5,873

* Adams, Columbia, Garfield, Lincoln, and Whitman.

The Bulk Handling of Wheat

Before the economic depression of the 1930's, the greater part of the grain of the Pacific Northwest moved from farm to market in burlap sacks. In the early years ship masters refused to carry bulk-grain cargo because of the danger of spoilage and the hazards of cargo shifting during the rough voyage around the Horn. Also, rail facilities for handling loose grain were limited. Even with the opening of the Panama Canal and improvement in cargo ships, the lack of adequate rail facilities from the interior to the coast terminals remained a barrier to bulk handling.

During World War I, sacks were in short supply and prices were high, which forced the development of bulk-handling equipment. Farm storage and country elevators were built, sack warehouses were converted to bulk storage, and the terminal facilities at coastal points were enlarged. After the war there was a return to the use of sacks, and in the 1929–30 season 62.7 per cent of the wheat received at Columbia River and Puget Sound terminals arrived in sacks.

In 1931, with the average farm price for wheat in the Pacific Northwest dropping to 37 cents per bushel, for the second time there was a marked increase in bulk handling of wheat. Another factor was the improvement in farm motor trucks and in quality and coverage of the "farm-to-market" roads.

Despite the trend toward bulk shipping, a considerable part of the wheat crop moved from farm to country elevators and warehouses in sacks as late as 1940. The World War II and postwar years, with sacks again high in price and in short supply, accomplished what is probably the final triumph of bulk wheat handling.

Storage Facilities

The accumulation of some 120 million bushels of new wheat in the short space of 6 or 7 weeks is a problem affecting growers. In the past, rapid movement into trade channels during the harvest season often created a market glut and depressed prices. Today commercial and farmer cooperative grain elevators and warehouses and farm storage facilities are estimated to provide storage for 1 year's crops. Despite many elevators and warehouses, local capacity may be temporarily overtaxed during the harvest season, and then bulk wheat is piled in the open. In addition to the interior storage facilities, there is terminal storage at Spokane, at Columbia River barge ports, and at Pacific Coast ports.

Supply and Disposition of Pacific Northwest Wheat

The average annual supply of wheat and its disposition for a typical year is presented in Table 3. The wheat supply of local origin is augmented by imports from Montana and other areas. This import is justified chiefly on the basis of difference in quality. The wheats of the Pacific Northwest generally require blending with harder wheats from the Great Plains for the production of flour acceptable to the domestic baking industry.

The total regional requirements are not capable of exact measurement, but it is estimated that between one-fourth and one-third of

TABLE 3

Supply		Disposition	
	Bushels		Bushels
Carryover (July 1)	17,505,000	Seed	5,707,000
Production	101,102,000	Milled for flour	36,316,000
Imports		Feed	10,476,000
Montana	13,140,000	Water-borne exports	
Unidentified	2,230,000	Orient	40,315,000
		Other	16,286,000
Total supply	134,209,000	Total disappearance	112,076,000
Unaccounted for	186,000	Carryover	22,139,000
Total supply	134,215,000	Total disposition	134,215,000

the crop is consumed locally. Since two-thirds to three-fourths of it moves to outside markets, these are of more than casual significance. In most years more than one-half moves into foreign trade channels. If flour were included, the total would be even more impressive. Because of locational and quality disadvantages, little is shipped to domestic markets outside the local region.

The Prospects

The international wheat situation poses a difficult problem to the Northwest farmer who is highly dependent on export markets. Despite this, the future prospects must always be considered in terms of the special physical and climatic conditions in the dryland interior where soil deterioration and erosion are increasing in magnitude.

MINOR GRAINS

The Rise and Decline of Dried Field Pea Production

Of the secondary crops in the wheat country, only the field pea has reached major significance and between 1940 and 1950 on some farms exceeded the returns from wheat. Dry peas were generally limited to the subhumid zone, particularly the Palouse district of Washington and northern Idaho. There, the suitability of the soil and climate for peas had long been known, but market requirements had, until 1940, limited production to about 160,000 acres.

The Federal Government food-crop program, under conditions imposed by World War II, called for an increase in field peas output. The guaranteed price of dried peas was increased fourfold and was

met by a fivefold increase in production from the Pacific Northwest
(Table 4). The predominant cropping systems used were the con-

TABLE 4

FIELD PEA ACREAGE

	Acres, 1939	Acres, 1943	Acres, 1950
Washington	101,000	398,000	104,000
Oregon	2,000	54,000	12,000
Idaho	56,000	250,000	55,000

tinuous pea and the wheat-pea types, with summer fallowing introduced only when weed infestation became serious.

The postwar years brought a contraction in the market which resulted in a reduction of field pea acreage to its prewar level.

Oats

The excellence of oats as a feed grain and forage for livestock and
for processing for human consumption has given this crop a long
history in the farm economy of the Pacific Northwest. The plant is
particularly well adapted to the cool, humid climate and the heavy
soils of the farming districts west of the Cascade Mountains, and this
region early assumed leadership in oat production, a position which it
has maintained to the present. However, oats are not limited to
western Washington and Oregon. The large feed requirements for
the horse population of the interior wheat region, before the advent
of the automobile, truck, and tractor, were met in part by the use of a
considerable amount of cropland for oats, which were grown generally on the subhumid margin of the wheat region. The oat crop
also was found in the farming systems of the intermontane basins and
valleys of northern Idaho and western Montana and in the irrigated
districts of the arid interior.

Maximum oat production in the Pacific Northwest was reached in
the period from 1910 to 1920, when the annual crop was from 40 to 50
million bushels. As the number of horses declined there was a reduction in the acreage cropped to oats. This trend was partially offset
by an increase in the demand for feeds provided by growing dairying,
poultry, and other livestock industries. This market today is the
major outlet for an oat crop that averages about 25 million bushels
annually.

Attention has been given to the development of new oat varieties
better adapted to differences in environmental conditions and to

market requirements. Better growth, yield, and harvesting characteristics, resistance to disease, and improved flavor in varieties grown
for food processing are being sought.

The 8 per cent of cropland in oats indicates its position relative to
other crops. It is rarely a major source of farm income. Between
50 and 60 per cent of it is consumed on the farm where grown. Considerable oats are cut for hay. The oat-grain harvest varies considerably from year to year, chiefly in response to changes in the price
relationships between the various feed grains and forage crops. More
than 600,000 acres are ordinarily planted to oats, with the greatest
concentration in the Willamette Valley and a secondary concentration
in the Puget Lowland where no wheat is grown. These areas account
for approximately 45 per cent of the acreage (Fig. 37). The irrigated
lands of the interior account for approximately 30 per cent of the
total oat acreage, with Yakima and Kittitas counties in Washington,
Klamath county in Oregon, and the Snake River Plain of southern
Idaho the principal producing districts. The greater part of the remainder is located in the intermontane valleys of the northern Rockies.

Barley

The barley crop of the Pacific Northwest, averaged for the period
1940–49, occupied 800,000 acres, or some 7 per cent of the region's
cropland. The annual average is 28 million bushels, with Idaho first
in both acreage and production (Fig. 38). The distribution in terms
of bushels produced was Idaho, 42 per cent; Oregon, 33 per cent;
Washington, 22 per cent; and western Montana, 3 per cent.

Over one-half of Idaho's barley crop is located on the Snake River
Plain, where it is grown both by dry farming and irrigation. The
Palouse margin in Idaho with Lewis, Idaho, and Nez Perce counties
also has large acreages and this center expands into the Palouse wheat
region of Washington. In Oregon the major centers are the Willamette Valley, the Klamath irrigated district, and the eastern border
counties, which include the irrigated Snake River Valley and the high
basins of the Blue Mountains.

The demand for barley as a feed grain and the production of types
suitable for malting account for the position of this crop in the farm
economy. Varieties suitable for a wide range of environmental conditions have permitted the incorporation of barley into the cropping
systems. More than 90 per cent of it is harvested as grain. In Idaho
approximately 50 per cent of the barley is consumed on the farm
where grown. For Washington, the producer consumption is about

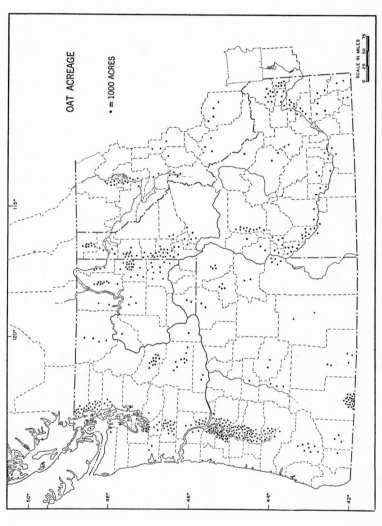

FIG. 37. Oat acreage. Each dot represents 1000 acres.

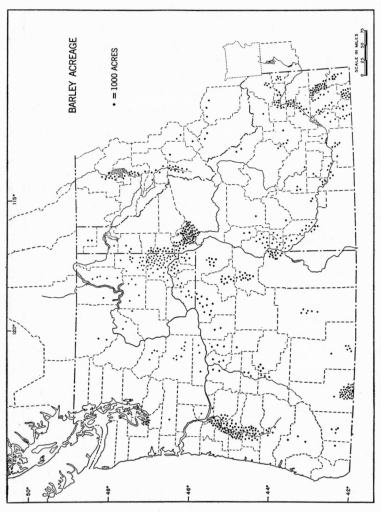

FIG. 38. Barley acreage. Each dot represents 1000 acres.

40 per cent of the crop. Oregon has the highest rank as a producer of barley as a cash crop, with about 70 per cent marketed off the producing farm. This type of disposition is accounted for chiefly by the Klamath district, which specializes in malting barley, and by the Willamette Valley, where a large livestock industry provides a market for grain feed. Barley production reached its maximum in 1942 when more than 1.2 million acres were seeded.

Rye

Rye is the least important of the small grains grown in the Pacific Northwest. For the period 1940–49 the crop averaged about 200,000 acres, or less than 2 per cent of the cropland of the region. Oregon led in acreage, with about 68 per cent of the total; Washington accounted for 26 per cent; and Idaho, 6 per cent.

Used chiefly for forage, nearly three-fourths of the seeded acreage is harvested as hay or used for pasture. This type of culture has its maximum importance in the semiarid interior in districts where poor soil, a short growing period, and moisture conditions limit the production of other forage crops. The use of rye as a cover crop for various legumes is a less important factor in its cultivation.

For the years 1940–49, an average of only 50,000 acres in rye was threshed annually, an indication of its minor importance as a grain. The average yield was approximately 800,000 bushels. The dry-farming area of central Washington and the semiarid farmlands at elevations generally over 4000 feet in south-central Oregon and in southern Idaho were the major centers for rye.

In general, one-half or more of the grain was retained on the farm for feed and seed. That which was sold as a cash crop found its principal markets as seed, for distilling purposes, as a feed grain, and for milling as flour.

REFERENCES

Baum, Richard K., "Industrial Utilization of Pacific Northwest Wheat," *State of Oregon Wheat Commission Research Report* 1, Pendleton, Oregon, March, 1950.

Cannell, Lewis D., "The Freight Rate Structure and Its Effect on the Price and Movement of Northwest Wheat," *State College of Washington Bureau of Economic and Business Research, Bulletin* 2, June, 1945.

"Controlling Wheat Smut," Agricultural Experiment Stations, Oregon State College, University of Idaho, Washington State College, *Pacific Northwest Bulletin* 1 (revised July, 1950).

Dreesen, W. H., *Wheat and Flour Exports from the Pacific Northwest, 1922–29,* U. S. Department of Agriculture, Bureau of Agricultural Economics, August, 1950.

Heisig, Carl P., Ahrends, Earnest R., and Merrick, Della E., *Wheat Production in War and Peace,* U. S. Department of Agricultural Economics, 1945.

Hurd, E. B., and Brough, O. L., Jr., "Farm Size and Land Use in the Wheat-Pea Area of Washington and Idaho, 1935–50," *Washington State College Agricultural Experiment Stations Circular* 169, September, 1951.

"Pacific Northwest Wheat Problems and the Export Subsidy," Stanford University Food Research Institute, *Wheat Studies* 1, X, No. 10, 1934.

Pubols, Ben H., and Heisig, Carl P., "Historical and Geographic Aspects of Wheat Yields in Washington," *Washington State College Agricultural Experiment Stations Bulletin* 355, 1937.

"Recommended Pacific Northwest Wheat Varieties," Agricultural Extension Services, University of Idaho, Oregon State College, Washington State College, *Pacific Northwest Bulletin* 4, 1951.

Smith, Henry W., "Nitrogen Fertilizer for Wheat Production," *Washington State College Agricultural Experiment Stations Circular* 85, 1950.

Snodgrass, Donald, and Harrington, A. H., "Supply and Disposition of Pacific Northwest Wheat," *Washington State College Agricultural Experiment Stations Circular* 196, 1952.

Taylor, Maurice C., and Baker, Vernon W., "Soil Conservation and Farm Income in the Palouse Wheat-Pea Area," *Washington State College Agricultural Experiment Stations Popular Bulletin* 186, 1947.

Wheat Statistics, Oregon and the Pacific Northwest, 1869–1947, U. S. Dept. of Agriculture, Bureau of Agricultural Economics, Portland, Oregon, 1948 (revised 1952).

Tree Fruit Industry

R. M. SHAW

Legend places the first orchard in the Pacific Northwest at Fort Vancouver. In 1824, at a dinner in London honoring Lieutenant Aemilius Simpson, R.N., and his men, who were about to depart for service in America, a woman dropped apple seeds from the dessert into Simpson's waistcoat pocket and bade him, in jest, to plant them upon his arrival there. When dining at Fort Vancouver 3 years later, he discovered the seeds in the pocket of the same waistcoat and gave them to the gardener of the Hudson's Bay Company, who planted them on the grounds of the fort. The story of commercial production, however, begins in the 1840's, when orchards were planted from grafted trees and seeds brought overland from the East by settlers. Development followed, reaching a point in the late 1850's and 1860's where various fruits were provided for local markets and apples for California.

Main expansion of the industry did not occur until the decade 1905–15, after transcontinental railroads were serving the region and fairly large irrigation projects were in operation. Men from all callings of life, in all parts of the country, were attracted to the fruit districts by stories of fortunes to be made in apples. Although distant from markets, the industry grew rapidly, and land suitable to fruit trees was planted about as fast as it was brought under irrigation.[1] The fruit

[1] During the 10-year period, 1940–49, nearly a fourth (23 per cent) of American peaches (4.7 per cent), pears (37.7 per cent), prunes (20.3 per cent), cherries (31.8 per cent), and commercial apples (30.5 per cent) was produced in Washington, Oregon, Idaho, and Montana. Of the 15,235,257 fruit trees (commercial and farm) in these four states in 1950, 50 per cent were in Washington, 40 per cent in Oregon, 7 per cent in Idaho, and 2 per cent (half of them apples) in Montana.

was sold in eastern United States in competition with that grown locally, as well as in many foreign countries.

Several factors, both natural and human, favored these early developments. Natural conditions, especially in the irrigated valleys, were favorable for growth of trees and heavy production of large, shapely, and well-colored fruit. Absence of summer rainfall minimized fungus diseases; irrigated soils were generally high in the elements of fertility, except for a deficiency in humus; an abundance of irrigation water existed; maximum sunshine promoted growth; cool nights colored the fruit; and insect problems were not serious. Human factors were important also, since northwestern growers did several things that were not done in the East. (1) Although early orchards contained many kinds and varieties of fruit, growers soon specialized in order to produce sufficient quantities of one type to ship in carload lots to distant markets at favorable rates. This also made it easier to advertise and establish a reputation. (2) Realizing that markets were distant and that a large portion of the selling price went for freight rates, growers found that it paid to ship only fine fruit. Hence, orchards were, as a rule, better pruned and more thoroughly sprayed than was common in the East, resulting in not only better fruit but also a higher average yield. (3) Careful grading, attractive packing, and certification of quality were the next contribution to sales promotion. Instead of barrels, boxes holding a bushel of fruit were used. Each box contained apples of even size and quality, individually wrapped in paper, and, to give further confidence to the buyer, was stamped with the names of the grower and professional packer as well as the number of apples.

Thus, large size and superior appearance of the fruit, careful selection of varieties, and attractive packing made it possible for northwestern growers to sell to eastern markets sufficiently above the price of eastern fruit to cover transportation costs.

During the depression, before our entering into World War II, the industry was not prosperous and many orchards, especially apples, were removed. This was reflected in the landscapes of many districts, by occasional areas of dead or uprooted trees and stumps and open spaces among the orchards in contrast to former days. A number of factors accounted for this condition. (1) To meet northwestern competition, eastern growers had improved their practices. Low-grade apples were rapidly disappearing from the orchards and superior varieties were taking their places. The barrel had almost disappeared being replaced by the bushel basket, and later by boxes for choice fruit. The best of the eastern pack now equals that of the Pacific Northwest in appearance and quality, thus reducing the advantage formerly enjoyed by northwestern growers. Apples, widely grown in the East, suffered most from this improvement. Sweet cherries, pears, apricots, prunes, and plums, which cannot be satisfactorily grown there, suffered less as they meet only the competition of other western districts. (2) Effective advertising increased sales of grapefruit, oranges, and pineapple, sold fresh, canned, or as juices, and thus the demand for northwestern deciduous fruits was lessened. (3) Increased expenditures for insect control and other expenses resulted in such high costs that, notwithstanding high yield per tree and acre, the cost of producing a bushel of apples was as high in some cases higher, than in eastern areas. (4) As production costs increased, the disadvantage of location was felt, the relatively fixed costs of transportation to eastern markets becoming disproportionately high to the return to the grower. (5) Most of the foreign market had been lost because of trade barriers, warfare, and economic inability to buy.

Any shift from tree fruits to other crops involves such problems as greater suitability of the area for orchards, toxicity of soil due to heavy and prolonged use of lead arsenate in spraying, mental attitude of former orchardists towards other kinds of farming, lack of income for a period of 2 to 6 years, investment costs of bringing new crops into production, and revision downward of property values (growers still regard land denuded of orchards of the same value as when raw during the boom period) so that other types of operators who need lower-priced land, such as dairymen, can buy it. For these reasons much of the orchardland in some areas remains idle.[2]

Location of Orchard Districts

Unlike the wheatlands of the Columbia plateau, the orchardlands of the Northwest are not of impressive extent, but appear as a score or more separate districts scattered about the region (Fig. 39). Most of them are in valleys that provide water for irrigation and sloping lands for air drainage, and are traversed by main or branch lines of railroads leading to Pacific ports and eastern markets. The intervening and adjacent areas are lacking in fruit because of ruggedness (mountain areas), cloudiness, and infertile soils (Pacific Coast), short-

[2] Of the 5004 acres of orchards removed from the area of Chelan, Grant, and Douglas counties (Washington), south from Entiat, during the 4-year period 1937–40, probably 80 per cent lies idle. The rest of the former appleland has been planted to alfalfa, corn, potatoes, and soft fruits.

ness of growing season (Upper Snake Valley), or lack of irrigation water (much of the Columbia Basin).

Most of the districts are arid or semiarid. All have dry summers, even though a few of the westernmost have rather heavy annual rainfall. Consequently, orchardists must irrigate or make some other adjustment (such as dry farming). In irrigated districts, permanent cover crops are maintained to enrich the soil. In the nonirrigated districts where there is insufficient moisture in summer for both trees and cover crops, orchards are subject to clean cultivation, although, as in the Willamette Valley, they may be sown to winter crops which are plowed under in the spring.

In Zone I (Fig. 39) the districts were originally wooded, and today peripheral orchards often merge with the bordering green forest tracts. Irrigation of fruit trees is scarcely practiced except in the Rogue and Hood valleys, where it was adopted only after commercial orchards had been established for a number of years. Before trees could be planted, the land had to be cleared of its timber. In the Hood River Valley, originally covered with oaks and conifers, Japanese laborers were brought in by landowners to transform the cut-over waste into a vast orchard. In the Umpqua Valley most of the land was open when the orchards were set, having been cultivated to small grains for a number of years.

Zone II, which contains the most districts, is characterized by low mean annual rainfall, original brown landscapes dotted with sagebrush or bunch grass (more easily cleared than the timber of the first zone), and irrigation projects. The Dalles district is the only one in which orchards are not irrigated. There is some well irrigation along the creeks but most of the orchards are too high up the slope to be reached by water. Construction of irrigation projects and planting of hundreds of orchards have greatly transformed the landscapes of districts in this zone. Row upon row of trees now grow upon the slopes in orderly succession, in spring a tumbling cascade of sweet-scented blossoms or in fall ruddy and gold with the burden of fruit. In addition to the lovely orchards, some districts are in sight of Mt. Adams, Mt. Hood, or Mt. Rainier, majestic iceclad volcanic peaks rising above the ridges of the Cascade Mountains. The knifelike division between sagebrush and orchards, frequently following the high line canal, vividly outlines the change wrought by man.

Zone III is similar to Zone I in that it was originally wooded and not all its orchards are irrigated. On the other hand, separated from it by the dry second zone and occupying an interior position, its winter

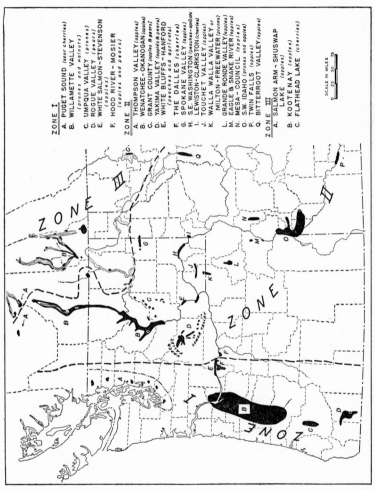

ZONE I
A. PUGET SOUND *(sour cherries)*
B. WILLAMETTE VALLEY
   (prunes and walnuts)
C. UMPQUA VALLEY *(prunes)*
D. ROGUE VALLEY *(pears)*
E. WHITE SALMON-STEVENSON
   (apples)
F. HOOD RIVER-MOSIER
   (apples and pears)

ZONE II
A. THOMPSON VALLEY *(apples)*
B. WENATCHEE-OKANOGAN *(apples)*
C. GRANT COUNTY *(apples & pears)*
D. YAKIMA VALLEY *(apples & pears)*
E. WHITE BLUFFS-HANFORD
   (peaches and apricots)
F. THE DALLES *(cherries)*
G. SPOKANE VALLEY *(apples)*
H. S.E. WASHINGTON *(peaches-apricots)*
I. LEWISTON-CLARKSTON *(cherries)*
J. TOUCHET VALLEY *(apples)*
K. WALLA WALLA VALLEY or
   MILTON-FREEWATER *(prunes)*
L. GRANDE RONDE VALLEY *(apples)*
M. EAGLE & SNAKE RIVER *(apples)*
N. MESA-COUNCIL *(apples)*
O. S.W. IDAHO *(prunes and apples)*
P. TWIN FALLS *(apples)*
Q. BITTERROOT VALLEY *(apples)*

ZONE III
A. SALMON ARM-SHUSWAP
   LAKE *(apples)*
B. KOOTENAY *(apples)*
C. FLATHEAD LAKE *(cherries)*

SCALE IN MILES
0 25 50 75

Fig. 39.   Tree fruit and nut districts of the Pacific Northwest.

temperatures are, in general, lower, its rainfall less (although more than in Zone II), and its fruit areas more elevated.

Districts with the largest number of fruit trees are Willamette Valley, Wenatchee-Okanogan, Yakima Valley,[3] Okanagan Valley (Canada), Umpqua Valley, Rogue Valley, southwest Idaho, and Hood River.

Kinds of Fruit

In 1950, commercial and farm orchards of Washington, Oregon, Idaho, and Montana contained 15,235,267 fruit trees. Of these, 30 per cent were apple, 23 per cent plum and prune, 19 per cent pear, 14 per cent peach, 11 per cent cherry, and 2 per cent apricot. The two major horticultural districts of British Columbia, Okanagan[4] and Kootenay, had 2,505,802 trees, 50 per cent of which were apple, 14 per cent pears, 13 per cent peaches, 10 per cent plums and prunes, 8 per cent apricot, and 5 per cent cherry.

Although each district produces all the deciduous fruits of the region, because of economic, historic, or climatic reasons each is characterized by one or two main fruits (Fig. 39).

Apples

The Canadian fruit districts specialize in apples. In 1949 the Okanagan horticultural district of British Columbia (Okanagan Valley, Salmon Arm, Shuswap Lake, Thompson Valley) produced 92 per cent of the province's apples; the areas forming the Kootenay horticultural district, 7 per cent. Most important fruit section is the Okanagan Valley. In its northern half 70 per cent (1950) of all trees are apple, but in its southern half they decline to 31 per cent and soft fruits increase in importance. Although the valley is much farther north than Yakima or Wenatchee, the growing of more tender fruits, such as peaches and apricots, is due to the presence of linear lakes. The orchards bordering Shuswap Lake and Salmon Arm form the

---

[3] In this chapter data for Yakima Valley are actually for Yakima County, in which most of the orchards of the district are located. Clark County in southwest Washington is considered a part of the Willamette Valley. The Washington-Okanogan district is made up of the Okanagan Valley of British Columbia, the Okanogan and Wenatchee valleys of Washington, and that part of the Columbia Valley that lies between the two latter valleys.

[4] The Okanagan district has 19 times as many trees as the Kootenay. Owing to the large number of trees that were frozen in January and February, 1950, when polar continental air flooded down the Okanagan (and Fraser) Valley, the count in the Okanagan horticultural district 2,297,308) is below normal. Losses were also considerable in the Okanogan-Wenatchee area.

most northerly district of the region; 80 per cent of its 97,329 trees are apple. In Thompson Valley there are 78,000 trees (mainly at Spence's Bridge, Lytton, and Chase), 84 per cent of which are apple. Scattered fruit areas, located at favorable sites on river benches and beside long, finger lakes in the narrow and deeply embedded valleys of the Selkirk and Rocky Mountains of southeast British Columbia, comprise the Kootenay district, in which 63 per cent of the 208,494 trees (1950) are apple. Creston Valley, that part of the Kootenay Valley between Kootenay Lake and the international boundary, contained 62 per cent of all the fruit trees in 1950 and is the most important part.

Orchards in the Yakima Valley (Plate 19B) and the section of the Wenatchee-Okanogan district in Washington enable that state to produce 73 per cent of the commercial apples in the American part of the Region. Two-fifths of all trees in the first area are apple; three-fourths in the second. Three smaller districts, Spokane Valley, Touchet Valley, and White Salmon-Stevenson, also specialize in this fruit and add to the state's output. The American division of the Wenatchee-Okanogan district is similar to the Canadian in that apples are all-important in the northern part. More southerly latitude rather than lakes (as in the Canadian counterpart) accounts for the increased importance of soft fruits. In the Yakima Valley there is a tendency for apples and pears to concentrate in the upper valley (two of whose districts are dissected plateaus) and stone fruits in the lower valley. At one time there were many apple orchards in the latter but the codling moth has become a serious pest there. The warm summer nights favor the flight of this insect. To control it requires about ten cover sprays, which increases the cost of production to a prohibitive point. Moreover, the acid and hot water needed to wash the spray from apples tend to lower their quality and shorten their storage life. Stone fruits are raised without cover sprays and Bartlett pears require fewer than apples. In the upper valley the temperatures are lower, especially at night, and infestation of the codling moth is less. Therefore, three or four sprays are sufficient in most parts, washing the apples is less difficult, a higher-quality product is more easily produced, and the cooler nights result in better color. The lower valley, on the other hand, possesses definite climatic advantages for stone fruits: high temperatures, somewhat less rain and therefore less splitting of cherries, and a growing season 1 or 2 weeks earlier, resulting frequently in a price advantage over fruits which reach the market later.

In Oregon, the greatest density of commercial apple trees is in Hood River Valley, which was developed as an export district; at one time 65 per cent or more of its apples were shipped to foreign markets. More recently the acreage of pears has so increased that pear production may soon equal the apple output. The larger Willamette Valley contains about the same number of apple trees but much of its acreage is not commercial. Two districts in Idaho, Mesa Council and Twin Falls, deal chiefly in apples but a third, southwest Idaho (Plate 19B), in which this fruit ranks second, has 1.5 times as many apple trees as both combined. The commercial apples of western Montana are produced largely in the Bitterroot Valley.

In the different parts of the region, emphasis on kinds of apples varies. In northerly British Columbia and in the Bitterroot Valley, most elevated of all districts except the Grande Ronde Valley of Oregon, the variety of first importance is the McIntosh. In the western districts of Oregon (including The Dalles, Mosier, and Hood River Valley with its Washington statellite, White Salmon-Stevenson) there is a preference for Yellow Newtowns and Spitzenbergs. In Washington, Idaho, and eastern Oregon most apple trees are Delicious, Winesap, Rome Beauty, and Jonathan. The Delicious is a favorite variety and ranks high in some parts of those areas favoring the McIntosh, Newtown, and Spitzenberg. In the Canadian portion of the region, the number of Delicious trees is equal to that of the McIntosh in the northerly Shuswap-Salmon Arm area and in the southern half of the Okanagan Valley there are 110,966 Delicious, 80,851 Winesaps, 56,346 Yellow Newtown trees, as compared with 46,397 of the McIntosh variety (1950). (In the Thompson Valley, the northern half of the Okanagan Valley, and in the Kootenay district, the McIntosh leads.) In Hood River Valley it outnumbers Spitzenberg trees and now ranks second to the Newtown. Apple trees less than 10 years of age in the American section of the Wenatchee-Okanogan district and the Yakima Valley are predominantly Delicious.

The future of the apple, first commercial fruit in the Northwest and still the leader in number of trees, became quite doubtful during the depression years. In two of the smaller districts, Hanford-White Bluffs [5] and Umatilla, apple trees have practically disappeared. In two of the larger districts, Southwest Idaho and Walla Walla Valley, many apple orchards have been removed and prune orchards are now more numerous. In other large districts, such as the Wenatchee-

[5] With construction of the Hanford engineering works, only a few scattered fruit trees are left.

Okanogan and Yakima Valley, although many apple trees have been uprooted, this fruit is still the favorite.

Prunes

Oregon produces 67 per cent of the prunes in the American section. Three valleys, Umpqua, Willamette, and Walla Walla, contain more prune than all other fruit trees combined. Half of the trees in the Southwest Idaho district are prune and in the Yakima Valley it comprises 4 per cent of all fruit trees. The prunes of the two western districts go to driers and canneries; those of the three eastern districts are sold fresh. The western prunes are thinner-skinned and more subject to internal brown rot during shipment than those grown in the higher and drier eastern districts. On the other hand, they are slightly larger and more suitable for canning and drying. The fresh Italian prunes of the inland districts are of high quality, those of the Walla Walla Valley usually bringing the highest prices paid in eastern markets. The demand for canned Italian prunes has increased steadily for a number of years, while the market for fresh prunes has held its own. The popularity of the dried prune, however, has shown a marked decline. In 1950 more than 200,000 prune trees were growing in the Okanagan horticultural district of Canada.

Pears

Four areas in Washington and Oregon, the Yakima, Rogue, and Hood River valleys and the southern end of the Wenatchee-Okanogan district, including Wenatchee Valley, produce most of the pears in the American section. Principal varieties are Bartlett, d'Anjou, Bosc, and Winter Nelis. More than half the acreage of the four districts is in Bartletts which predominate in all but Hood River where d'Anjous are more important. The Bartlett is the first to ripen and the only one sold both fresh and canned. The other varieties are winter pears and are sold fresh. They keep longer in storage (the d'Anjou until April) and so may be marketed over a long period.

The outstanding district is the Rogue River Valley (Plate 19A). A combination of climatic and soil conditions has been extremely favorable for the growing of high-quality pears. Moderate winters and summers which are hot and dry are well suited to the ripening of pears.[6] Much of the soil is a rather heavy adobe and is better for

[6] In the Umpqua and Willamette valleys, the other districts of western Oregon, pears are grown commercially but are not included among the most important fruits. Summer temperatures are lower than in the Rogue Valley and not warm enough for the best development of most pear varieties.

pears than for other tree fruits. About 35 per cent of the pear trees are Bartlett, 26 per cent d'Anjou, 24 per cent Bosc, 9 per cent Comice, and 4 per cent Winter Nelis. A portion of the Bartlett tonnage each year goes to canneries in Willamette Valley and California (only 5 per cent is canned in Rogue River Valley); the remainder is shipped as fresh fruit to eastern markets. The Comice pear, which thrives in only a few areas in the United States, is found at its best in the Rogue district. Many are sold in fancy gift boxes for the Christmas trade and advertised in magazines under the name Royal Riviera.

Cherries

Four districts, Puget Sound Lowland, The Dalles, Clarkston-Lewiston, and Flathead Lake, specialize in cherries, though there are two others, Willamette Valley and Yakima Valley, containing greater acreages. Because rains crack sweet cherries, the black Bings and Lamberts and yellow-red Royal Anns are grown in the drier areas. Sour cherries are produced in Puget Sound Lowland.

More than half the cherries in The Dalles and Willamette Valley districts are Royal Ann. At the time that plantings were made, the chief demand was in the canning field, Royal Anns being the accepted variety for that purpose. For that reason cherries of these districts are largely processed. In the remaining sweet-cherry districts the black varieties predominate and a large part of the crop is shipped East as fresh fruit. The trees on the east side of Flathead Lake are young, some 60,000 trees (mainly Lambert) have recently come into bearing. Slow maturation, due to cool nights tempered by the lake, makes for meaty rather than juicy cherries, which adds materially to their keeping and eating qualities. In general, sour cherries are canned or frozen, Bings and Lamberts sold fresh, and Royal Anns canned, brined for the maraschino trade, or sold fresh early in the season before the black sweet cherries mature.

Apricots and Peaches

Apricots and peaches bloom earlier than other fruits and are grown where greater security from spring frosts can be expected. As already noted, the ameliorating influence of lakes permits the growing of these fruits in the northerly Okanagan Valley of Canada. In the only two districts, both small, that specialize in peaches and apricots, Hanford-White Bluffs (Columbia Valley) and Southeast Washington (Snake River Valley), summers are long and hot. Orchards are frequently placed on foothill slopes where drainage of cold air is expedited. Five districts stand out in numbers of peach trees: Yakima Valley, Okanagan Valley (Canada), Wenatchee-Okanogan, Willamette Valley, and Southwest Idaho. In the American section, 61 per cent of the peaches are produced in Washington, 29 per cent in Oregon, and 20 per cent in Idaho. The three districts with the largest numbers of apricot trees are the Wenatchee-Okanogan, Okanagan Valley (Canada), and Yakima Valley. Most of the trees of the latter are in the Tieton area, a dissected plateau in the upper valley. Although cooler than most other parts of the district, it has excellent air drainage. More recent plantings, however, indicate a future shift of apricot production to the recognized soft-fruit areas of the lower valley. The apricots of The Dalles district are of excellent quality and their production has increased since 1925.

Walnuts and Filberts

English walnuts and filberts are grown west of the Cascade Mountains, where both summers and winters are mild, in the Puget Sound Lowland, but mostly in Willamette Valley (especially in the northern half), where they rank next to prunes in acreage. After harvest, they are artificially dried and the walnuts bleached and graded for size. Most of the nuts are marketed through cooperatives in 50- or 100-pound lots; however, there is a tendency to sell them in small cellophane bags, and a considerable volume has been marketed as shelled nuts. They are disposed of largely in the central and eastern states.

Size of Orchards

The average size of the Region's orchards, located chiefly on valley slopes and benches, is 10 to 40 acres. There are some large ones,[7] among which are the Mesa Orchards (1200 acres) in the Upper Weiser Valley of Idaho, and the A.Z. Wells Orchard (265 acres) at Azwell and the Beebe Orchard (500 acres) near Chelan, both in the Columbia Valley. Such orchards are self-sufficient, procuring their own irrigation water, packing, storing, and marketing their own fruit, and maintaining clusters of cabins and houses for the workers.

[7] During the expansion period, an orchard of 8000 acres (world's largest) was planted on the plateau south of The Dalles district. The promoters sold individual investors separate lots on the basis of perpetual care, the owners to reap annual dividends when the trees bore fruit. The soil was fertile, but the moisture, though sufficient to produce large crops of wheat by dry-farming methods, was inadequate for fruit and no irrigation was handy. Eventually the owners grubbed thousands of trees and planted the land to grain. Similar ventures on a smaller scale were not uncommon, many of the lots being sold to absentee easterners.

Seasonal Activities

Changing seasonal landscapes and activities are typified by the Tieton area. In winter the trees are bare and dormant and pruning is the chief activity. In spring, when the trees in bloom flaunt their promise of a coming harvest, orchardists clean ditches and open furrows, spray, disc the cover crop, irrigate, and pollinate with rented hives of bees. During the summer the growers continue to irrigate and spray; in addition, they thin the fruit, prop the bending branches, and harvest cherries (July 1), apricots (July 15), and pears (Auggust 20). The autumn harvest begins September 1 with the picking of Jonathan apples; other varieties are picked in succession, and by November 1 the activity is completed. This is the busiest season of the year (Plate 20A). Low-wheeled wagons or sleds, pulled by horses or tractors, distribute empty boxes through the orchards and haul filled ones to the road or to the growers' packing houses. Trucks carry empty boxes over the highways to the orchards and filled ones back to commercial packing plants in Yakima. Great numbers of itinerant workers, who live in cheap tourist cabins or on public camping grounds in trailers and tents, drift in to augment local labor.

Marketing

The fruit may be marketed in various ways, as exemplified by the Yakima and Wenatchee valleys. Ranking first are large corporative and private organizations through whom growers may dispose of their products to buyers all over the United States and, in the past, Europe. Their frame packing houses and brick-and-tile cold-storage plants are scattered through the valley. Other growers form cooperatives, owning their own packing and storage plants (Plate 20B) and doing their own marketing. A few pack and sell their fruits themselves. Three large canneries, a vinegar plant at Yakima, and a small dehydrator at Buena absorb a portion of the local output. Grocery-store chains and west coast canneries send in buyers for another part. Some fruit is trucked to nearby nonfruit-producing areas, and during seasons of heavy production a considerable tonnage is handled through the Federal Surplus Marketing Administration.

Market Centers

The urban centers that have developed to serve the fruit districts reflect the activity. Orchards come down to their limits and single or small groups of trees wedge their way within. Scarce is the yard without a blooming tree in spring. The horticultural character of the surrounding country is seen in the packing and storage houses and processing plants that comprise a part of their landscapes. Small villages, such as Entiat in the Wenatchee-Okanogan district, are dominated by a packing shed and cold-storage plant. In larger towns, like Milton-Freewater, northeastern Oregon, a string of such buildings stretches out along the railroad track for a quarter-mile or more. Largest and most pretentious area is "produce row" at Yakima, which with Wenatchee and Medford are the three largest "fruit" cities in the region.

REFERENCES

Blodgett, E. C., "Cherry Industry in the Lewiston Orchards with Cultural Recommendations," *Agricultural Experiment Station Bulletin* 171, University of Idaho, Moscow, 1930.

Ellison, J. W., "The Beginnings of the Apple Industry in Oregon," *Agricultural History*, Vol. 11, pp. 322–343, 1937.

Freeman, O. W., "Apple Industry of the Wenatchee Area," *Economic Geography*, Vol. 10, pp. 160–171.

Heisig, C. P., and B. H. Pubols, "Fruit Trees in Yakima County," *State College of Washington Agricultural Experiment Station Bulletin* 359, 1938.

Miller, Elbert E., and Richard M. Highsmith, Jr., "Geography of the Fruit Industry of Yakima Valley, Washington," *Economic Geography*, Vol. 25, pp. 285–295, October, 1949.

"Plum and Prune Growing in the Pacific States," *U. S. Department of Agriculture Farmers' Bulletin* 1372, Washington, D. C., 1938.

Schuster, C. E., "Filberts," *Oregon State College Agricultural Experiment Station Circular* 108, Corvallis, Ore., 1934.

Schuster, C. E., "Walnut Production in Oregon," *Oregon State College Agricultural Experiment Station Circular* 108, Corvallis, Ore., 1934.

CHAPTER 19

Small Fruits and Vegetables

OTIS W. FREEMAN

The Pacific Northwest has certain sections with soil and climate extremely favorable for the commercial production of small fruits. The industry is further benefited by satisfactory transportation, labor, and marketing conditions. The culture of small fruits and vegetables is most important in the Puget-Willamette Lowland, where producers find them an important source of income. Economic success for a berry grower depends a great deal on his ability to keep abreast of changing markets and advances in knowledge of fruit culture, control of pests, handling of labor, etc. The human factor equals in importance the natural factors.

Berries

Berries in general require a fertile, well-drained soil, an adequate rainfall without excessive moisture in the harvesting season, and relatively early springs so that most of the crop may be sold before the markets have been glutted. Requiring less sunshine than commercial orchard fruits, berries flourish in the foggy, cloudy climate on the west side better than east of the Cascades. In general there is no shortage of land suitable for berry production. Limiting factors are more commonly the farmer's lack of experience, lack of labor in picking season, and distance from market rather than adverse conditions of soil or climate. Most berries, however, do not grow well on wet overflow land or on poor leached soil. The principal areas of production are fertile bottomlands and benchlands, and, west of Portland, rolling uplands.

Labor as a factor in berry production is of prime importance in the picking season. An owner may be able to trim and cultivate several acres of strawberries or cane fruit; but berries are such a perishable commodity that they must be picked quickly during the season, so that an acre of small fruit may require the services of many pickers. Both local residents and itinerants find employment in the berry-picking season.

The three recognized commercial outlets are (1) the local market for fresh fruit, which in the larger cities like Seattle, Portland, Vancouver, and Spokane is of considerable magnitude; (2) outside markets in other parts of the United States, including Alaska and Hawaii; (3) local canning, freezing, and preserving plants. Fresh fruit, whether sold locally or shipped, must be consumed within a few days to avoid deterioration. The shipping distance for small fruits, being perishable, is limited to markets that can be reached within a few days. Glutting of markets may occur from overproduction, too rapid ripening by hot weather, or competition with other producing areas. Shipments of small fruits in season are regularly made as far as the Twin Cities, and occasionally loganberries have gone to Chicago and further east, but beyond Montana or the western Dakotas competition with other areas generally makes shipment unprofitable. Besides local sales, hundreds of carloads of West Coast small fruits are sent in refrigerator cars to important market centers for distribution east of the Cascade Mountains.

Berries are very valuable per acre of producing land. Whereas an acre in wheat may produce a crop worth $25 or $50, the same area in berries may provide an income of many hundreds of dollars. The returns from a berry crop in a single year may even exceed the selling price of the land. However, this is not all profit, and in order to produce bumper crops, careful culture and painstaking care are necessary. In addition, large sums are paid to the pickers, and for boxes, transportation, and other expenses that make up the cost of raising and marketing the fruit. Not everyone can raise commercial-quality fruit at a profit, but the small-fruit industry does provide large incomes on small areas of cleared land, which is a big advantage where cut-over land covered by huge stumps is very expensive to clear. The farms in berry-producing sections are generally small since a few acres are usually all a grower can care for properly. Berry raising is frequently a part-time occupation, especially for people living near large city markets.

Processing Small Fruit

Oregon and Washington are the leading states in the canning of small fruits. Exclusive of blueberries, the two states produce three-fifths to three-fourths of the canned berries of the nation. Nearly a million and a half cases of berries come from the Northwest each year: blackberries, loganberries, raspberries, strawberries, and gooseberries in that order. Oregon is first in the packing of loganberries and gooseberries, Washington in the other three. Of all loganberries canned in the United States, 98 per cent are processed in Oregon and Washington. The two states also supply a large majority (60–70 per cent) of the national pack of blackberries and gooseberries and nearly half the strawberries and raspberries. Some of the pack is exported, especially loganberries to Great Britain. Canned berries are nonperishable and it is possible to ship them longer distances than the fresh fruit. Favorable locations for canneries are in situations where not only small fruits are available but also vegetables like spinach, peas, beans, tomatoes, or asparagus. Some orchard fruits, especially cherries and prunes, may also be processed in the same plants that handle the berries. The overhead of a cannery is about the same whether it operates 1 month or 5 months. When several different fruits and vegetables for canning can be secured, operations are naturally much more economical than if there is an attempt to make a profit from the processing of only one or two kinds of crops.

In addition to the berry pack, fruit juice, especially that of loganberries, is bottled. At one time 10 per cent of this fruit was processed in this way, but the output of juice has declined of late years, partly because of lack of advertising. Some berry juice is made into liqueurs. Jams and jellies provide another outlet by which the small fruits are marketed at times of the year and to distances which would otherwise be impossible. More preserves, jams, and jellies are made of berries than of all other fruits. More than half the total preserves and jams are strawberry.

The use of cold packing for preserving berries began about 1911, and since 1920 the quantity of small fruits preserved by freezing has increased nearly every year. The Pacific Northwest packs more frozen berries than any section of the country. In this form the berries will keep in prime condition for many months. A large part of the pack is shipped east in refrigerator cars and sold to bakers, confectioners, restaurants, and ice-cream manufacturers. Strawberries make up about two-thirds of the frozen fruit and loganberries much of the remainder. Advantages of the cold pack are that the fruit tastes almost fresh, it can be shipped greater distances than when fresh, the processing is cheaper than canning, and the fruit reaches bakers and other buyers in prime condition. Around a hundred thousand

50-gallon barrels (400 pounds net) of frozen berries were sold each year between 1925 and 1930. During the next two decades, the output of frozen fruit, divided between western Washington and Oregon, increased considerably.

Cane Fruit

The cane fruits include the raspberry, blackberry, loganberry, youngberry, boysenberry, and dewberry; the bush fruits include currants and gooseberries. The blackberry and dewberry, and even the raspberry in places, grow wild in the Pacific Northwest. The blackberry and raspberry were artificially crossed to produce new fruits, called after their respective discoverers the loganberry, the youngberry, the boysenberry, etc. No part of the world furnishes cane fruits of finer quality than the Pacific Northwest, and numerous varieties grown have been originated there. Probably twice as much acreage is in cane fruits as in strawberries, but the acreage of no single cane fruit equals the acreage of strawberries. Commercial production of the cane berries is concentrated in the Portland area, in the Willamette Valley, and in the northern half of the Puget Sound Basin. The cane fruits are produced both west and east of Portland south to Salem in important quantities.

In Washington, the Puyallup Valley and other fertile areas adjacent to Seattle, Tacoma, and Olympia are leading producing areas, with important amounts of fruit coming from around Bellingham, the Skagit and Snohomish valleys, and other sections north of Seattle. The small-fruit industry of the Puyallup-Sumner (Plate 20A) area of Pierce and King counties is in a section devoted largely to the culture of berry crops and has the advantage of nearby labor supply from Tacoma and Seattle. The building of canneries was another favorable factor. In the specialized berry area of King and Pierce counties the berry farms average 5 to 20 acres in size, with many of them 3 acres or less. They are intensively cultivated with but little waste land. The ideal climatic and soil conditions, combined with care and skill exercised by growers, result in heavy yields. The land is high in price, but the berry crops return interest on the high valuations. The cane fruits are grown mainly on the bottomlands and strawberries more frequently on the upland soils.

The yield of small fruits varies widely, depending on care given the variety of fruit, the natural conditions, etc. A survey in Oregon indicates that the usual yield in tons per acre was for strawberries 1.70, red raspberries 1.75, blackberries 3.50, blackcaps 1.05, loganberries 1.85, and gooseberries 2.15. The volume of berries per unit of weight varies with the fruit but can be estimated at around 1000 quarts per ton of berries. Certain factors, especially the greater availability of moisture in the small-fruit districts of Washington, cause berry yields to exceed usual yields in Oregon by 25 to 50 per cent.

Strawberries

Strawberries are grown under a variety of conditions by small growers who must use land at their disposal; but the fruit is exacting in its soil and climatic requirements, and commercial districts must have favorable factors of soil, drainage, slope of lands, and freedom from frost hazards, and in addition they must be close to transportation and labor supply. Gently sloping land with well-drained, fine sandy-loam soil, underlain by a firmer-textured subsoil, is best. Such soil should be fetrile and contain abundant organic matter. Care must be used in setting strawberries, in mulching the patches where severe winters occur, and in keeping the soil in good tilth and free of weeds and pests. Obviously experience and careful attention are required to grow quality strawberries successfully.

Strawberries are the leading small fruit. In the United States as a whole, strawberries account for one-half the acreage of berries, but the proportion in the Northwest is somewhat less than this. Production of strawberries is especially important in the Willamette Valley, and in the entire Puget Sound Lowland, including the island counties. The Hood River Valley, Spokane Valley, Kennewick, Walla Walla, and Umatilla districts east of the mountains are other areas. In Washington about 1,150,000 crates of strawberries are harvested from an estimated 7700 acres annually, and in Oregon about 13,600 acres are planted to the fruit. Some berries are grown in the Snake River Valley, especially the western portion, in northern Idaho, in the Bitterroot and Flathead valleys of Montana, and in the Fraser River Valley and Vancouver Island of British Columbia. About 37 million pounds of strawberries are sold from Oregon and 25 million from Washington per year, in addition to those consumed by the producers.

FACTORS AND ACREAGE. Both cane and bush fruits require, for optimum growth, fertile soil, humid conditions, and absence of excessively hot, dry weather. Since a market and labor for picking are prime essentials, most cane and bush fruits are grown near centers of population on the west side of the Cascades, where sufficient land suitable for the crop is available.

According to the census, the acreage devoted to commercial small fruits in the Northwest is between two and three times the number of farms that report production, which indicates that the average grower has about 2½ acres in strawberries or other small fruits. In all, over 5000 farms in Washington and nearly 10,000 farms in Oregon sell small fruits of various sorts, with the acreage in Washington approximating 13,700 and in Oregon 27,000. Most of Idaho's production of small fruits is on a small scale. Thus, whereas 3000 farms report strawberries, the entire acreage is less than 700, and with 5000 farms reporting bush or cane fruits the acreage is little more than 800 acres, so that the state is hardly self-supporting in this respect. The same situation exists in western Montana. As the small fruits are listed separately by the census, there is some duplication involved in the total farms.

RASPBERRIES. Raspberries are the most important of the cane fruits in the Willamette-Puget Lowland, especially in Washington, which has 4500 acres in raspberries, compared to 1500 in blackberries, loganberries, and youngberries. Oregon has 2500 acres of raspberries, 2100 acres of loganberries, youngberries, and boysenberries, and 780 acres of blackberries and dewberries. Gooseberries and currants are of limited importance.

MISCELLANEOUS FRUITS. Increasing quantities of grapes, mostly of the Concord variety, are being marketed from the Yakima Valley for home consumption. At Kennewick, Washington, a factory bottles grape juice from its own vineyards of several hundred acres and, in addition, buys grapes from farmer growers. Concord grapes, for juice, are picked when fully ripe, and the juice is pasteurized and kept at proper temperature to prevent spoilage until bottled, which is done throughout most of the year.

Washington fruit juices are now the basis for a growing wine-making industry on both sides of the Cascades. The Hood Canal district of western Washington has a grape-growing, juice-bottling, and wine-making industry centering in Mason County. In eastern Washington, districts such as the Yakima Valley have established wineries using grapes; wines and cordials are also made from apples and berries.

Cranberries are highly localized, in Pacific County near Willapa Bay and near Grays Harbor in Washington, and Coos Bay in Oregon. They were introduced from the East and have found their natural conditions near the seacoast in peat bogs "fertilized" with acid sand

and will thus utilize situations where possibilities for agriculture are poor. Since the Northwest does not supply its own consumption of cranberries, there is an expansion potential here. Considerable expense is required to prepare a bog for cranberries. Numerous pickers are needed to gather the crop. Usually the Washington output of cranberries totals about 25,000 barrels and that of Oregon 12,000.

Several hundred thousand gallons of wild huckleberries are marketed from the mountains of the Northwest each year, and much larger quantities than this are wasted. Experimental canning of the fruit has been tried at Libby, Montana, and other places, but no large output like that of the blueberry of the Northeast has yet resulted. There seems little doubt that, by artificially propagating and taking care of huckleberries and planting them for canning purposes on cut-over land now out of use, a valuable new industry might be developed.

Vegetable Production

All kinds of vegetables flourish in the Northwest. Vegetables are produced in home gardens for domestic use, and they are grown in market gardens and on truck farms to supply the demand for fresh produce in the urban centers. Like small fruits, the value of vegetables per acre is high in proportion to that of wheat or other field crops. For instance, in 1949, about 90,000 acres in Washington produced vegetables that sold for nearly $15,000,000. Forty thousand Oregon farms grow vegetables for home use. In 1949 over 3600 Oregon farms grew vegetables for sale on 91,000 acres, and these crops sold for $16,738,000. The largest acreage was in green peas, sweet corn, green beans, and onions. Some asparagus, lettuce, tomatoes, etc., are shipped outside the state, especially eastward into Montana, but on the whole the marketing of vegetables is a local business.

Some 30,000 acres of rich diked land along the lower Columbia River below Portland is well adapted by soil, climate, and water supply to peas, beans, and other vegetables. Typical yields in tons per acre are: string beans, 6–8; carrots, 12–15; beets, 12–14; cabbage, 15–30; and unshelled peas, 3–6. Green beans, beets, carrots, and peas have been extensively canned in this district. A quick-freeze packing plant is located at Hillsboro. Growers also sell quantities of fresh celery, cauliflower, broccoli, and cabbage from the diked lands.

Onions are grown extensively in the northern Willamette Valley. The Umpqua and Rogue River valleys are other important districts for certain vagetables, including tomatoes. The Northwest is comparatively free of insects and fungus diseases affecting truck crops.

In Washington lettuce is the most valuable vegetable crop, especially during the summer when hot weather elsewhere in the United States precludes the growing of good head lettuce. In the Kent district and other sections of Puget Sound, 2000 acres are devoted to lettuce each year. Western Washington lettuce considerably exceeds the consuming capacity of the local area, and hundreds of carloads are exported each summer, some to distant markets.

Commercial asparagus is grown in the Yakima Valley, around Kennewick, and at Walla Walla. The Walla Walla district is also noted for its spinach. The acreage of tomatoes has been increasing rapidly. Melon and squash are found mainly in the irrigated sections east of the mountains, especially along the Columbia and in the Yakima and Walla Walla valleys, with the Roseburg district leading in western Oregon. Cucumbers are raised both for marketing fresh and for pickling.

Many sections of the Northwest raise peas which are dried and shipped to eastern markets, where they are either processed for food or are used to supply seed distributors. The larger part of the pea seed comes from southeastern Spokane County and around the Blue Mountains. The Twin Falls region, Idaho, and the Bozeman district of Montana also market dry peas.

DEVELOPMENT OF CANNERIES. To an increasing degree vegetables are being grown for sale to canneries. Although canneries are rather widely distributed, the principal producing areas are: in Washington, the Walla Walla, Dayton, Waitsburg, Ellensburg, Mt. Vernon, East Stanwood, and Montesano regions; in Montana, the Bozeman area; in Idaho, the Payette district; in Oregon, the Athena and Milton-Freewater districts, and the diked lands from Portland to Astoria. Among freezing plants for peas and other vegetables are those at Snohomish, Kent, Monroe, and La Conner in western Washington.

Peas are by far the most important of all vegetables grown for canning in this region. The output of peas, both in the northern Puget Sound district and upon the slopes descending from the Blue Mountains of Washington and Oregon near the towns of Dayton, Walla Walla, Athena, and Milton-Freewater, supports a large canning industry. Washington is now one of the leading pea-packing states though as recently as the 1930's the output was inconsiderable.

Along the foothill regions bordering the Blue Mountains in Washington and Oregon, canning peas come from different elevations. Because of varying rates of growth, these areas supply the canneries for a run of several weeks. This district alone supplies one-fourth of all the peas canned in the United States. Pea canneries in areas that can raise other vegetables, such as spinach, asparagus, and tomatoes, often process them during seasons when peas are not available. This is especially true of Washington canneries.

Such vegetables as green beans, cabbage, asparagus, carrots, beets, spinach, and tomatoes as well as some sweet corn are also packed. The Payette region produces and cans sweet corn and tomatoes; Dayton and Walla Walla process almost all vegetables mentioned. A factory to manufacture cans is located at Walla Walla.

By furnishing a definite cash outlet for small fruits and vegetables, canneries have helped materially to stabilize the farmer's market. The haul from the farm to the plant usually is short, and the grower delivers his vegetables or fruit when they are prime.

CONCLUSIONS. On the whole the Puget-Willamette Lowlands are more important in the vegetable and truck industry than areas east of the mountains, probably owing to a combination of proximity to large consuming centers of the Northwest combined with marine-type rainfall, relative coolness, and a long growing season. Another factor is that west-side cutover land is expensive to clear, so that it is almost necessary to grow something of high value per acre like vegetables or small fruits on the small acreage cleared, rather than to devote the space to field crops.

REFERENCES

Crowley, D. J., "The Cultivated Cranberry in Washington," *State College of Washington Agricultural Experiment Station Bulletin* 349, Pullman, 1937.

Physical and Economic Geography of Oregon, pp. 171–182, Oregon State Board of Higher Education, 1940.

Seaman, A. K., "Cranberry Industry of the Pacific Coast," *Economic Geography*, Vol. 17, pp. 180–186.

"Strawberry Growing in Washington," *Extension Service Bulletin* 246, State College of Washington, 1938.

Sulerud, George L., and M. N. Nelson, "An Economic Study of the Small Fruit Industry in Oregon," *Oregon State College Agricultural Experiment Station Bulletin* 274, Corvallis, 1931.

Specialty and Forage Crops

HOWARD J. CRITCHFIELD

At least one-third of the farm income of the Pacific Northwest is derived directly from specialty [1] and forage crops, and a large part of the income from dairying and livestock raising depends indirectly on forage crops. Although production of these crops is rather widely scattered throughout the northwestern states, there is a marked concentration in four general areas: the Willamette Valley of Oregon, the Puget Sound Lowland and Yakima Valley in Washington, and the Snake River Plain in Idaho.

Several factors influence the distribution and quantity of production of specialty crops. Moisture, temperature, and soil conditions together or singly often determine the best locality for a specific crop. Because many specialty crops can be grown successfully only under certain climatic conditions, those localities which have naturally suitable climates or where moisture deficiencies can be overcome through irrigation have the majority of such crops. Forage crops have a wider distribution which bears a relation to the animal industries but they play an important role in the rotation systems on specialty crop farms and are frequently grown as cash crops. Insect pests and diseases are significant factors in the growing of most specialty crops, especially seeds. Some crops experience a shift from one locality to another solely because of insect or disease infestation. Specialty crops in general require intensive use of the land and large amounts of labor. The difficulty of securing seasonal labor is being met increasingly by mechanization, however. For some crops expensive growing, processing, storage, and marketing facilities are necessary, and the availability of the facilities or the capital to provide them frequently contributes to the localization of production. Fluctuations in the market

[1] For definitions of specialty farms see Chapter 16.

347

price for a crop are normally reflected in varying production. Competition from other regions of the United States or foreign sources may directly affect prices, although government subsidies and tariffs counteract these factors in some instances. There is also considerable competition among the various specialty crops for arable land. If the market price for one crop decreases in relation to other crops it is likely to be replaced by one of the higher-paying specialties.

Many of the specialty crops grown in the Pacific Northwest were introduced from the analogous climate of the British Isles and northwestern Europe. Plant varieties and cultivation methods suited to local conditions have been developed by government agencies and farmers to the point where the United States is no longer dependent upon European countries for such imports as hops, vegetable and grass seeds, and flower bulbs. Experimentation is being carried on in the Pacific Northwest, and the acreage, yields, and number of specialty crops may be expected to increase.

Potatoes

Potatoes are grown throughout the Pacific Northwest both for domestic consumption and commercially. Although the potatoes from small patches found on most farms are an important subsistence crop and may even enter local commerce, the bulk of production comes from larger acreages in irrigated areas where growing conditions can be more easily controlled. The trend in commercial potato production in recent years has been away from nonirrigated areas as competition between potato-growing districts has increased. This is especially true in Oregon, where acreages have declined in the Willamette Valley while there have been increases in the irrigated lands in the central and eastern parts of the state.

The principal potato-growing areas of the Pacific Northwest are in the Snake River Plain of southern Idaho, the valleys of western Montana, the Yakima Valley of Washington, and the irrigated lands of central and eastern Oregon, especially in Deschutes, Klamath, and Malheur counties.

1951 POTATO PRODUCTION IN NORTHWEST STATES

	Acres	Bushels
Montana	10,000	2,150,000
Idaho	134,000	37,520,000
Washington	29,000	11,600,000
Oregon	34,000	11,220,000

The warm days and cool nights characteristic of the Pacific Northwest summers are ideal for potato production. Because they do not require such a long frost-free season potatoes may be grown in valley bottoms, whereas slopes and benchlands are reserved for more delicate crops such as fruits. The precipitation factor is not critical where production is carried out under irrigation. But whether it is furnished by rainfall or irrigation a steady supply of soil moisture is necessary for the smooth, well-formed tubers demanded by the retail market. The preferred soils for potatoes are loams, silt loams, or sandy loams with deep subsoils and good drainage. Generally potatoes respond well to organic fertilizers and their requirement of potassium is relatively high. Commercial fertilizers consisting of varying amounts of nitrate, phosphate, and potash are applied by many farmers. Rotation with legumes is also widely practiced to help maintain soil fertility and combat diseases and insects.

Commercial potato growers usually prefer to plant certified seed as a safeguard against certain diseases and to insure uniform quality. Certified potato seed is frequently grown outside the areas of commercial production where the factor of isolation favors disease control and purer varieties. The parent seed for seed-potato production is usually brought in from a distant area; much of that used in the Pacific Northwest is developed in California.

In the areas of commercial production, potatoes are planted, cultivated, and harvested almost entirely by machinery. Combination digging and sacking machines called "potato combines" are becoming common because they reduce the amount of labor needed for harvesting.

Potatoes compete with truck crops or sugar beets for land in most irrigated areas, and acreages fluctuate appreciably in response to the relative prices of these crops. The average commercial potato grower is equipped with machinery that may be used for any of several row crops, and his acreage of potatoes in any one year is influenced by market forecasts. Because the retail consumer buys in small quantities throughout the year, storage is one of the problems of the potato industry. In high-producing districts the crop is usually stored in large cooperative potato cellars for gradual release into trade channels. There is but a minor market for processed potatoes. During World War II dehydration was developed in southern Idaho and in Oregon, but the special conditions which favored this outlet for potato surpluses no longer exist.

Sugar Beets

Sugar beets have had an erratic history in connection with irrigation agriculture in the Pacific Northwest. The first sugar-beet factory was established at Idaho Falls in 1903, and southeastern Idaho remains the principal producing area. Between 1920 and 1930 curly-top disease was the cause of decreased yields throughout the intermountain region of the western United States. As a result factories in the Yakima Valley were forced to close. Use of curly-top-resistant varieties has permitted a revival of production in some of the affected areas, and both world wars have brought a stimulus to sugar-beet output. Government subsidies, tariffs on imported cane sugar, and the competition of other row crops for the land have also influenced acreages. Today the centers of production and refining are in the Snake River Plain region of Idaho and adjacent Oregon, in the Columbia Basin and Yakima Valley, and in widely distributed Montana localities. In 1951 Idaho ranked as the third sugar-beet-producing state, with an output of 1,253,000 tons.

The optimum climate for sugar beets is virtually the same as for potatoes. Cool nights and sunny days are conducive to the formation of a high percentage of sugar in the sugar-beet root. Moisture requirements are met by irrigation, and the quality of the beets can be controlled to some extent by irrigation procedures. The best soils for sugar beets have a slightly alkaline reaction and a high organic-matter content. Because organic matter is ordinarily deficient in the dry-land soils of the Pacific Northwest it is commonly provided by a green-manure crop in the crop rotation.

Sugar beets are grown under contract agreement with the refineries, and the sugar-beet companies supply disease-resistant varieties of seed. Seed is produced to some extent throughout the sugar-beet-growing areas, but there is a tendency to bring it from remote localities. Much of the seed sown in the Pacific Northwest comes from Utah, Arizona, and California, and sugar-beet seed production is being developed in the Willamette and Rogue River valleys of Oregon. In common with most other row crops sugar-beet production is becoming mechanized in all its phases. Considerable hand labor is still employed, however, Mexican laborers forming a large share of the working force in several localities. About three-fourths of the sugar-beet crop is taken to the refinery by rail from open storage dumps situated at convenient places in the producing areas. The value of sugar beets is high and increased sharply during World War II. In the Yakima Valley, for example, the total returns per acre from the refinery and the government subsidy increased from $93.20 in 1938 to $245.78 in 1945.[2]

Beet tops, beet pulp, and molasses are valuable by-products of the beet-sugar industry, and all are important as livestock feed. They form the principal feeds for fattening thousands of lambs and beef cattle, especially in the Snake Valley.

Expansion of sugar-beet production in the Pacific Northwest depends largely on international sugar economics and the maintenance of government price supports. Some 40,000 acres near Moses Lake, Washington, are expected to be in beets as Columbia Basin irrigation is developed.

Hops

Almost all the commercial hop yards of the United States are in the states of Washington, Oregon, and California. Idaho and New York each have a small production. The major producing areas in the Pacific Northwest are in the Willamette Valley and in the Yakima Valley districts of Tampico, Moxee City, Sunnyside, Mabton, and Prosser. There is minor output in the Rogue River Valley near Grants Pass, the Puget Sound Lowland near Tacoma, and in the Snake Valley near Twin Falls.

HOP PRODUCTION IN PACIFIC NORTHWEST, 1951

	Acres	Yield per Acre, pounds	Total Yield, pounds
Idaho	1,500	1695	2,543,000
Washington	15,300	1790	27,387,000
Oregon	14,900	1260	18,774,000

Hops are grown for use primarily in the brewing industry as a flavoring and clarifying agent. They have a limited market for use in the manufacture of breakfast foods, yeast, and certain pharmaceutical preparations. The hop plant has rather rigid soil and climatic requirements for maximum yields and it is subject to attack by several diseases, the most troublesome of which is downy mildew. Hop production demands much hand labor; thinning and training of the vines on trellises are still hand operations, but cultivation and harvesting (Plate 20B) have become largely mechanized. In the Yakima Valley,

[2] C. Emil Nelson and Everette Kreizinger, "Sugar Beet Production in Irrigated Central Washington," *State College of Washington Extension Service Bulletin* 365, p. 2.

98 per cent of the hops are harvested by machine but in the Willamette Valley three-fourths of the crop is still picked by hand.[3] After harvesting, the hops are cured in kilns and then baled in burlap for shipment to markets all over the United States. For a time after World War II hops were exported to Europe, but this market is decreasing as the European hop yards become rehabilitated. The quantity of hops produced in the Pacific Northwest is related to foreign competition as well as to demand among United States brewers.

Fiber-Flax and Flaxseed

Fiber-flax has been grown in the Willamette Valley since the middle of the last century, but it did not become an established crop until a flax mill was constructed at the Oregon State Penitentiary in 1915. The Willamette Valley is now the only significant fiber-flax producing area in the nation. Increased demands and government subsidies during World War II were a stimulus to production, and facilities now exist in the Willamette Valley for fiber from 20,000 acres. Actual acreages vary somewhat from year to year, however. The total area fell from 18,000 acres in 1942 to 1000 acres in 1950 but rose again to 3300 acres in 1951. Mechanical methods of harvesting have eliminated part of the heavy labor requirement but foreign competition with respect to both price and quality is a principal factor in holding down production in peacetime.

The flax fiber produced in Oregon is used primarily in cordage, sackcloth, and other coarse materials. The short tangled fibers, known as tow, have several uses, among them being in the making of paper for currency. Improvement of quality to a standard satisfactory for fine linen can be achieved through improved cultivation and harvesting methods and more careful selection of flax varieties.

Flax for seed is grown in several farming areas of the Northwest, but the Willamette Valley is the leading area for this crop also. The center of linseed-oil pressing in the Pacific Northwest is Portland. The products of flaxseed pressing are linseed oil, which is used extensively in the manufacture of paints and enamels, and linseed meal, which is valuable as a livestock feed. Except for a portion kept for sowing, flaxseed removed from the straw of fiber-flax at the mill is also sold to be pressed for its oil.

[3] Elbert E. Miller and Richard M. Highsmith, Jr., "The Hop Industry of the Pacific Coast," *Journal of Geography*, February, 1950, p. 66.

Specialty Nursery Crops

A number of nursery crops are adapted to the climate and soils of western Washington and Oregon. Acreages of young fruit trees, berry plants, and ornamentals have been increased largely in response to the expanding market in the Pacific Northwest. Thousands of species and varieties of trees, shrubs, and bushes are grown. Some nurserymen concentrate on a few items; others grow many kinds of nursery crops. Holly is a crop that has had a considerable increase in production in the past decade, particularly in western Oregon.

Cut flowers, flower seeds, and bulbs are grown chiefly in the Puget Sound Lowland and the Willamette Valley, but these specialties are now being developed on a small scale in other parts of the Pacific Northwest. The leading bulb crops are lilies, gladioli, narcissi, irises, tulips, and dahlias. Flower-bulb production in the Nooksack Valley north of Bellingham is carried on by descendants of immigrants from Holland. Curry County, Oregon, ranks high in the production of Easter lilies, and Puyallup, Washington, is a daffodil center. The principal cut flowers grown in the open are chrysanthemums, asters, peonies, and daffodils, although others may be marketed by bulb growers to supplement their income. Flower seeds are grown commercially in widely scattered areas, usually in small acreages.

Vegetable Seeds

In the past a large part of the vegetable-seed requirements of the Pacific Northwest was met by imports from abroad, chiefly Europe. In both world wars there was a marked increase in acreage of vegetable seed crops, and today the Northwest produces surpluses of several garden seeds. Areas in which vegetable growing is profitable are not necessarily suited to production of vegetable seed. Insect pests and diseases are often critical factors and contribute to risk in production. Special care is necessary for most vegetable-seed crops and a great amount of hand labor is required. During the flowering period the seed fields are "rogued" by hand to remove weeds and plants that are poor in quality or of the wrong variety. Most of the common garden vegetables are biennials, requiring 2 years' use of the land for a seed crop.

Garden-seed production is a highly localized activity because only certain areas have soil and climatic conditions suitable for growing a specific type of seed. Cabbage, cauliflower, rutabaga, turnip, radish, and beet seeds are grown primarily in the Puget Sound Lowland.

The major producing area for seed peas is in North Idaho and eastern Washington, especially the Palouse Hills. In Idaho onion seed is a specialty near Lewiston, and garlic seed is produced near Parma. Cucumber and squash seeds are grown chiefly in the Willamette Valley. Similarly other vegetable seeds are harvested in widely separated locations.

Miscellaneous Specialty Crops

Several crops with highly specialized uses and limited markets occupy small acreages in the coastal areas or in the interior on irrigated land. Peppermint, grown for the essential oil in its leaves, is one of the most important of these. The value of the 1951 crop in the Pacific Northwest exceeded $6,000,000. Peppermint is grown in the Willamette Valley, along the Columbia River on both sides near its mouth, and in the Yakima Valley from Yakima to Kennewick. In the Willamette Valley the acreage has more than doubled since World War II in response to high prices.

Mustard seed for use in condiment manufacture is grown chiefly in Montana and Washington, the acreage varying greatly from year to year. Idaho is the only state with a significant production of rapeseed. Other crops grown on a small scale as food seasonings or for medicinal purposes in the western counties of Washington and Oregon are dill seed, ginseng root, golden seal, sage, caraway, anise, safflower, and pyrethrum.

Forage Crops

Grasses and legumes rank high in the acreage of land devoted to crops because of their value both as a basis for the livestock industries and in crop rotation for soil conservation or insect and disease control. There is an increasing tendency toward "grassland farming," particularly west of the Cascade Range, where the milder climate permits a longer pasture season. It has been estimated that about 90 per cent of the farmland of coastal Oregon is used for the production of forage crops.[4] Because of the labor saved, pasturing is the most economical method of converting grasses and legumes into meat or dairy products. Various pasture seed mixtures are sown according to local conditions of soil, climate, and drainage. The more common constituents of pasture mixtures are white, red, alsike, or ladino clover,

---

[4] H. B. Howell and Arthur S. King, "Forage Crops for Coast Counties of Oregon," *Oregon State College Extension Bulletin 707*, p. 3.

rye grasses, bent grasses, crested wheat grass, orchard grass, alta fescue, creeping fescue, brome, timothy, and meadow foxtail. Alfalfa is sometimes included in place of one of the clovers in irrigated pastures. Similarly other species are sown in certain localities for special purposes. Reed canary grass is adapted to lowlands subject to flooding. Lotus major is a legume that thrives on acidic soils. Burnett, a member of the rose family, is a useful pasture plant on logged-off lands west of the Cascades.

The same grasses and legumes which are sown for pastures are also harvested for hay and silage. Largely because rain at haying time may cause damage to hay crops there has been a trend toward silage as a more efficient way of storing forage crops. Drying grass by means of artificial heat is also a method of preserving forage. Aside from direct pasturage, however, hay still ranks first as a method of utilizing green forage crops.

The leading hay crop of the Pacific Northwest is alfalfa. Of the perennial legumes it produces the highest yields per acre and has the highest quality in terms of feed value. Although it is generally grown for hay it is also used in pastures and silage. Alfalfa is tolerant of alkali soils and yields well in the irrigated areas of the interior valleys and plains, where it is the fundamental link in the crop-livestock association. It has also been an important crop on cutover forest lands, especially in Idaho and Montana, but lime and fertilizers are required to establish alfalfa on forest soils. Since alfalfa is a perennial the fields are usually kept in production for several years and the crop assumes a different role in crop rotation from most other forage crops. The leading areas of production are the Snake River Plain, Yakima Valley, and Malheur County in eastern Oregon. Most of Montana's alfalfa acreage lies east of the Rocky Mountains.

1951 ALFALFA PRODUCTION

	Acres	Tons
Montana	657,000	1,018,000
Idaho	726,000	1,888,000
Washington	303,000	621,000
Oregon	217,000	575,000

Alfalfa enters into interstate and interregional commerce more than any other hay crop. For many irrigated farms it is a cash crop to be sold locally to livestock or dairy producers or to be shipped, usually by truck, to remote dairying or animal fattening centers. In Washington and Oregon there is a general movement of baled alfalfa from the irrigated farms of the arid interior to the coastal areas where alfalfa is not suited to soil and climatic conditions.

In addition to the pasture plants commonly cut for hay and silage, the grains are also important fodders. Oats is the principal small grain cut for hay in many localities, and corn is an important silage crop on the Snake River Plain. Sorghums, millets, and Sudan grass are grown in drier parts of the Pacific Northwest as forage crops, but the total acreage has never been great.

Grass and Legume Seeds

Harvesting of grass and legume seeds is a logical adjunct to hay and pasture production, and the dry summers characteristic of the Pacific Northwest generally favor expansion of this phase of grassland farming. Grass seed is increasing as a cash crop in irrigated lands where it may be used as a soil builder and at the same time provide a cash income. Most localities specialize in one or two species that are well adapted to the local conditions. The most important producing areas are in the Snake, Yakima, and Willamette valleys. The last has climatic advantages that have favored its development into one of the leading grass seed areas of the United States. The Willamette Valley is particularly noted for the production of rye grass, bent grass, and fescue seeds. Oregon supplies virtually all the nation's rye-grass seed and a large proportion of the lawn-grass seeds. Idaho is the leading state for white-clover seed. The irrigated Yakima and Snake valleys are leading producers of alfalfa seed. Washington has the highest per acre yield of alfalfa seed among the states and in 1951 was second to California in total production with 294,000 bushels.

Because of widespread production of hay and forage crops in the Pacific Northwest there is a heavy demand for seeds within the region. Seeds are also marketed in many parts of the United States according to the demand. Certain seeds have special markets. Alfalfa seeds find a market in the Great Plains and in California. Vetch and seed peas are sold chiefly in the southeastern states. Austrian field peas have been grown extensively in the Palouse area and in eastern Oregon for sale in the United States and for export.

Dry peas and dry beans are grown in the interior districts both on irrigated and nonirrigated land for human consumption as well as seed. Washington produces over two-thirds of the dry field peas in the United States and Idaho is the third ranking state in dry-bean production.

REFERENCES

Klages, K. H. W., *Ecological Crop Geography*, The Macmillan Co., New York, 1942.

Miller, Elbert E., and Richard M. Highsmith, Jr., "The Hop Industry of the Pacific Coast," *Journal of Geography*, Vol. XLIX, No. 2, pp. 63–77, February, 1950.

Oregon State College Agricultural Experiment Station Bulletins 365, 425, 437, 455, 484, 677, 692, 694, 696, 701, 707, 713; *Oregon Agriculture Series* 1, 2, 8; and *Station Circulars* 114, 133.

State College of Washington Agricultural Extension Bulletins 319, 365; *Extension Circulars* 28, 48, 81, 83, 109.

U. S. Department of Agriculture Farmers' Bulletins 1539, 1722, 1903, 1988; *Leaflet* 93; *Bureau of Agricultural Economics Annual Summary of Crop Production*, 1951.

University of Idaho Agricultural Experiment Station Bulletins 140, 224.

CHAPTER
21

Livestock in the
Pacific Northwest

WILLIS B. MERRIAM

Early explorers in the Columbia Basin and other unforested areas throughout the Northwest commented upon the vast expanse of luxuriant grasslands. In time, these lands were stocked with cattle and sheep, which were succeeded later by waving wheat fields, but there are still thousands of acres where grazing is dominant. The livestock business is of special value to the Northwest because it makes use of the thousands of acres of "too" lands—lands too rough, too dry, too mountainous, too wet, too frosty, or too remote from market for cultivation. Grazing and animal fattening are also complementary to certain types of agriculture, since they utilize forage crops and by-products otherwise wasted, such as sugar-beet tops and pea vines. Grazing and fattening of livestock are so widely scattered over the Northwest that in a larger sense the region may be regarded as one vast animal pasture.

Early Cattle Raising

Although a few head of livestock were brought in by early settlers, the industry really began in the middle 1820's. Cattle raising to supply meat to the various fur-trading posts was inaugurated at Fort Vancouver in 1825, and in 1826 small herds appeared in the Colville and Okanogan valleys. Cattle driven across the plains were a feature of the Wallula settlement in 1824, and it is estimated that 200,000 head were in the Walla Walla country by 1855. The Indian wars after 1855 caused a reduction in numbers, but with the arrival of more settlers during the 1860's and 1870's cattle again increased. During the 1860's herds from Utah and California were driven into Idaho and western Montana. Somewhat later, cattle drives of breeding stock came north from Texas. There were two main reasons for the rapid rise of range stock at this time: the growing local market centered mainly around military posts and the gold camps in the mountains of Idaho and British Columbia. After the decline of this mining, many drives of Oregon cattle (as all Northwest stock was called) were made to Nevada and Wyoming railheads for shipment east.

The Diminishing Range

During the early years much of the Pacific Northwest was a free range open to anyone, but markets were few and distant and livestock was not profitable. Before 1880 overgrazing became common and the range had deteriorated. Stockmen, however, were determined to make a fortune while the grazing lasted. Not only did overgrazing and overproduction handicap the cattlemen of this time, but severe winters periodically destroyed the natural increase of the herds on the open range. Tremendous numbers of cattle were lost during the bitter winter of 1861–62. The winters of 1885–86 and 1889–90 also killed thousands. As a result, the more progressive stockmen began to provide some winter shelter and hay for their stock, introducing the first fixed agriculture to many parts of the Northwest.

Settlers also took up much of the best grazing land for homesteads, in spite of opposition on the part of the stock ranchers. In Washington desirable free range had almost vanished by 1880. The completion of the Northern Pacific Railroad in 1883, followed by other railroads, helped further to change the character of the livestock business. It became easier to ship cattle to market and more profitable to improve the stock, but the railroad also encouraged settlement by farmers. Each new farm and fence crowded out more stockmen, thus hastening the end of the free range in the better areas. Here alfalfa fields and permanent haystacks brought a change to pure-blood stock and the marketing of baby beef and caused a shift to dairy herds.

Conditions Affecting the Livestock Industry

Except on the western slopes of the Cascades and Coast Range, the Pacific Northwest is characterized by a limited rainfall and generally low humidity. The dry climate and moderate temperatures of the interior plateaus, desert plains, and mountain pastures are, on the whole, favorable for livestock. Except in high mountains the snowfall is moderate, sleet storms seldom occur, and animals require little or no shelter even when temperatures become quite low, although hay or other forage must be supplied in cold or snowy weather. Untilled grasslands, open woods and forest meadows, wet pastures, and both irrigated and dry agricultural lands make their contribution to the livestock industry. Census figures indicate about 175,461,000 acres of land in the area encompassed by this study of which only about one-tenth is actually in crops. In the states comprising the region, percentage of all land in farms ranges from about 22 per cent for Idaho to 38 per cent for Washington. The balance is made up of national forests, Indian reservations, national parks, and unappropriated governmental land or miscellaneous privately owned lands, much of which is also used for grazing.

Present Grazing Area

Of 52,997,120 acres of land in Idaho, about 40,888,000 acres (77 per cent) are classified as actual or potential grazing land, including about half of the 12,503,000 acres in "farms." In proportion, Washington has less grazing land than the rest of the Northwest; of its 42,865,-280 acres about 16,720,000 are in farms (38 per cent), of which 6 million acres provide grazing. There is very little usable open range in Washington but considerable forest pasture, both publicly and privately owned, is available, raising the total to 14,870,000 acres or 35 per cent of the state. With 61,664,000 acres, one-quarter (25.8 per cent) of Oregon's total area is in public domain; most of this is range and grazing land located mainly in the dry central and southeastern sections. Nearly half (42 per cent) of Oregon is privately owned land of which 16 per cent is in crops, 43 per cent in timber, and 57 per cent in grazing land including some forestland.

ACREAGE OF RANGE LAND IN THE PACIFIC NORTHWEST *

(in thousands of acres)

State	Idaho	Oregon	Washington	Montana	Total
Total acreage	52,997	61,664	42,865	17,935	175,461
Private woodland pastured	946	1,529	1,252	213	3,940
Private rangeland	6,230	10,056	6,427	1,675	24,388
National forest	20,162	8,680	3,923	8,792	41,537
Grazing district and public domain	12,748	13,211	577	2,320	28,836
Indian lands	802	1,804	2,713	3,000	8,319
	40,888	35,280	14,872	16,000	107,040

* From the U. S. Department of Agriculture.

Including mountainous western Montana's seventeen counties, most of which are rangeland, probably 107 million acres of the northwestern states are or could be used for grazing.

Decline in Carrying Capacity

The area available tells only part of the story since the carrying capacity of the range varies widely. Feed for one cow may be provided by an acre of wet pasture or 100 acres of semidesert herbage. Where serious deterioration of the range has occurred, the carrying capacity may be only one-third of what it was originally. Government surveys indicate that virgin forage has had an average decline of 68 per cent in southern Idaho and 65 per cent in eastern Oregon. A survey by the Federal Land Bank of Spokane shows that the range in the mountain counties of western Montana has deteriorated 56 to 63 per cent. Where formerly 2 or 3 acres of virgin grazing land per month sufficed to feed one cow, now 5 to 8 acres are needed. This depletion has therefore materially decreased the carrying capacity of the area.

Income from Livestock

Annual farm income for the three northwest states and western Montana averages about $850,000,000 from crops and $575,000,000 from livestock and animal products.

Although dairy produce and poultry are included in the totals shown by the table, the income from sale of beef, mutton, pork, and wool totals well over $285,000,000 per year for the Northwest. From the range alone, livestock operations provide approximately 24 per cent of the agricultural income, running as high as 40 per cent in western Montana, 20 per cent in Oregon, 25 per cent in Idaho, and 11 per cent in Washington.

Present Livestock Conditions

From the standpoint of value, beef cattle represent the leading aspect of the Northwest livestock industry, with some 2,150,000 beef-class cattle having an assessed valuation of over $300,000,000. Cattle are rather evenly distributed over eastern and southern Oregon, the less mountainous parts of Idaho, western Montana (Plate 24B), northeastern Washington, the valleys and plateaus of southern British Columbia, and the Scablands, semideserts, and rough uplands of the Columbia plateau. The lowlands in western Washington and Oregon and the rugged northwest mountains are minor areas of production.

Some beef animals are marketed every year from the dairying and general farming sections on both sides of the Cascades.

Beef Cattle

The beef-cattle industry has been undergoing a number of changes. The former practice was to stock the range to the limit of carrying capacity and keep the steers on pasture until they were 3 to 5 years old and weighed 1300 to 1600 pounds. Present market demand favors undermature animals, yearlings, and 2-year-olds averaging 900 to 1200 pounds, which require more and better fodder, especially during the winter. The number of animals on the range has not changed appreciably since 1920, although local increases have occurred where more land is in permanent or cultivated pasture.

Beef prices rose sharply during World War I, declined in the 1930's, again rose sharply during World War II, only to decline again in the early 1950's. At the same time taxes, general costs of production, and priming for market have increased to such a point that the livestock industry is not considered as profitable as in earlier times. In the days of the open range a steer could be raised for as little as $3 per head per year, but costs are now many times that amount. On average range land, about 40 acres are required for a cow per year. The grazing season in the mountain counties is 7 to 7½ months, and the winter feeding is about 4½ months. Hay is the usual winter feed, prices averaging $20 to $30 per ton, in contrast to $6 to $8 per ton during the 1930's. Compared with most farming operations, relatively little hired labor is required on a stock ranch. Range cattle country therefore supports only a sparse population.

Since 1915, the range has suffered from time to time from decreased rainfall. In addition to drought with its resultant shortages of hay and grass, price and cost fluctuations have handicapped the range cattle men.

Range Management

Overgrazing, with its resultant lack of feed and deterioration of the range by erosion, is one of the greatest problems. Natural rehabilitation of the better native grasses is an extremely slow process, and it may not be economically feasible for private owners to seed their land with grasses. Poisonous and nonedible plants tend to increase with overgrazing. To help rehabilitate the public range and ultimately improve conditions for livestock, Congress passed the Taylor Grazing District Act in 1935. Under the Taylor Act the Administration proposes to conserve the range resources of the public domain by a system of temporary permits and by the reduction of grazing animals to the number that will permit maintenance and improvement of the native herbage.[1]

Sheep in the Northwest

The number of sheep in the Pacific Northwest totals 2,628,000 in contrast to 7 million in 1910. Most noticeable is the decline of nearly 50 per cent since 1940. Exceeding the national trend, the reduction in Northwest sheep may be attributed to restricted range, lack of herdsmen, and a trend toward more beef cattle. The Northwest has fewer sheep today than at any time since 1890.

The largest producer of sheep in the Northwest is Idaho, with more than a million head, most of which are in the central and southern plains, plateaus, and mountains. Oregon, with its Snake River slopes, arid plateaus, and northeastern mountains, as well as "wet" pastures in the Willamette Valley and along the coast, ranks second; eastern Washington, the northern highlands, and the Yakima and Kittitas valleys are centers of concentration for Washington.

Sheep utilize mediocre grazing to better advantage than cattle and tend to replace cattle on poor pastures.

Sheep Practices

It is a common practice to stock with dual-purpose breeds. The range-sheep industry centers around ewes that produce fat lambs for summer and fall shipment to packing centers and supply wool in the spring. Sheepmen in the Northwest have developed a hybrid breed by crossing the Merino and Rambouillet with Lincoln, Cotswold, Hampshire, or Romney. This hybrid, called "Columbia," "Corriedale," or no-name, is best adapted for quick development of lambs for market and for a high average-weight wool clip. These crosses produce prolific ewes that herd together well and have heavy fleeces of excellent-quality wool. The ewes are kept for 6 to 7 years, and the fat lambs are usually sold at 5 months of age, weighing 85 to 95 pounds each.

Seasonal transhumance, using the lowlands for winter ranges and mountain forest pastures for summer grazing, is a common practice. In

---

[1] Since May 1, 1951, the fees have been 10 cents per animal unit month, having been raised at that time from 6 cents. An animal unit month is the amount 1 horse or 1 cow or 5 sheep will eat or graze in 1 month. There is also a range improvement fee of 2 cents an animal unit month.

eastern Oregon sheep winter in the lower valleys, where feed has been stored, or graze on semidesert herbage. In summer the flocks are taken into the Blue Mountains, the Cascades, and other ranges for several months on green pastures.

In Coos and Curry counties in coastal Oregon, the raising of sheep is confined to hilly and logged-off land and to the coastal moors; here they do not require attendant herding or supplementary feeding but go through the winter in excellent condition. This long-staple wool, similar to that of the Penine and Cheviot hills of England and southern Scotland, has been in special demand for army blankets.

Kittitas Valley Sheep

Within the boundaries of Kittitas County, Washington, may be found sheep practices that are typical of southern Idaho and most other arid pasturelands of the Northwest.

In the fall the animals are grazed on irrigated pastures. As winter approaches, they are usually moved eastward to the sagebrush and grass-covered slopes that descend to the Columbia River. In spring, the foothills provide range, and for summer feeding there are the national forests in the high mountains of the Cascades (Plate 21A).

Some range is owned by sheepmen, but most of it must be leased from the government or railroad and lumber companies. Owners can graze sheep in the national forests only on restricted allotments. Nearly all the grazing land has been leased, and the recreational areas in the national forests have reduced the land available for sheep. Regular driveways connect the various allotments. The Forest Service limits a band to 1250 ewes and 1500 lambs. Other restrictions intended to protect the forests and scenic beauty prohibit a band from bedding in the same spot more than one night, from grazing within a quarter of a mile of a highway, and from bedding down near running water that might become polluted. Also a herder must leave at least 25 per cent of the palatable vegetation. The average season for grazing sheep in national forests is from the middle of June to mid-September. In July the top lambs are sent to market, being trailed down to a corral for loading in trucks for transportation to Seattle or to the nearest railroad stockpens for shipment east.

The herder, who must be very faithful, rarely keeps his herd in one locality more than a week. He is assisted by a pacer, who brings in salt for the sheep and food for the two men, and by several dogs without whose aid herding sheep in large bands would be nearly impossible.

The cultural pattern connected with the range sheep industry is, in the words of Dr. R. M. Shaw:

. . . shiftlessly picturesque rather than substantially impressive. Corrals are makeshift affairs quickly arranged in any suitable pattern by merely wiring wooden panels to poles quickly driven into the ground and frequently supported by boulders. Sheds, unpainted and weather-worn, stand in varying stages of dilapidation. The home of a herder may be a canvas-covered wagon in open country, a tent at any season, or a shack or abandoned farm house if he is to remain in an area for some time, as on winter range. The industry involves thousands of acres of land; its imprint is but lightly stamped upon the landscape. People are scarcely cognizant of it except in the fall when sheep are on the valley pastures.

Idaho As a Sheep Center

Sheep constitute the major livestock of Idaho, 22 per cent of all farms in the state keeping sheep. In southern Idaho farm flocks of 50 to 100 have proved a valuable means of utilizing surplus feeds and by-products such as beet tops, grain stubble, and bean and pea straw. Some farm flocks are also found in Oregon and Washington, and more could be kept.

The Idaho sheep business is carried on primarily for mutton production, the lamb crop providing the greatest returns. In general, income from lambs and mutton is twice that from the sale of wool. Lambs are fattened in irrigated sections where there is an abundance of alfalfa hay. In the neighborhood of the Idaho sugar factories, extensive use has been made of beet plup as priming feed. Range lambs weighing about 60 pounds are sometimes primed to about 85 pounds before being shipped to Chicago, Omaha, or West Coast markets.

Ranches usually handle between 2000 and 3000 head. The whole of southern Idaho is a sheep-raising area, with the chief feeding sections in the southeast, the Snake River Plain, and the irrigated land of the Boise Basin. In summer a million sheep graze in the national forests of central Idaho.

Value and Future

The annual wool clip of the Northwest totals some 23 million pounds, worth around $11,000,000 with Idaho, Oregon, and western Montana in the lead. Early in the 1940's the clip exceeded 46 million pounds.

Since sheep produce two money crops per year, lambs and wool, and can utilize poorer feed than cattle, they are often a better economic risk. There would seem to be room for an increase in farm flocks that would consume fodder and by-products now largely wasted.

Swine

Lacking rich cornfields for use in fattening, the region raises only some 600,000 hogs annually. Cash receipts from farm marketing of hogs are about $8,000,000 annually, with Oregon and Idaho in the lead. Important centers are communities with grain, dairy, and fruit farms, where hogs are a valuable means of utilizing feed materials wasted. These include skim milk, field peas, cull potatoes, fallen fruit, pumpkins, and certain concentrated field crops such as the cheaper grains. A few animals are fattened on kitchen scraps. Near the larger cities garbage is sometimes collected for use in feed lots. Another practice is the pasturing of pigs on alfalfa fields, the green feed being supplemented by grain.

Market demands for hogs in the Pacific Northwest are far in excess of the local supply, and shipments are made regularly from the Great Plains and Midwest to packing plants in Portland, Seattle, and Spokane. The state of Washington produces less than 35 per cent of its consumer requirements.

Horses and Mules

Horses in the Northwest around 1950 numbered some 255,000, a continued decline from more than 600,000 in 1940, and more than a million in 1910 and 1920. This decline is due to increased use of power machinery on farms. Horses are not raised systematically on a large scale, but many farmers and ranchers keep mares to work and have a few colts every year to sell or break to harness or saddle for their own use. They can in this way raise colts at a cost low enough to discourage professional horse breeders. A few race and riding horses are raised in the irrigated sections or around the larger cities.

There is a small but steadily decreasing number of mules in the Northwest, about 7000 in 1950, in contrast to 43,000 in 1930 and 47,000 in 1920. Some mules are still used by the Forest Service, Park Service, and private individuals to reach lookouts, trail crews, or camp sites.

Goats

In some parts of western Oregon goats are kept on fenced land to help clean up brush and make clearing easier. A few milk goats are found near most cities. Since goat's milk is highly recommended by dieticians and sells at a good price, and the goat needs comparatively little feed, it might be used to advantage on more small subsistence and part-time farms.

Role of Livestock

Although the days of cheap cattle and low-cost sheep produced on the open range are past, 25,000 livestock farms and ranches in the Northwest yield animal products that exceed a half-billion dollars annually.

REFERENCES

Atkinson, A., "Beef Cattle," *Montana State College Extension Service Bulletin* 136, Bozeman, 1933.

Johnson, R. G., "Some Oregon Grazing Problems," *Commonwealth Review*, Vol. 19, pp. 261–267, Eugene, 1937.

Maddox, C. S., "Fattening Cattle in Washington," *State College of Washington Extension Service Bulletin* 238, Pullman, 1934.

McCall, R., "Beef Cattle Feeding Experiments," *State College of Washington Agricultural Experiment Station Bulletin* 302, Pullman, 1937.

Physical and Economic Geography of Oregon, pp. 195–202, Oregon State Board of Higher Education, 1940.

Rinehart, E. F., "Wintering Range Stock," *Ext. Serv. Circ.* 39. University of Idaho, Moscow, 1931.

Watts, L. F., C. Huritt, *et al.*, "The Western Range," *Senate Document* 199 (1936), U. S. Government Printing Office, Washington, D. C.

CHAPTER

22

The Dairy Industry

WILLIAM H. PIERSON and OLIVER H. HEINTZELMAN

Place of Dairying in the Northwest Economy

As a source of revenue for the Pacific Northwest, dairying is exceeded only by the total of all field crops and by the lumber industry. Milk production is the largest single source of cash farm income. Sales of milk and butterfat, which amount to about $180,000,000 yearly, represent one-eighth of the entire income from agriculture. When to sales are added the $23,000,000 of milk consumed upon farms, the income from dairy animals sold for meat, the money realized from the sale of purebred breeding stock at home and abroad, the $25,000,-000 added by the manufacture of dairy products, and the revenues from wholesale and retail distribution, the role of dairying in the region assumes major proportions. According to the census a total of 565 million gallons of milk was produced in the three Northwest states in 1950.

Approximately 20 per cent of all Northwest farms are classed as dairy farms,[1] but the operators of several thousand farms classified otherwise are engaged in dairying in combination with such enterprises as poultry, fruit growing, and general farming. Milk cows are kept on some 170,000 farms, 70 per cent of all those listed. To these primary producers must be added nearly 4000 persons in factories making dairy products, and the thousands of others engaged in marketing and handling activities.

Dairying can be measured by specific values added to the money economy of the Northwest. Its contributions are less visible but basic to the resource wealth of the region and to the development of permanent agriculture. The use of land for pasture instead of for continuous

[1] A dairy farm, according to Bureau of Census usage, receives at least 50 per cent of its income from milk or dairy produce.

cropping and the addition of valuable animal manures improve soil fertility, and the maintenance of a grass cover on sloping land protects against soil erosion. In his practice of grassland agriculture the dairyman contributes to the up-building of the Northwest.

Correlation with Climate

The climate of the Pacific Northwest is generally favorable for dairy cattle, especially the breeds that were developed under similar conditions in northwestern Europe. The temperate marine climate of western Washington and Oregon, with its mild, rainy winters and relatively cool summers, is essentially the counterpart of the climate in which the Jersey, Guernsey, and Holstein breeds had their origins. These breeds are at their best in the marine Northwest, milk production per cow is high, and expenditures for shelter and winter feeding are low.

East of the Cascades temperature conditions are less ideal although favorable in general. Winters are severe, but less severe than those of the highly developed Great Lakes dairy belt. In eastern Oregon, in the Snake River Plain, and in the Columbia Basin, midsummer temperatures during 2 or 3 months are too high for maximum milk production, although wherever irrigation has overcome the limitation imposed by aridity, dairying can be practiced profitably.

Factors Affecting Regional Distribution

The distribution of the 680,000 dairy cows in the Pacific Northwest (Fig. 40) is influenced by a complex of factors, chief of which are (1) quality of pasturage, (2) the availability of feedstuffs, (3) the competition of other farm enterprises for land and labor, and (4) the proximity to urban markets and processing plants.

Good pasturage is naturally abundant in the rainy sections west of the Cascades and can be efficiently provided in the irrigated areas on the east side. In the dry-farming sections of the interior, pastures are poorly suited to dairy needs, with the result that milk cows are kept in small numbers, frequently only one or two on a farm, and these often of beef type or mixed breeds. Hay crops as well as pasture grasses flourish west of the Cascades and in the irrigated sections, but on dry-land farms they are inadequate to sustain large-scale dairies. Even in the irrigated sections the high costs of land and water tend to favor use of cropland for more intensive purposes such as orcharding, except in the immediate vicinity of urban centers and in

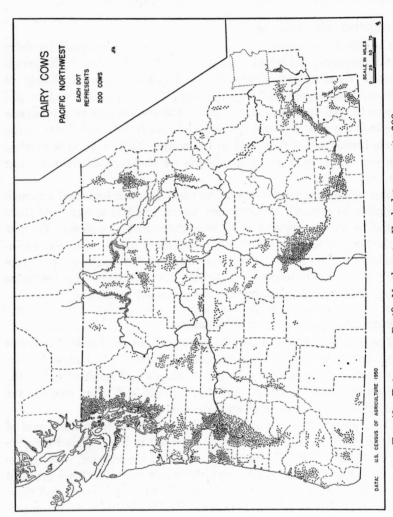

Fig. 40. Dairy cows, Pacific Northwest. Each dot represents 200 cows.

certain districts where soil and drainage are unfavorable for horticulture.

The grain feeds are readily grown at moderate cost in nearly all parts of the Northwest except in the rain-soaked coastal region; here the lush growth of grass for pasture and hay offsets the deficiency of concentrated feedstuffs.

The Puget Sound Lowland

The lowland of western Washington between the Cascades and the coastal mountains is the prime dairy region of the Pacific Northwest, with five of its ten leading dairying counties. About 60 per cent of the milk cows of Washington are found here.

Climatic conditions closely approximating those of the best dairy countries of Northwest Europe, large urban markets near by, and agricultural conditions more favorable to intensive use of cropland than to general farming, all combine to favor dairy specialization. Precipitation, which ranges from 30 to 50 inches, is ample for rich pasturage and hay crops. A tendency to drought during 2 summer months is largely offset by the seepage received in the alluvial soils on which most farming is done. The dryness of the summers permits the growing of oats, wheat, and corn for fodder, thus providing a well-rounded supply of feedstuffs. Not entirely self-sufficient, this lowland imports some grain and alfalfa hay from eastern Washington.

The best agriculture is in the valleys of the numerous rivers crossing the lowland. Many upland farms on relatively sterile glacial outwash are found in the vicinity of the larger cities. These small part-time farms producing small amounts of milk are a response to adjacent urban markets and often to the desire of urban workers to enjoy country life while supplementing their income.

Valley farms are usually small, owing in part to the high cost of preparing cutover land. Stump removal costs more than the initial purchase price of good, raw land, and clearing is sometimes prolonged over many years of farm occupancy, although bulldozing can effect rapid clearance. Woodland pasture and forest are characteristic of many farms except in the older settled areas. As the result of the high value of cleared lands, agriculture is specialized and intensive. Dairy farms containing more than 80 acres are few, and most are between 30 and 70 acres, a satisfactory size.

A typical dairy farm in Whatcom County, leading dairying county of the Northwest, contains 48 acres, of which about half is cropped. Clover, timothy, and rye grass, usually grown together and used interchangeably as meadow or pasture, occupy 15 to 18 of the 24 acres cultivated. Oats, for grain or cut for green feed, occupy most of the remaining acres cropped. Corn for forage, a potato patch, and a family garden and orchard utilize small acreages. The uncleared portion of the farm is thick woods or stumpy noncrop pasture of low carrying capacity. The dairy barn is usually larger than the modest dwelling and shelters some 14 to 18 cows, well-selected grade Guernseys, Holsteins, and Jerseys. Many dairy farms include poultry as a sideline or perhaps as a major enterprise of equal importance.

This is a region of high specialization, good farm techniques, and well-organized marketing services. More than 65 per cent of the milk is sold as fresh market milk, Seattle and Tacoma taking most of it. Many creameries and condenseries together with a few cheese factories make this region also a heavy shipper of all types of dairy produce.

Willamette Valley

The fertile and long-settled Willamette Valley is the most important agricultural region of Oregon, and one of the two dominant dairying regions of the Pacific Northwest. Here are found six of the ten chief dairying counties of Oregon and three of the first twenty dairying counties in the Pacific Northwest.

This region differs from the Puget Sound Lowland in several ways. Here is found a broad expanse of level farmland with soils more fertile than all but the best alluviums of the Puget Lowland. Winters are colder, although not severe, and summers are warm and dry. Although annual precipitation ranges between 40 and 50 inches, summer drought is sufficiently pronounced to limit the season of natural pasturage to about 3½ months. Supplemental irrigation, by which the pasture season is lengthened to 6 or 7 months and the hay crop improved, is now increasing. Summer drought necessitates considerable grain feeding.

Instead of the predominant milk production found in the Puget Lowland, other types of specialized farming prevail. More than 80 per cent of all cropland, however, is in pasture, hay, and grains such as wheat, oats, corn, and barley—crops basic to dairying.

Dairy farms average 155 acres, with about 80 acres in crops, most of the remainder being brushy pasture. Such farms have about 14 milk cows. Many other farms keep a few cows and add to the regional output. The productivity of cows within the Willamette Valley, over 6400 pounds of milk per year, is exceeded in the Pacific Northwest only in the Puget Sound Lowland.

The greatest dairying density is found in the vicinity of Portland, which, with 25 per cent of the population of the state, is the one large urban market within Oregon. Its milk comes from dairy farms in four adjacent Oregon counties as well as from Clark County across the Columbia River in Washington. With its million people the Valley constitutes a prime market, with seasonal shortages of fluid milk made up by imports from the coast and from mountainous southern Oregon.

Coastal Region

Climatically the narrow fringe of lowland in Oregon and Washington between the Coast Range and the ocean is the Ireland of the Northwest. All-year coolness and heavy and persistent rainfall favor lush growth of grasses on upland terraces, river valleys, and tidal flats, but virtually prohibits the ripening of grain. Even the curing of the grasses which grow so abundantly is difficult because of the high humidity and fogginess of late summer, the least-rainy season.

The short valleys facing the sea and separated by mountain spurs contain all the cropland, and dairying is almost the only type of agriculture. Nearly every farm keeps cows, the percentage of dairy farms being higher than in any other section of the Northwest.

This is a region of pasture dairying, based upon abundant grazing for 7 or 8 months. Practices are adjusted to the advantages and limitations of the environment, cows being freshened in spring for peak production during the long pasture season when feed is abundant and labor demands are at a minimum. To economize on hay and grains, milk production is allowed to slacken during the winter months. Much hay and virtually all feed grains must be purchased outside. Many dairymen clip their lush spring pastures for grass silage, and high cylindrical silos as well as pits for storage are features of many farmsteads.

Farms often contain large acreages of uncleared or rough mountain land, with only 30 to 35 acres in crops. As in the Puget Lowland stump and brush removal costs between $50 and $100 per acre so that only the alluvial soils are cropped. Pastureland is valued at $150 to $400 per acre.

The lack of large urban markets for fresh milk and the markedly seasonal nature of production result in the sale of the bulk of the milk to cheese factories and creameries. Tillamook, Coos, and Curry counties in Oregon are noted centers of cheesemaking.

Tillamook County, one of the most distinctive dairy areas of the Northwest, forms a unit in the coast region. In this county, which is populated largely by farmers of Swiss ancestry, dairying is predominant, with four-fifths of the arable land in grass and more than 90 per cent of the farm income derived from milk. Diversification is lacking; more than 80 per cent of the milk is made into 12 million pounds of cheddar cheese annually. A modern plant at Tillamook, erected at a cost of $3,000,000, is one of the largest cheese factories on the Pacific Coast.

Irrigated Districts of Eastern Washington

The chain of irrigated districts strung along the base of the Cascades from Okanogan County to Klickitat County, thence eastward to include Walla Walla County, contains the major portion of the dairying of eastern Washington. In this region of low rainfall dairying is almost entirely limited to the irrigated sections. Alfalfa hay and cheaply obtainable grains provide suitable feeds, but high summer temperatures and dust render the production of high-grade dairy products more difficult than in western Washington.

In this irrigated region crop-specialty and fruit farms prevail, but each district contains a number of dairy farms, especially near urban centers; dairying is dominant over considerable areas in Kittitas and Yakima counties. Farms of all types have cows for home milk supply, and dairying is a well-developed sideline on many of them. The feasibility of such operations on irrigated land in competition with high-value specialty crops is largely determined by the cost of land and water and the market value of alfalfa hay sold as a cash crop. Dairy farms tend to occupy the less-valuable irrigated lands, as well as valley bottoms where frost constitutes a fruit hazard; they often contain wet and other untilled land usable for pastures during the spring months.

Yakima County is the regional leader, with about 10 million gallons of milk yearly to rank sixth in Washington. Kittitas and Okanogan counties are lesser producers. About 30 per cent of the milk is consumed fresh and most of the remainder made into butter.

Northeastern Washington and Idaho Panhandle

Ferry, Stevens, Pend Oreille, and Spokane counties in Washington, together with Kootenai and Bonner counties in Idaho, comprise a dairy region in which many farms are nonirrigated. In the hills and mountain valleys precipitation of 20 to 30 inches permits pasture, hay, and forage crops. Farms are large and usually contain much woodland pasture of moderate carrying capacity. Similar conditions exist in the scablands south of Spokane. Milk production per cow is lower than in the irrigated districts east of the Cascades.

Dairy farms are located in valleys having transportation facilities for marketing milk and cream in Spokane, the largest center of butter manufacturing in Washington. Spokane and Stevens counties are the leaders.

Snake River Plain

With the exception of the small amount in the Panhandle, Idaho dairying is on irrigated land where abundant alfalfa hay and excellent pastures are supplemented by large quantities of by-products such as beet tops, pea-vine silage, and cull potatoes. The broad Snake River Plain contains three rather distinct dairy sections, all based upon irrigation but differing in intensity.

The Boise Valley of Canyon and Ada counties is the outstanding dairying section of Idaho. These two counties, ranking fifth and seventh in the Pacific Northwest, contain one-fifth of all milk cows in Idaho. Fresh milk is marketed chiefly in Boise, Nampa, and Caldwell, the surplus going to the factories.

A lesser concentration occurs within the Middle Snake Plain in Twin Falls, Gooding, Jerome, Cassia, and Minidoka counties.

In the upper Snake River Plain dairy farms are thinly dispersed over the area. On farms growing potatoes, sugar beets, and seed peas, milk as a sideline is sufficient to run creameries and cheese factories in the larger towns.

The only noteworthy area of irrigated dairying in Idaho outside the Snake River Plain is in Franklin, Bear Lake, and southern Bannock counties in the southeast corner of the state. Here in high intermontaine valleys much milk is produced along with hay, grain, poultry, and range livestock. In Cache Valley, extending from Franklin County into Utah, dairy farms are the dominant type.

Valleys of Western Montana

Agriculture in western Montana is limited to the floors of the several elongated valleys between the mountain ranges, where environmental factors both favor and hinder dairy activities. Because of high altitudes and remoteness from moderating oceanic influence, winters are severe. Farms lie between 2500 and 6000 feet, with 67 per cent of all croplands above 4200 feet. The growing season is short, varying with altitude from less than 90 to about 130 days. A few high districts such as the Big Hole Valley in Beaverhead County produce only grass and hay. Precipitation of only 13 to 16 inches makes irrigation necessary except on a few tracts of naturally subirrigated land.

In the irrigated valleys of western Montana more emphasis is given to dairying than is general in the state. Dairy centers in the Rocky Mountain Trench, extending from the head of the Bitterroot Valley in southern Ravalli County, northward through Missoula, into Lake and Flathead counties, produce one-half of the milk in western Montana. Nearly 70 per cent of the state's milk is produced in the thirteen western counties, Ravalli and Lake counties ranking first and second in mild production within Montana.

Missoula, Anaconda, and Butte receive fresh milk from western Montana valley farms, but the largest of these urban markets contains only some 50,000 people. Rural population is likewise sparse in this region of grazing range and large farms. Montana must therefore sell the greater part of its milk in the form of butter and cheese.

Areas of Local Intensity

Throughout the Northwest are a number of other centers, mainly in irrigated districts or near cities, where dairying has local significance. For instance, in the Umpqua and Rogue River valleys west of the Cascades in southern Oregon, some dairying is done along with horticulture and general farming. Fresh milk from these valleys is marketed in Medford, Grants Pass, Roseburg, and Eugene, and the surplus goes to butter and cheese factories. The Blue Mountain region of Oregon is a recognized center, and local dairy herds supply the urban markets of Baker, La Grande, and Pendleton.

Manufacture of Dairy Products

The processing of milk is one of the important industries of the Northwest. Over 500 plants manufacture dairy products or prepare fresh milk for market. Butter takes the bulk of the milk supply, 60 million pounds being made annually in 175 establishments. Butter-making is a part of the multiple operations of many plants scattered throughout the region, but a number of creameries located in areas remote from markets for fresh milk make only butter.

Surplus supplies of fluid milk together with growing markets have stimulated the manufacture of such concentrated dairy products as condensed and evaporated milk, ice-cream mix, and the nonfat milk solids. Together, these condensed products rank second to butter in the amount of milk utilized. Washington leads in canned-milk production, with factories at Arlington and Mount Vernon in the Puget

Lowland and at Sunnyside in the Yakima Valley. Idaho is second, with factories in the Snake River Plain at Buhl and Nampa.

Cheese plants are the third greatest users of factory milk. Eighty-two plants, more than two-thirds of which make only cheese, manufacture approximately 54 million pounds annually. Cheddar cheese, made from whole milk, is the dominant type and represents 80 per cent of the total production. Oregon leads in cheese production, followed by Idaho, these two states producing about 85 per cent of the cheese manufactured in the Northwest. Though found throughout the dairy regions, the cheese factories are concentrated in the areas of excess milk supply within the Snake River Plain and the Pacific Coast region.

Approximately 400 plants engage in the preparation of fluid milk for distribution to consumers and in the making of cottage cheese, ice cream, and other dairy products. Skim milk and whey concentrates and casein are valuable by-products of many plants.

Marketing of Dairy Products

Northwest dairy products are, in the main, consumed within the region. Washington is slightly deficient in aggregate dairy production, buying both butter and cheese. Oregon, Idaho, and western Montana are surplus producers, shipping millions of pounds of both butter and cheese to California. The very small quantities of Northwest dairy products reaching eastern markets are more than offset by cheese imports. Special types of cheeses are also imported from foreign countries in small amounts.

The industry is well stabilized. Markets for its products have grown as population increased on the Pacific Coast. In the future little further expansion is expected, however, chiefly because the region is already a surplus producer selling against stern eastern competition and because of the increasing consumption of oleomargarine. Nevertheless, with admittedly favorable environmental conditions and an industry skilled in scientific methods, the Pacific Northwest will continue to be one of the important dairy regions of the nation.

REFERENCES

Oregon State College Agricultural Experiment Station Bulletins 272, 305, 328, 335, 338, Corvallis.

State College of Washington Agricultural Experiment Station Bulletins 295, 309; *Extension Service Bulletins* 164, 239, 273, Pullman.

University of Idaho Agricultural Experiment Station Bulletins 214, 215, 216, Moscow.

CHAPTER

23

The Poultry Industry
and Minor Animals

JOHN C. SHERMAN

Since 1917 the Northwest states have experienced a boom in the production of poultry and poultry products. This business constitutes the fourth most important farm industry in terms of dollars returned to farmers. Poultry and poultry products make up almost 6 per cent of the total income received from sales by farmers. Of the approximately $2,250,000,000 worth of farm products sold in 1950, over $70,000,000 came from poultry.

Its major concentration is in the Puget-Willamette Lowland. Development here has been particularly rapid, three stages of growth being evident. First, before 1917, was a period of early development during which flocks and equipment, both for raising and processing poultry, were built up. This period was associated with large-scale influx of population before and after World War I. The infant industry was unable to supply the local demand for eggs and poultry, making necessary their importation from outside sources. The second stage, between 1920 and 1940, was a period during which a national reputation was established and tons of poultry and millions of eggs were shipped to eastern markets. For example, in 1930 over 10 per cent of the eggs consumed in metropolitan New York were produced in Washington state. During this stage great advances were made in primary production, processing, and marketing of poultry. Flocks were so improved that this region ranks among the highest in the United States in egg production per hen. A large number of poultry farms were established on which, through selective breeding, heavy-laying and meat-producing strains were developed. Over the years breeders have established a national and international reputation for high quality (Plate 21B).

During this second stage large poultry cooperatives were established. At first they were primarily marketing organizations, but they now process and sell poultry products in their own plants and through their own marketing organizations; they purchase and prepare feeds of all kinds and equipment of almost every type needed. The cooperatives have been largely responsible for the standardization that gives Northwest poultry a high reputation for quality. They have, also, through their profit-sharing plans, made possible a far higher dollar return to poultrymen.

The third stage in the development of the poultry industry, 1940 to the present, has been a period of market changes. Production has been stabilized since 1930.[1] During this time supply and demand became nearly balanced so that at present less than 1 per cent of the eggs are marketed in other states. The large growth in population, approximately 37 per cent, in Washington and Oregon, during the decade 1940 to 1950 absorbed the surplus formerly shipped to outside markets. The continued high cost to consumers of meats and other protein sources, including dairy products, has been a second important factor. Local consumption has become so large that some importation of eggs has become necessary.

Turkey raising in Washington increased to about 1 million birds in 1950; it has been stable in Oregon since 1940, with nearly 1.7 million turkeys. The same factors, population increase and better competitive prices, have favored turkeys as they have chicken and eggs. Only in Montana and Idaho is there any decline in turkeys, about 10 per cent between 1944 and 1950.

Measured in terms of producing farms, the labor employed, and the income received, eggs and chickens for meat represent the most important part of poultry production.

In 1950, there were on Northwest farms almost 8.5 million chickens. Annual sales are over 11.5 million birds. In 1950, production of eggs in dozens numbered: Washington 36,312,000; Oregon, 24,237,000; Idaho, 8,626,000; and western Montana, 1,705,000.

[1] Production of poultry in the northwest states has remained almost static.

	Chickens Raised	Eggs Produced
1930	10,000,000	850,000,000
1935	8,500,000	778,000,000
1940	8,500,000	824,000,000
1945	10,942,000	814,000,000
1950	9,000,000	800,000,000

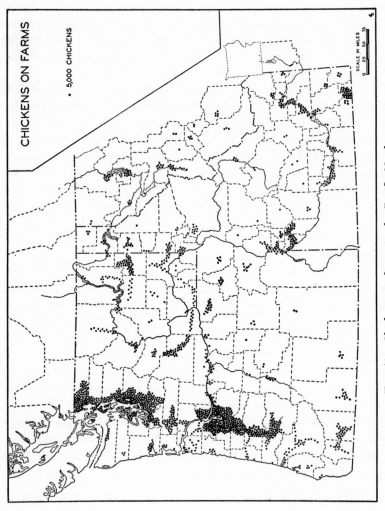

Fig. 41. Chickens on farms in the Pacific Northwest.

The map (Fig. 41) shows the distribution of chickens and indirectly of eggs. The concentrations are of two kinds: (1) within the western part of Washington and northwestern Oregon in the most densely populated portion of the region and (2) in the irrigated sections of all four states east of the Cascades. Whatcom, King, and Pierce counties in Washington and Clackamas, Lane, and Washington counties in Oregon are the leaders for chickens and eggs (see Table 1). In-

TABLE 1

THE MAJOR POULTRY-PRODUCING COUNTIES OF THE PACIFIC NORTHWEST *

County	Chickens on Farms	Chickens Sold	Eggs Sold, dozens
Washington			
Whatcom	499,392	626,037	6,764,311
King	410,510	960,883	4,212,568
Pierce	397,412	880,007	4,104,380
Lewis	260,129	603,773	3,123,445
Snohomish	241,719	557,231	2,760,708
Oregon			
Clackamas	368,631	762,744	3,621,146
Lane	339,919	466,134	3,516,160
Washington	302,694	482,282	3,411,204
Marion	267,750	297,521	2,468,233
Douglas	159,990	174,910	1,414,793
Idaho			
Canyon	152,843	241,452	959,638
Franklin	149,416	130,404	1,340,781
Ada	100,947	70,717	596,637
Twin Falls	90,497	77,356	515,545
Bingham	84,503	36,252	440,958
Montana			
Ravalli	59,808	36,562	379,551
Lake	56,951	36,881	285,973
Flathead	56,942	62,507	379,004
Missoula	29,273	90,384	115,276
Madison	27,655	9,877	100,374
Total	4,056,711	6,604,914	40,510,685
Per cent of regional production	48	57	57

* Data from Preliminary 1950 Census of Agriculture, *Farms, Farm Characteristics and Farm Products*, Bureau of the Census, U. S. Department of Commerce.

cluding other western counties almost 60 per cent of all chicken and egg production in the region would be found in the Puget-Willamette

Lowland. Secondary concentrations center in the populous Yakima Valley and the Snake River Plain. Outside the main areas for poultry, most farmers keep a small flock of hens which add to the total output.

The breed of chicken is primarily determined by the type of production desired. The white Leghorn is favored for eggs. Large commercial poultry farms may cover only a few acres but are aptly described as egg factories. Young hens are the best layers and can be forced through special diet and lighting to lay a maximum number of eggs. The average lay per hen in this region is 150 eggs per year as compared to a national average of 136. Careful breeding programs, disease prevention, replacement of poor layers, and carefully timed and regulated feeding have made this possible.

The so-called colored chickens, Rhode Island and New Hampshire Reds, have been increasing in popularity. These two breeds are better for dual-purpose chickens: good layers and heavy meat birds. They grow fast and make excellent fryers; moreover, laying hens produce almost as many eggs per year as Leghorns. From year to year these breeds often establish records in national laying contests. Some of the best breeding flocks have averaged as high as 260 eggs per year. Individual records are as high as 335 per year. Rhode Island and New Hampshire Reds are popular with the many small-scale and part-time poultrymen.

A major problem in this region, particularly in the Puget Sound area, is feed, which is locally insufficient. Wheat, oats, and corn are shipped in from outside.

Cooperative Associations

The Washington Cooperative Egg and Poultry Association and the Oregon Egg Producers have played a large part in the advancement of the industry. They furnish their members with information concerning methods of feeding and care of their flocks. Their personnel handle and properly mix much of the feed used by the poultrymen and also supervise the grading of eggs and dressed poultry to assure uniformity. These cooperatives maintain a fleet of trucks, both for collection and distribution. Their ability to buy in quantity gives members prices much lower than would otherwise be possible.

The Washington Co-op is the larger of the two organizations and maintains a network of processing plants and stations over all of Washington and part of Idaho. The Oregon Egg Producers operate only west of the Cascades. Some southwest Washington poultrymen are served by this organization.

Specialization

Some poultrymen specialize in hatching baby chicks which are sold to the general trade, and there are also many commercial and custom hatcheries. The annual production of baby chicks in Washington is between 18 and 19 million per year. As a group the breeders in the northwest states have achieved a high reputation, and consequently the demand for their chicks is wide. Many ship chicks and hatching eggs all over the United States, and to Hawaii, Alaska, Canada, South America, and even to Asia. One of the major advances has been the technique of sexing day-old chicks. Although egg and poultry prices have more than tripled since 1935, feed costs in the Northwest have quadrupled, but better breeds and strains, more feeding know-how, sexing, and excellent processing and marketing help keep the industry profitable.

Turkeys

Turkey raising has increased greatly since 1935 but has remained quite stable since 1945. The mature turkey is a hardy bird. This is not true of the young poults, which are much less hardy than young chickens. Although the drier climate east of the Cascades would seem more favorable than that of the damper west side, the major producing area is western Washington and Oregon. Since turkeys provide meat, it would seem logical for them to be raised near major feed sources, but nearness to market actually is the dominant locational factor. The maps of both turkeys and poultry (Figs. 41 and 42) reveal a close correlation. Concentration of both appears in the most densely populated and most highly urbanized section of the Northwest.

Turkey raising is geared to fall and early winter markets. This holiday trade which has been the traditional target for turkey raisers lasts for such a short time that annual incomes may be seriously affected. Consequently there has been a concerted effort to make turkey a meat that is consumed all year round. Advertising has helped create this market, but of even greater significance has been the increase in the number of small, family-sized birds such as the Beltsville. These turkeys, eviscerated and packaged, weigh from 5 to 8 pounds. The increasingly common practice of cleaning and packaging so as to make poultry oven-ready has made necessary expansion of processing plants and higher costs.

Despite the increase of small-turkey production, the larger breeds,

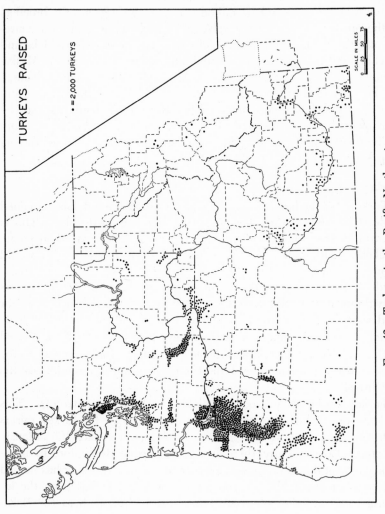

Fig. 42.   Turkeys in the Pacific Northwest.

such as the broad-breasted Bronze, are still the major type marketed. Unlike chickens, a large percentage of turkeys is shipped east.

Poultry diseases in this region are one of the main problems. State experiment stations as well as feed companies and pharmaceutical firms are vigorously combatting the menace of disease. Research is carried on concerning all phases of poultry diseases and information is issued concerning methods of control.

Miscellaneous

Ducks and geese are kept on many farms where water and feed are available. The raising of dogs and other pets is both a hobby and source of income. Breeders of rabbits and pigeons for sale and food are found mostly among suburban and small-town residents.

Bee Keeping

Although the production of honey does not rank as a major industry in the Northwest, it is of some importance in both coastal and interior sections. In some irrigated areas an interesting phase of the business is connected with fruit culture. Some apple orchards find it desirable to bring in many bee colonies to aid in pollination of the blossoms during the short flowering season. Because the amount of honey gathered will not pay the expense of bringing in the extra colonies, owners of the bees are paid for the trouble. Ordinarily, the colonies cannot be kept near the orchards after the blossoming season because the poison in the sprays would kill the insects. Bees are of considerable benefit as pollinizers of seed crops in parts of Oregon. Alfalfa, sweet clover, sage in the deserts, and fireweed on the coast are among the blossoms that provide pasture for bees. The leading honey-producing area is southern Idaho. Other important sections include the Yakima, Malheur, and Willamette valleys.

Fur Farming

There are hundreds of fur farms in the Northwest states and in British Columbia and Alaska, where the cool climate and other conditions are favorable. In Oregon about $450,000 annually in furs is sold by about 230 fox and 175 mink farms. The silver fox is the most widely distributed animal raised for its fur in the Northwest. Other preferred animals are mink, muskrat, and chinchilla rabbits. The feeding of fur bearers like mink and foxes must be done skillfully to insure a superior pelt, and the animals must be carefully managed to prevent loss from disease. Fish and special fish-scrap feeds available in quantities in the Northwest are much used for fur farms to provide needed elements in the diet. Horsemeat is also fed by some growers. In Alaska, offshore islands are utilized for fur farms on which the animals are raised in semicaptivity.

Conclusions

Poultry production is about evenly divided between the large-scale commercial and the small-scale and part-time growers. Commercial farms, although not usually occupying large acreages, require full time of the operator because of the large number of fowls kept and the highly organized character of the business. Chicken raising, however, is also profitable as a part-time occupation. Scattered around all of the major urban areas are large numbers of part-time farms. Chickens in moderate numbers, 50 to 500, fit into this farm system, and this type of operation has increased to the point where it supplies a large share of the poultry raised. A considerable number of breeding farms also fit into this category.

Unlike chickens, turkey raising is not well adapted to the part-time farm. The susceptibility of the young poults to disease and the care required to bring them to maturity require full time and attention. It is a common practice to raise both turkeys and chickens on the same farm. Chickens provide the year-round product, whereas the turkeys are prepared for the late fall and early winter market.

The two maps (Figs. 41 and 42) indicate clearly that poultry is an urban and not a ranch industry. Proximity of markets, collecting and processing facilities, availability of labor, and transportation services are all factors that favor such location.

Although there has been a large influx of population into the Northwest, only 5 per cent of the national egg production is carried on here. Any decline locally will inevitably open this market to outside competitors. The established reputation, the highly organized character of the industry, and the proved ability to maintain a reasonable profit margin should all act to gear production trends closely to gains in population. Therefore, a small, steady increase in the poultry industry in the Pacific Northwest is to be expected.

Industry, Commerce, and Urban Development

The natural and agricultural resources of the Northwest are moved to processing plants and distant markets over highways, railroads, and shipping routes. The fifth part of the book begins with a chapter on the transportation pattern, followed by a discussion of manufacturing and the regional industries and the foreign trade of the Northwest. The final chapter of *The Pacific Northwest* describes urban development, with particular attention to the larger cities.

CHAPTER

24

The Transportation Pattern

FRANCES M. EARLE

Physically isolated from the settlements of eastern United States by the barriers of distance, mountains, and deserts, the Pacific Northwest was for many years oriented toward the sea. The first great routes used in exploration, early trade, and settlement were the sea lanes from eastern United States via Cape Horn to the Columbia River and Puget Sound. Because little was known of the interior of this vast region, settlements were of necessity located by access to water until an alternative overland route was established. Settlers moved westward over the famous Oregon Trail, a heavily traveled wagon road, by way of the Missouri and Platte rivers, thence to the valleys of the Snake and the Columbia. Approximately 15,000 people crossed the plains and mountains to Oregon between 1840 and 1850.

With the establishment of permanent inland settlements, "wagoning" became the chief mode of transport. Topography, climate, great distances, and poor roads combined to make wagoning both slow and expensive and to increase the demands for better overland facilities.

The Columbia River has always been a dominant influence in focusing the westward movement of explorers, traders, and settlers. Beginning in 1811 with the establishment of the American trading post of Astoria, through the 1820's and 1830's when the Hudson's Bay Company was active, to the 1840's and 1850's when the American pioneers arrived in their covered wagons, using the Columbia route for the last part of their westward trek, it has played an increasingly important role. Attracted by the discovery of placer gold in Idaho and Montana, men and supplies were moved upstream to the interior by paddle-wheel steamers during the 1860's and 1870's, and Portland, Umatilla, Walla Walla, and Lewiston became supply centers. By providing the only water-level route across the Cascade mountain barrier to the Pacific Ocean, the river also helped to locate railroad lines and motor highways.

The completion of the transcontinental railroads [1]—the Northern Pacific in 1883, Union Pacific in 1884, the Great Northern in 1893, and the Chicago, Milwaukee, St. Paul and Pacific in 1909—made possible the opening up and settlement of the Northwest and contributed to the rapid growth of agriculture, mining, and lumbering.

The completion of the Panama Canal in 1914 provided a further stimulus to economic development, particularly in opening up both eastern and European markets for lumber, fruit, wheat, and wool. As a result of competition with intercoastal steamship lines there were some reductions in rail freight rates. The availability of refrigerated cargo space also forced the railroads to offer similar services for the rapid transport of perishable fruits and vegetables. Port facilities were greatly expanded on Puget Sound and the lower Columbia.

The gradual development of lighter, faster, and more varied equipment put the railroads in a better competitive position. The great increase in passenger cars, motor buses, and trucks is another significant trend. Air transport has grown even faster. An extensive system of airports is used by international, transcontinental, coastwise, and connecting lines, which offer both scheduled and nonscheduled passenger and freight services.

Railways

During the westward movement in the late 1850's a 2-mile portage (mule powered) was established to facilitate the transfer of cargo from boats on the upper Columbia to those connecting with Portland. In 1863 this portage was rebuilt into a 6-mile steam railroad, the first to operate in the present state of Washington. The Northern Pacific, the first line authorized to construct a railroad to the Northwest, selected Tacoma as its terminus and several years later completed the tracks to Seattle. In the following decade both the Union Pacific and the Great Northern reached the Pacific Northwest (Fig. 43).

Within the region short lines were built to serve local needs, as from New Castle mines to Seattle to transport coal and from the Walla Walla area to the Columbia River to move wheat. There were also

[1] Construction of transcontinental railways was encouraged by land grants given by the Federal or state governments. Usually these grants covered alternate sections of land for a specified number of miles, sometimes as much as 40 miles, on both sides of the right of way. Thus the railroads acquired large tracts which might be sold to prospective settlers.

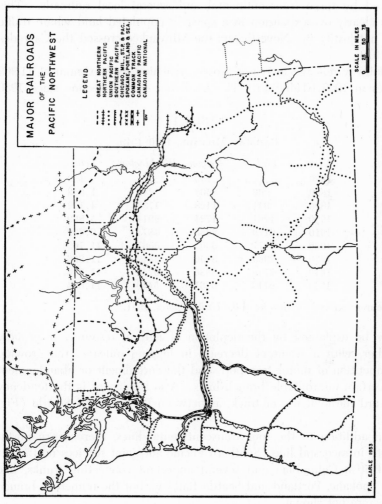

Fig. 43. Major railroads of the Pacific Northwest.

many logging railroads, some of which were abandoned after the timber was cut. By indirectly stimulating the growth of agriculture, these local lines contributed to speculative land booms.

With a total population of 737,491 in 1890, the Northwest was served by three transcontinental and several local railroads. This was clearly overexpansion in a sparsely populated land where traffic did not justify it. Nevertheless the Milwaukee crossed the Cascades in 1910.

Railway mileage increased slowly, reaching its maximum of 11,963 miles in 1930 (Table 1). The small but steady decline since 1930

TABLE 1

RAILWAY MILEAGE, 1870–1949

Year	Idaho	Oregon	Washington	Total
1870	....	159	....	159
1880	206	508	289	1,003
1890	941	1428	1783	4,152
1900	1261	1724	2914	5,899
1910	2179	2285	4875	9,339
1920	2877	3305	5587	11,769
1930	2965	3456	5542	11,963
1940	2746	3386	5243	11,374
1949	2713	3231	5140	11,084

Source: *Statistical Abstract of the United States*, 1951.

may be explained by the depletion of natural resources, especially timber, with a resultant decrease in logging mileage, the growing competition of motor transport, and the curtailment or abandonment of certain unprofitable branch lines. Also significant is the tendency toward the joint use of track, as between Portland and Seattle (Fig. 43).

In addition to the four transcontinental lines, there are a north-south intracoastal line (Southern Pacific and joint services northward to British Columbia) and several important connecting trunks, like the Spokane, Portland and Seattle Railway, but the numerous branch lines are not shown.

The major problem confronting the railroads is insufficient freight for the available facilities. In comparison with other parts of the country, transcontinental railroads serving the Northwest operate at a disadvantage in both freight and passenger traffic.

The total tonnage of commodities originating in the region and shipped out by rail exceeds the volume shipped into the area by 9,915,000 tons (Table 2). This disparity in tonnage shipped and

TABLE 2

RAILROAD TRAFFIC. VOLUME OF MAJOR COMMODITIES, 1950 *

(1000 tons)

	Oregon		Washington		Idaho		Total	
	Origi-nating	Termi-nating	Origi-nating	Termi-nating	Origi-nating	Termi-nating	Origi-nating	Termi-nating
Products of agriculture	1,636	1826	2,971	2,590	3189	1489	7,796	5,905
Animals and products	72	112	97	195	238	96	407	403
Products of mines	911	1840	1,607	3,492	1290	1865	3,808	7,197
Products of forests	11,680	2630	9,371	7,203	1756	670	22,807	10,503
Manufactures and miscellaneous	2,311	2744	4,367	4,564	703	968	7,381	8,276
Total	16,610	9152	18,416	18,044	7176	5088	42,199	32,284

* Washington and Oregon data, 1950; Idaho, 1948.
Source: *Reports of Interstate Commerce Commission*, 1952.

tonnage received is explained by the fact that the region is shipping great quantities of raw and semifinished products which are heavy and bulky. The dominance of forest products in the regional economy is shown by the 12,304,000-ton export surplus; furthermore, forest products provide the major tonnages originating in both Oregon and Washington. The region also shows an agricultural surplus, self-sufficiency in animals and products, but has large deficits in both minerals and manufactures.

Because the Pacific Northwest must export a large proportion of its production to distant markets and, at the same time, obtain from distant markets part of its raw materials and the bulk of its manufactures, the matter of freight rates is vital. For example, in 1950 Washington's rail shipments of forest products [2] included the items tabulated below. Equalization of eastbound and westbound freight rates is also a problem for the entire Northwest.

[2] *Carload Waybill Analyses*, 1950, Interstate Commerce Commission, No. 5143, August, 1951.

	Tons	
Wood pulp	840,500	To 16 states
Paperboard, fiberboard	129,100	
Building woodwork and mill work	134,000	To 27 states
Wrapping paper	73,000	
Newsprint	53,000	
Paper bags	50,600	
Printing paper (n.o.s.)	31,200	
Wallboard	23,500	
Woodenware	21,200	
Furniture	14,200	To 13 states

Except for the Puget Sound area and the Willamette Valley, the Northwest is sparsely settled and centers of population are generally quite widely separated. With approximately 8 per cent of the land area of the United States, the Northwest has about 5 per cent of the railway mileage but less than 3 per cent of the population. In proportion to population there is a large tonnage but not a high value of freight. The distance between centers within the region, the long distance to markets, and the relatively low density of traffic and relatively high transportation costs constitute real problems.

Highways

Little attention was given to road building in the Northwest until after the middle of the nineteenth century, the local need for all-weather haulage being partially satisfied by corduroy roads. Federal programs were initiated, and after achieving statehood in 1859 Oregon was required by Act of Congress to use 5 per cent of the net proceeds from the sale of public lands for road building and other internal improvements. Rugged topography and vast distances were handicaps, and progress was slow. Hard-surfaced highways belong strictly to the twentieth century, the automobile providing the basic stimulus.

Road building expanded rapidly to meet the conditions created by the growth and shifts of population and by the increased use of motor vehicles.[3] In 1949 the ratio of population to motor vehicles in the Northwest was 2.3 and registrations (including passenger cars, buses, and trucks) totaled 1,698,000, which was more than a 50 per cent increase over 1940. Technological advancement has made possible higher speeds with greater ease; the average speed for all vehicles

[3] State and county roads are financed by motor fuel tax receipts. In 1950 the Pacific Northwest received $44,311,000 in motor fuel taxes. *Highway Statistics, 1950*, U. S. Bureau of Public Roads, 1952.

increased from 41 miles per hour prewar to 53 miles per hour in 1951. Heavier automobiles and particularly larger buses and trucks put such strain on roads and bridges that it has been difficult to build and maintain highways capable of meeting the growing motor-traffic demand. Trucks moving up and down the West Coast weigh about 70,000 pounds and carry a 30,000-pound payload, which may include a hundred different items.

The highway pattern (Fig. 44) is based upon a number of east-west trunk lines which, like the railways, took advantage of the relatively low passes in the Cascades. Only two of these highways extend entirely across the region: U.S. 10 in the north and U.S. 30, or the Oregon Trail Route, in the south. The main north-south routes are through the Puget Sound-Willamette Trough (U.S. 99), the Pacific Coast highway (U.S. 101) and east of the Cascades U.S. 97 extends from Canada southward through the Okanogan Valley, Yakima, and The Dalles to California. Another north-south highway extends from the Canadian border through the Idaho panhandle and Lewiston (U.S. 95) to the Snake Basin, thence to Nevada. County roads serve as feeders to the state and national highways (Table 3).

TABLE 3

HIGHWAY MILEAGE, 1950 *

Type	Idaho	Oregon	Washington	Total
Federal and state park, forest, reservation roads, etc.	6,216	13,348	4,773	24,337
State highways	4,708	7,268	6,292	18,268
Urban extensions of state highways	202	396	443	1,041
County and other local roads	25,438	32,534	39,947	97,919

* *Highway Statistics, 1951*, U. S. Bureau of Public Roads.

Agricultural settlements tended to establish the road pattern, and the density of the net is indicative of the intensity of land use as well as the type of products. Orchards and truck farms, for example, need a denser net so that shipping points will be economically accessible, whereas the more extensive wheat areas require a less dense pattern. The secondary lines not only serve agriculture but also cover thinly the areas of forest exploitation and mining. The growth and diversification of industry has created new demands for roads, just as areas set aside for reservations and tourist attractions also have their requirements.

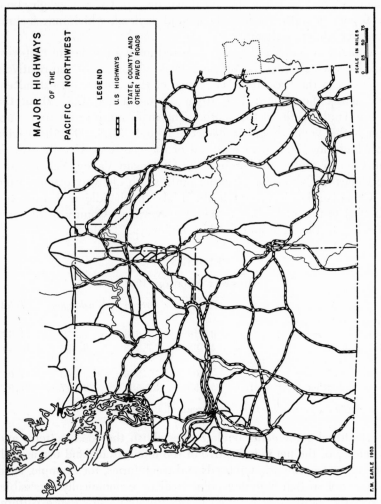

Fɪɢ. 44. Major highways of the Pacific Northwest.

By far the heaviest flow of highway traffic in the Northwest is from the Canadian border through the Puget Sound-Willamette Trough, which is not only the most densely populated area but also the most highly industrialized (Fig. 45).

From Seattle the heaviest traffic flow eastward follows U.S. 10 via Snoqualmie Pass [4] to Ellensburg, thence southward through the irrigated and densely populated Yakima Valley and Kennewick, through northeastern Oregon to connect with the highways serving the agricultural lands of the Snake River Plain. The second major east-west route extends from the mouth of the Columbia to Umatilla, with state and national highways serving both sides of the river. Intersecting the great north-south artery (U.S. 99) at Portland-Vancouver, these highways along the river carry an increasing volume of eastbound traffic to the Columbia Basin, where traffic is increasing in direct proportion to the expansion of irrigation agriculture.

California is reached by three main routes: the heaviest traffic flow is south from the Willamette Valley through Grant's Pass and Medford in the Rogue River Valley, by a fast desert route east of the Cascades through Bend and Klamath Falls, and by the picturesque but longer coast route which is less heavily traveled. In Oregon this highway is fed by several roads which cross the Coast Range while in Washington the main highway loops around the higher Olympic Mountains.

Although new links may still be required in the road net, attention is being given to improvement of routes, gradients, and curvature, to a better-directed flow of traffic, and to greater safety. Comprehensive surveys have been made for the purpose of coordinating highway planning with the present and potential patterns of population, land use, and traffic.

Inland Waterways

From the earliest settlements in the Northwest to the coming of the railroads, population clusters were oriented to water transportation. Some of the settlements that were originally served by ships are now oriented to highways, thus leaving the waterways mainly to fishing and pleasure craft. The Columbia is the most significant inland waterway (Table 4).

---

[4] The Lake Washington floating bridge on U.S. 10 is now toll free, and to expedite traffic eastward from Seattle a second lake bridge is planned. A far more ambitious project to bridge Puget Sound to the Olympic Peninsula is being studied.

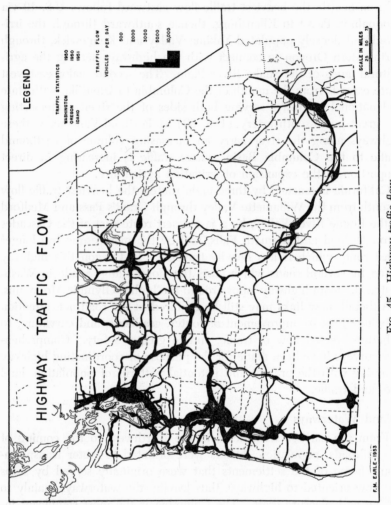

Fig. 45. Highway traffic flow

TABLE 4

COMMERCE ON PRINCIPAL RIVERS AND CANALS, 1944–49 *

(1000 short tons)

	1944	1945	1946	1947	1948	1949
Columbia and lower Willamette below Vancouver and Portland	15,701	16,635	14,232	15,938	15,592	18,369
Columbia from Vancouver to The Dalles	1,509	1,417	1,826	2,005	2,684	3,034
Willamette above Portland and Yamhill River, Oregon	5,236	2,877	3,979	4,942	4,170	4,149
Snohomish River, Washington	2,000	1,778	1,783	1,882	1,637	1,699
Lake Washington Ship Canal	3,006	2,183	2,167	2,015	2,115	2,012

* Source: *Statistical Abstract of the United States*, 1951.

Waterways, navigable for shallow draft vessels and barges, extend far inland in the Columbia system. Improvements, including the Bonneville dam and navigation lock, extend facilities for ocean shipping to The Dalles, 188 miles inland.

The Columbia River trunk waterways, considered navigable to Lewiston on the Snake, to Priest Rapids on the Columbia in central Washington, and to Albany on the Willamette in Oregon, are being improved in order to increase their effectiveness as arteries of commerce.

Columbia traffic has been showing a sharp upward trend. The principal downstream movement is in forest and agricultural products, especially wheat and flour; the major upstream commodities are forest and petroleum products and building materials—sand, gravel, and cement. Development of the Columbia Basin under the Grand Coulee project and the further improvement of navigation in the Columbia system should be mutually stimulating.

The Lake Washington Ship Canal handles over 2 million cargo tons annually, most of it consigned to industrial plants around Lake Union. Lesser tonnages are recorded on the Snohomish River. Minor navigable waterways include lakes such as Pend Oreille, Coeur d'Alene, Flathead, Chelan, and also Lake Roosevelt extending from Grand Coulee Dam to the Canadian border.

PUGET SOUND

Navigation on Puget Sound

Like the more famous Mediterranean between southern Europe and North Africa, the great inland sea of the Northwest serves as an easy highway between many ports in the United States and Canada. From Cape Flattery on the west, from Olympia at its far-south tip, and including the Strait of Georgia which leads to the spectacular but quiet Inland Passage to Alaska, this inland sea separates the many communities on its perimeter but at the same time increases their accessibility. There are excellent harbors with deep channels open 12 months of the year that provide sea lanes northward to Alaska and westward to the Pacific Ocean, thence to world markets.

Early explorers sailing into Puget Sound and finding Indian villages along the coasts noted that the dugout carved in one piece from a cedar log was the universal mode of travel from village to village. Long voyages were sometimes made in these sturdy boats.

The same sailing ships which brought the early loggers and pioneer settlers to western Washington served to open up a coastwise trade in lumber, coal, and wheat. The *Beaver*, first steamboat on the Sound, started operating in 1835. At an early date various types of vessels were built at Port Orchard, Port Blakeley, Port Madison, and Salmon Bay. Settlements were located by access to navigable waterways, and economic development was dependent upon trade by water, at first by fleets of canoes and by sailing ships and Sound steamers, later by regularly scheduled packets.

Deepwater bays, inlets, and sloughs provided anchorage around the entire extent of the Sound. Many of the east-side rivers, such as the Fraser, the Skagit, the Snohomish, and the Duwamish, were navigable for some distance. As with the Indian villages, connection between settlements was invariably by water, a situation that continued well into the twentieth century.

With the building of roads along the coast, the extreme importance of waterfront location gradually diminished. For example, the rich La Conner Flats on Swinomish Slough, once served entirely by steamer and barge, is now oriented to highways and its water traffic is minor. Rapid transportation by highway and railway caused the decline of passenger traffic on the Sound. Steamships that formerly operated between Seattle and the ports of Tacoma, Olympia, and Bellingham have disappeared, but regular service is still maintained between

Seattle, Victoria, and Vancouver. Certain ferry services are still active
and the busiest route is that from Seattle across to Bremerton and its
Navy Yard. There is daily ferry service from Anacortes via the San
Juan Islands to Sydney, from Port Angeles to Victoria, between Sydney
and Vancouver, and from Nanaimo to Vancouver. In 1952 there were
only eight routes offering daily service in Washington waters.[5]

Although the passenger significance of the Sound has declined, the
freight function has increased. Forest products, especially logs which
are rafted within the area, account for the largest tonnages; sand,
gravel, cement and crushed rock, and petroleum products move in an
endless stream. One of the larger tugboat companies operates about
50 vessels for towing, 20 tank barges for bulk petroleum products, 2
or 3 railroad car ferries, and 110 barges for bulk freight, including
several for hogged fuel and mud. Various types of craft move a large
volume of cargo within the waters of Puget Sound and the Strait of
Georgia.

Government vessels, including transports, mine sweepers, battle-
ships, and carriers, are also heavy users of Puget Sound waters. Since
1942 there has been a great increase in shipping as various bases were
activated and men and matériel moved overseas. Among the larger
permanent centers are the Bremerton Navy Yard, Smith Cove (Navy),
and the Port of Embarkation in Seattle and the Canadian naval base
at Esquimalt.

Modern fishing vessels, including trollers, purse seiners, gillnetters,
tuna clippers, and halibuters, operate from the home ports of Seattle
and Bellingham, Vancouver, and Victoria; the fleet is active in the
deep waters and in certain rivers during the season.

There are thousands of miles of sheltered passages in the Northwest
open to boating enthusiasts, and Washington now leads the United
States in small-boat ownership. The Sound was formerly visited by
the palatial yachts of wealthy Europeans, but most of the locally
owned craft are modest. Inland cruising in the Northwest attracts
many active participants, but the various races—crew, sailboat, speed-
boat, and tug—draw an even larger number of spectators.

[5] Washington State ferries in operation: Mukilteo to Columbia Beach; Seattle
to Winslow; Seattle to Bremerton; Fauntleroy-Vashon-Harper; Lofall to South
Point; Anacortes to San Juan Islands; Edmonds to Kingston; and Pt. Defiance to
Tahlequah.

Airways

Air transportation is well developed, with international, national, and local lines offering both scheduled and nonscheduled passenger and freight services. The leading airports, Seattle-Tacoma, Spokane, and Portland, handle a steadily increasing volume of passengers and cargo, and feeder lines extend services to dozens of small communities. The number of airports and airfields more than doubled between 1940 and 1950, the 1950 total being 438; this number included 182 municipal, 96 commercial, and 12 military types.

Through the Seattle-Tacoma International Airport, served by eight certificated carriers, the Northwest has direct and frequent service to Canada, Alaska, Hawaii, Japan, and, via Portland or Vancouver, British Columbia, to Australia and New Zealand. By using stratocruisers to make longer hops, the Tokyo-Seattle flight is made in 16 hours. Trans-Pacific tourist service began in 1954. Triweekly freight service over this route was inaugurated in 1953; goods consigned to eastern United States are unloaded and go through customs inspection at the Seattle-Tacoma International Airport.

Alaska traffic reached a new peak in 1952, with four certificated carriers giving daily service. In contrast to the transit type of trade with the Far East, about 90 per cent of the cargo for Alaska originated in Seattle. New developments are the transportation of construction workers by air and the mass migration of 5000 to 6000 fishermen northward in June and southward at the end of the season (Table 5).

TABLE 5

TRAFFIC SEATTLE-TACOMA INTERNATIONAL AIRPORT, 1948–52 *

Year	Total Air Freight, pounds	Revenue Passengers, number
1948	7,870,463	469,985
1949	13,565,996	510,222
1950	18,573,026	629,552
1951	19,725,239	751,529
1952	23,869,002	910,412

* Includes Boeing Field.

Because of postwar shipping shortages on the Pacific, air traffic has greatly increased and Seattle-Tacoma ranks second to New York City in the volume of its air cargo. In 1951 the Seattle-Tacoma International Airport showed a 6 per cent increase in freight over 1950, a 19 per cent increase in passengers, 29 per cent in mail, and 12 per cent in express.

In addition to their commercial services, certain certificated carriers contracted with the Military Air Transport Service to fly the great-circle route to the Orient. When one of these airlines reported the completion of its one-thousandth round trip between July, 1950, and October, 1952, it had flown 31,593 soldiers and 9,509,859 pounds of military cargo across the Pacific in the airlift to Tokyo.

REFERENCES

The Columbia River, Bureau of Reclamation, U. S. Department of the Interior, 1947.

Interstate Commerce Commission, various publications.

Highway Statistics, Bureau of Public Roads, U. S. Department of Commerce, Annual.

U. S. Army Engineers, port series and annual reports.

World Railways, 1950–51, Chicago, 1951.

Winther, Oscar Osburn, *The Old Oregon Country: a History of Frontier Trade, Transportation, and Travel,* 1950.

CHAPTER
25

Manufacturing in the
Pacific Northwest

SAMUEL N. DICKEN

In the Pacific Northwest more persons are engaged in manufacturing than in primary agriculture, fisheries, and mining combined. Likewise the "value added" to the raw materials by manufacturing exceeds the total value of farm products, minerals, and fish; a wide variety of processing is included under the term "manufacturing."

Lumber (Plate 22A) and various wood products, such as plywood, paper, hardboard, and furniture, are of paramount importance. Metals and metal products, machinery, instruments, and tools are also included, as are the canning, drying, grinding, and freezing of foods. Textiles, clothing, printing, chemicals, petroleum refining, rubber, and leather are also examples of the fabricating process. Manufacturing includes all processing plants from a small sawmill, turning out rough lumber, to an airplane factory, and from a cranberry packing plant to an aluminum rolling mill.

The number of workers employed is one measure of the relative importance of manufacturing. The Pacific Northwest with 290,000 production workers, representing about 6.5 per cent of the population, is below the national average of nearly 12 million, or about 8.3 per cent of the total population. Before World War II the corresponding figures were 4.5 per cent for the Pacific Northwest and 6 per cent for the United States. Another method of showing the relative importance of manufactures is the value added. During the period 1939 to 1947, the value added per capita for the Pacific Northwest increased from $137 to $374 while that of the United States as a whole increased from $187 to $519. The population in the three Pacific Northwest states, plus seventeen mountain counties of western Montana, increased from 3,567,861 in 1940 to 4,721,104 in 1950. Manufacturing in the Northwest increased more rapidly than the population, but less rapidly than in the United States as a whole. The graph (Fig. 46) shows the changes in manufacturing, measured in terms of production workers, and also reveals the relative importance of the

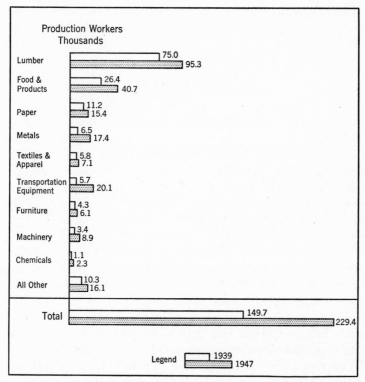

Fig. 46. The distribution of production workers in Oregon, Washington, and Idaho for the years 1939 and 1947. In 1951 the number of production workers was approximately 290,000. (*Data from U. S. Bureau of the Census.*)

various industries. Lumber, paper, and furniture combined account for half of such employees.

The Pacific Northwest has many advantages for the development of various kinds of manufacturing on a fairly large scale. It has an abundant water supply, not only fresh water for industrial uses and the generation of hydroelectric energy, but also sea water from which chemicals may be extracted. There is an abundance of certain minerals, although some are in scant supply. Minerals include common salt, limestone, and the ores of lead, zinc, copper, mercury, iron, chrome, phosphate, magnesium, manganese, and antimony. Coal resources are unsatisfactory for large-scale industrialization. The region also has an increasing supply of agricultural raw materials which can contribute to the industrial potential. Forest industries provide a broad base of raw material which, with the aid of tree farms, sustained yield practices, and more complete utilization, also contributes to the manufacturing potential. Further studies must be made of the resource potential in order to develop selective industries best suited to the region.

LOCATION FACTORS

Location factors may be summarized in terms of raw materials, power, human skills (labor), transportation, and market. For example, the location of raw materials is more significant to the production of lumber than to the furniture industry. Both use wood, but the furniture factory not only adds more value to the raw materials and can, therefore, pay a higher transportation charge, but it also needs a greater variety of woods, some of which must come from distant sources. Similarly, the power factor is of little concern to light industries or to a sawmill using waste materials for fuel, but it is of vital importance to the aluminum industry which requires large quantities of hydroelectric energy. Likewise, some industries, such as food processing, need little trained labor, whereas others, metalworking for example, require more skill.

The rapid increase in population in the Northwest and in California is bringing about continuous changes in the market factor, making it possible to manufacture articles locally that were formerly produced more economically in the populous East. Technology is constantly changing. Of special significance is the increasing mechanization of the wood-products industries with a decline in workers per unit of production. On the other hand, there is an increasing need for expansion in the transport equipment and machine industries. Defense demands materially affect northwest industries, for example expansion or contraction in light metals and airplane factories.

Raw Materials and Supplies

In the Pacific Northwest, the most significant raw materials are the products of forests, agriculture, mining, and fisheries.

Hydroelectric power, available in large blocks at low rates, partially compensates for the scarcity of fuels. The principal coalfields are on both flanks of the Cascades (Fig. 47), but it is necessary to import superior quality coal from Utah, British Columbia, Montana, and Wyoming. Iron ore is widely distributed, but the deposits are small and the quality low. Little is used locally, although small shipments

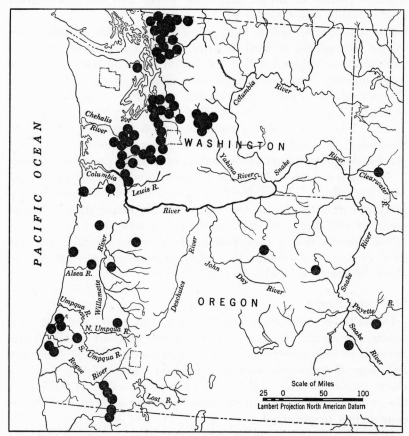

FIG. 47. The known occurrences of coal in Washington, Oregon, and western Idaho. In most cases, however, the coals are of little or no commercial value at present. (*From the Bonneville Power Administration.*)

of ore have been made to Japan. It is significant that the deposits of ore and coal are not adequate for a complete iron and steel industry. Some steel is made from scrap, and converters have been in operation for some time in Seattle and Vancouver, Washington, but most of the supplies are shipped in.

Some of the metallic ores are of great strategic significance but, after simple concentration in the region, are shipped elsewhere for final processing, particularly chrome, mercury, tungsten, and manganese. Important metal-mining districts include the Butte, Montana, area, famous for copper and zinc, and also northern Idaho and the adjacent portion of British Columbia, where lead and zinc are the most valuable (see Chapter 9).

Forest products, such as logs, pulpwood, and other materials, contribute increasingly to local industry. Formerly, most of the forest products were shipped out of the region in crude form, as logs or rough lumber. The processing is now more complex, and the value per unit added to forest products has increased. Considerable emphasis is placed upon the use of wood for paper, plywood, and hardboard. A large part of this manufacturing is localized in the Puget Sound and Willamette lowlands because these regions are well supplied with transportation, labor, and other facilities for manufacturing.

Perhaps the most widespread of all the raw materials are derived from agriculture. Vegetables and fruits are canned or otherwise processed near the farms, but less-perishable crops, such as wheat, are often milled at some distance from their source.

The fisheries are an important source of raw materials, only partially exploited. Canneries and other processing plants are located along the coasts of Washington and Oregon.

Fuels and Power

Of the three common sources of energy, coal, petroleum, and water power, the Pacific Northwest possesses only the last in abundance. Because of heavy precipitation and high elevations, the Northwest has more hydroelectric energy, developed and potential, than any other comparable part of the United States, especially in the Columbia Basin where numerous dams have been built and others are under construction or projected.

Cheap hydroelectric energy encourages the location of many industries. This applies particularly to aluminum and others using electroprocesses. These latter include the refining of many metals, such as zinc; also the production of artificial abrasives, chlorine, caustic soda, and other chemicals. Cheap hydroelectric energy also contributes to woodworking, agricultural processing, and other establishments. However, power production will have to be expanded rapidly in the years to come if the increasing demands of industry are to be met.

Labor

Labor finds the Northwest an attractive place in which to live and work. Labor receives slightly higher wages here than in comparable regions, but in many of the urban centers living costs are also higher. The large growth of population during the 1940's was associated with the increasing demands for workers in war industries. Workmen are in greatest supply in the Willamette-Puget Lowland, but other sections of the Northwest, for example the Spokane area, also have rather large work reservoirs. Labor demands created by the future expansion of industry can be satisfied by immigration and natural increase in population.

Transportation

Two aspects of transportation are of concern to industry. Externally, the Pacific Northwest is at some disadvantage because of the remote source of some raw materials as well as the long distance to the great markets. Rail transportation is available to all parts of the country, but the rates are relatively high and this precludes economical marketing of many manufactures. Water transport via the Panama Canal is of considerable advantage for the export of heavy commodities, such as lumber and other wood products.

Internally, the transportation system of the Northwest is satisfactory but there are certain difficulties and handicaps. The Cascade Range, once a serious barrier, is crossed by many railroads and highways. North-south transportation is good through the Willamette-Puget Lowland, and this region has reasonable access to other parts of the Northwest. Satisfactory inland waterways are available only in the Puget Sound region and in the lower Columbia River. Plans to improve the upper Columbia to enable heavy freight boats to reach the Inland Empire are under way but are not likely to be completed for several years. Airways form a fairly complete network for most parts of the region.

Markets

The internal market of the Northwest is provided by the nearly 5 million people who live in the region. This market is constantly expanding, not only in the number of people involved, but also in their per capita income and consumption. Externally the forest industries of the Northwest are able to compete successfully with other regions of the United States, most of which are closer to the great eastern market. The increasing population in California also has an important effect, since large quantities of lumber, agricultural products, and other materials are marketed in that state.

Other Location Factors

The relative importance of the several locational factors varies with time and area. The abundant power available at Bonneville or Grand Coulee does not necessarily mean that an industry is located exactly at these points. Since hydroelectric energy is flexible and can be transported for considerable distances, other factors in location may have a more specific influence, such as labor supply, transportation, or market.

The precise physical location of an industry may depend upon a good available site. Level land, nearness to railroads or to water transportation, and similar factors may determine the actual location of a manufacturing establishment. It is important, therefore, to distinguish between the general location factors and the factors that tend to localize the industry on a specific site. A lumber mill, for example, can be satisfactorily located within any district and at any point where logs and other forest products are available, but it is also desirable to locate the mill on level land near a water supply.

DISTRIBUTION AND NATURE OF MANUFACTURING

More than 290,000 workers are employed in industry; 159,000 are in Washington, 114,000 in Oregon, and 18,000 in Idaho (Fig. 48). Most of these employees are concentrated in a few areas, many counties having few or no workers engaged in manufacturing. The distribution of industries together with the percentage of workers and

TABLE 1

County	Number of Workers (1947)
King (Washington)	44,000
Multnomah (Oregon)	41,000
Pierce (Washington)	14,000
Snohomish (Washington)	8,000
Spokane (Washington)	8,000
Lane (Oregon)	8,000

the percentage of value added to the raw materials are shown in Table 2. The value added by manufacturing is generally in proportion to the number of employees. The census of manufactures for 1947 shows that the Pacific Northwest added value to raw materials to the extent of $1,654,000,000.

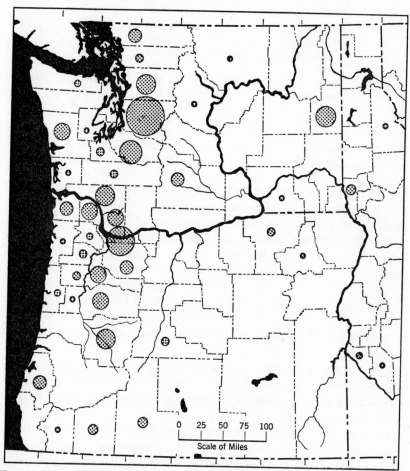

Fig. 48. The distribution of production workers in the Pacific Northwest, 1947. The largest circle, for King County, Washington, represents 44,000 workers; the smallest represents approximately 1000 workers. Counties without circles have less than 1000 production workers. (*Data from Census of Manufacturers.*)

Detailed studies of the individual industrial districts reveal the special location factors that have been of greatest influence. King County, Washington, the Seattle area, has the greatest industrial production. The obvious advantages are a tidewater location and good

TABLE 2

Industry	Number of Workers	Value Added to Raw Materials, millions of dollars
Lumber	95,000	686.5
Food products	40,000	300.1
Transportation equipment	20,000	86.7
Metals	17,000	83.1
Paper	15,000	172.4
Machinery	9,000	45.1
Printing	6,800	72.0
Furniture	6,000	28.6
Clothing	4,000	18.5
Textiles	3,100	15.4
Chemicals	2,300	29.0

transportation facilities. In earlier days this region had large forest resources, some of which are now depleted. In King County the air-craft industry contributes most to the value added by manufacturing.

Industries in the Portland metropolitan area are similar, in many respects, to those of the Seattle area. Portland leads in textiles, lumber, furniture, and paper, but Seattle is far ahead in transportation equipment. Portland is a river port and has access to the Inland Empire country east of the Cascades via the Columbia Gorge. It is also in a good position to gather and process the materials produced in the Willamette Valley, which is the most productive area of its hinterland.

The variety and scope of manufacturing in the two great metropolitan districts, Seattle (King County) and Portland (Multnomah, Clackamas, and Washington counties in Oregon and Clark County in Washington), are summarized in Table 3.

Outside the Seattle and Portland manufacturing areas industry is less concentrated but is by no means unimportant. Approximately 60 per cent of the industrial workers are in smaller cities and towns (Fig. 48). In the Willamette Valley, Linn, Marion, and Lane counties average more than 4000 production workers each, and in the lower Columbia district, Clatsop and Columbia counties in Oregon and Cowlitz County in Washington likewise average about 4000 workers. Grays Harbor, Snohomish, and Pierce counties in Washington have slightly higher averages. In most of the counties mentioned the chief industry is wood products.

TABLE 3

INDUSTRIES OF THE SEATTLE AND PORTLAND METROPOLITAN DISTRICTS*

| | Seattle | | Portland | |
	Establish-ments	Workers	Establish-ments	Workers
1. Food and kindred products	218	6,150	229	6,583
2. Textile-mill products	9	139	14	2,486
3. Apparel and related products	94	1,999	42	1,655
4. Lumber and products, except furniture	105	5,092	255	8,471
5. Furniture and fixtures	58	937	52	2,629
6. Paper and allied products	17	660	26	4,388
7. Printing and publishing industries	169	1,942	178	1,762
8. Chemicals and allied products	62	608	55	608
9. Petroleum and coal products	4	34	7	230
10. Rubber products	4	32	5	102
11. Leather and leather products	14	294	18	208
12. Stone, clay, and glass products	48	958	45	529
13. Primary metal industries	31	2,209	43	3,398
14. Fabricated metal products	129	2,926	103	3,116
15. Machinery, except electrical	104	2,589	98	2,633
16. Electrical machinery	18	661	23	714
17. Transportation equipment	56	16,814	32	2,190
18. Instruments and related products	15	59	10	.....
19. Miscellaneous manufactures	66	565	61	780
Total	1221	44,668	1297	42,675

* U. S. Bureau of the Census, 1947.

The industrial district centering around Spokane is rapidly growing in importance. The nearness to Grand Coulee Dam with its cheap power determined the location of aluminum and magnesium refining and other metalworking establishments. The processing of wheat, meat, and timber is also important. Manufacturing in northern Idaho and western Montana consists mainly of the processing of timber and ores.

GROWTH IN MANUFACTURING

Since 1940, manufacturing has expanded rapidly in the Pacific Northwest and in the United States (Fig. 49). Industrial pay rolls in the United States increased from 20 per cent of all individual incomes in 1939 to 22 per cent in 1947. At the same time in the North-

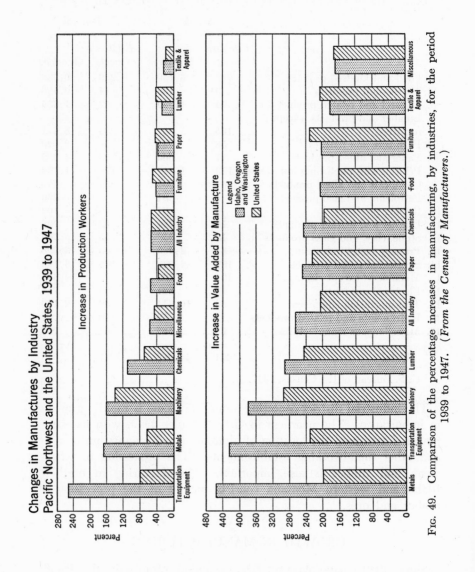

FIG. 49. Comparison of the percentage increases in manufacturing, by industries, for the period 1939 to 1947. (*From the Census of Manufacturers.*)

west manufacturing pay rolls were 17 per cent of all income payment in both 1939 and 1947. Manufacturing increased more in Oregon than in other Northwest states. The increase in production workers during the 1940's was 61 per cent in Oregon compared with 50 per cent in Washington, 48 per cent in Idaho, and 52 per cent in the United States.

Expansion in manufacturing has not been uniform. Some counties, such as King County in Washington, showed an increase of 89 per cent, chiefly associated with the expansion of the aircraft industries. In Multnomah County, Oregon, the increase was 72 per cent, largely because of the development of heavy industries and the increase in food processing. Light metals contributed to the increase in Spokane County and vicinity. In southwestern Oregon, especially the Eugene area, the increase in wood processing accounted for a large part of the expansion.

The amount of growth for the separate industries varies. Heavy industry, machinery, metals, and transportation equipment show the largest increase of workers and value added. Aircraft, truck bodies and parts, sawmill equipment, steel products, and aluminum are expanding. Machinery, metals, and transportation equipment accounted for 20.3 per cent of all wage earners in 1947 compared with 10 per cent in 1939. The extent of these industries is still small, employing less than 1 per cent of all the workers. Forest-product industries still dominate the economy. Lumber and basic timber products, such as pulp, paper, and furniture, employ nearly half of the workers. The relative importance of these industries declined from 61 per cent of all workers in 1939 to 54 per cent in 1947. Machinery, transportation equipment, metals, and chemical industries are the only products in which the rate of increase in value added by manufacturing in the Northwest exceeds the rate of growth in the nation.[1]

Although manufacturing is growing rather rapidly in the Pacific Northwest, it is lagging behind the population. During the 1940's large numbers of immigrant workers were attracted to the construction industries. These industries boom in times of expansion of population, but as population stabilizes it is expected that more of these construction workers will be freed for manufacturing. Indeed, industry in the Pacific Northwest must provide jobs for these workers freed from the other occupations. It is also apparent that future

[1] The average worker in the Northwest earned $2859 in 1947 compared to $2538 in the United States as a whole.

growth of industry in the Pacific Northwest will depend partly upon an increased supply of hydroelectric energy, more efficient utilization and processing of raw materials, and improved transportation.

Forest Industries

Forest industries, including lumber, plywood, pulp, paper, hardboard, and furniture, account for more than half of all the workers engaged in manufacturing and for more than one-third the value added. Furthermore, they will continue to expand as new processes are developed. Their distribution is wide; nearly every county has some forest industry, but the greatest concentration is in the Willamette-Puget Lowland, near the great forests of the Coast Range, the Olympic Mountains, the Cascades, and the Rocky Mountains (Plate 22A). Centers of forest production are constantly shifting; in general, the movement was to southward, with southwestern Oregon showing the greatest increase. Likewise, the emphasis is also changing with the increasing production of paper, plywood, millwork, and hardboard.

The first sawmill in the Pacific Northwest was established 5 miles above Fort Vancouver in 1827. After 10 years this mill was enlarged and rebuilt, and 1-inchboards were exported to the Sandwich Islands. As settlement advanced into the Willamette Valley and the Puget Sound Lowland, small sawmills were established to supply lumber for frame houses and other buildings. Soon ship communication was established, mills were enlarged, and lumber exported to California. Railroads opened up new areas for exploitation as well as new markets by using large quantities of ties, bridge timbers, and lumber of other dimensions. The expansion of public and private highways and logging roads and the increased use of the caterpillar tractor, bulldozer, and other mobile equipment have made it possible to extend forest exploitation into remote areas.

By-products from the mills include alcohol, recovered at Springfield, Oregon, and Bellingham, Washington; naval stores distilled from pine stumps in the Klamath Falls region; vanillin, made in Seattle from pulp waste lignin; as well as yeast, wax, tannin, insulating material, Prestologs, and charcoal.

Plywood

An important development in wood industries is the manufacture of plywood (Plate 22B). When a rotating blade is applied to peeler logs, the wood is peeled off in strips or sheets, called veneer. These thin strips are then glued together, for maximum strength the grain running in alternate directions in the several layers. This enables the manufacturer to add more value to the raw material than is possible in the production of lumber alone. New plywood plants are being established notably in southwestern Oregon, where there is still a good supply of peeler logs. When these are exhausted it is probable that plywood will be replaced in part by hardboard. In this process wood particles are subjected to steam and expanded by the release of pressure to form hardboard pulp. Thus it is possible to utilize the former waste of sawmills as well as old wood from overripe trees.

Paper

The paper industry has expanded rapidly along the shores of Puget Sound, the lower Columbia River, and in the Willamette Lowland. Production is concentrated mainly in fifteen cities extending from Port Angeles and Everett on the north to Coos Bay and Springfield on the south. In the interior, mills are operated at Lewiston, Idaho, and Spokane. A variety of woods are used, including hemlock, spruce, balsam fir, white fir, Douglas fir, cedar, and cottonwood. Paper is made from the waste of sawmills, from scraps of wood, as well as from logs unfit for lumber. In addition to wood, the paper mill needs power, water supply, a flowing stream to carry away waste, and a small amount of chemicals which in some mills are partially recovered for reuse.

Three processes are used in papermaking, the choice depending largely upon the kinds of wood available. The sulfite (acid) process is used largely with hemlock and white fir. It produces a bleached pulp of high quality, some of which is converted to rayon, newsprint, and tissues. The sulfate (alkaline) process utilizes western cedar, Douglas fir, red fir, and other woods of rather high resin content, and produces a variety of papers, including newsprint, wrapping paper, and cardboard. In the mechanical (ground-wood) process the wood, usually hemlock, white fir, or cottonwood, is reduced to fine particles by huge, revolving stone grinders. This consumes more power than the other processes but gives a high yield of good-quality pulp suitable for newsprint, tissues, and other purposes. Census reports list 44 establishments for Washington, Oregon, and Idaho producing pulp, paper, or allied products, with a total of more than 5000 workers employed. Among the later developments is a big plup and paper mill and hydroelectric plant at Powell River, British Columbia, north of Vancouver.

Furniture

The furniture industry utilizes the best of the local softwoods and hardwoods but, of necessity, must import other hardwoods.   Local supplies of maple, red alder, and myrtle account for a limited amount of furniture.   However, large quantities of softwood are used in the form of plywood for inner structures, such as drawer bottoms and sides, thus reducing the amount of high-grade hardwood veneer needed for the exposed surfaces.   Hardwoods are obtained from eastern United States and from the Philippines and other tropical areas.   In addition to wood, the furniture industry uses plastics for table tops, cloth for upholstery, and metals.   The furniture industry is localized chiefly around Portland and Tacoma, but there are small factories in many of the larger cities.   Furniture is marketed mainly in the Pacific Northwest and the Rocky Mountain area.

Food Processing

Second in importance to the forest industries, food processing is expanding.   It includes milling, fruit and vegetable canning, freezing, and dehydrating, and certain other processes for converting the raw materials of agriculture into more satisfactory consumer items.   Raw materials include wheat and other grains, fruits and vegetables, and meat animals and milk.   In general, the food-processing industries are located near the source of the raw materials, but there are some exceptions.

FLOUR MILLING.   The major wheat-producing areas are in north-central Oregon and southeastern Washington, with flour mills located not only in the wheat belts, for example at Spokane, but also in the Willamette Valley and the Puget Sound region.   Since wheat can be transported easily and is in great demand, large tonnages are shipped without further processing.   However, this movement may be interrupted at some point, such as Portland, Tacoma, or Seattle, where the wheat is milled and exported as flour.

The first flour mill in the Northwest, constructed at Fort Vancouver in 1828, was a small "grist" mill manufacturing flour not only for local use but also for export to California.   As settlement advanced, mills were established in other areas, including the Willamette Valley and the newer wheat belts east of the Cascades.   Although the number of flour mills has been decreasing, the surviving mills are generally large and the number of wage earners employed, the value of the products, and value added by manufacturing have been slowly increasing.

CANNING AND PACKING. The canning, freezing, and packing of fruits and vegetables constitute an important part of Northwest manufacturing. The deciduous fruits, particularly cherries, peaches, plums, prunes, apples (Plate 23A), and pears, are processed in large quantities, as are certain vegetables, including peas, beans, corn, broccoli, cauliflower, and spinach. In addition to tree fruits, the principal orchard areas in Washington and Oregon produce large quantities of small fruits, such as strawberries and raspberries. The largest canning and freezing centers are in the Puget Sound-Willamette Valley area, but large quantities of peas and asparagus are processed in southeastern Washington and adjacent portions of Oregon.

Portland, Seattle, Spokane, and Vancouver, British Columbia, are the leading meat-packing centers, although beef cattle and lambs usually come from the drier parts of the region east of the Cascades. The industry does not produce enough meat to supply the regional demand. The shortage of pork is especially noteworthy. The canning and freezing of fishery products are concentrated largely in the Astoria region of Oregon, in southwestern Washington, and around Puget Sound. Tuna and salmon are the most important items.

DAIRY PRODUCTS. Over 500 factories are engaged in the manufacture of butter and cheese, canned milk, milk powder, and ice cream. The humid parts of Washington and Oregon and some of the irrigated areas east of the Cascades are well suited for dairy production, and the steadily growing urban population provides a good market. Because of the bulk and perishable nature of fluid milk, most factories are located near the producing areas. Plants are concentrated in the Puget Sound-Willamette Valley, near Spokane, and in the Snake River Plain of southern Idaho. Other important dairy areas are Tillamook County, Oregon, and Whatcom County, Washington. Throughout the Northwest more milk is used in the manufacture of butter than cheese, Idaho leading in butter production. Oregon leads in the manufacture of cheese, mainly cheddar, most of the production coming from the Willamette Valley and Tillamook County. Washington is the largest producer of evaporated milk.

METAL INDUSTRIES

Plants for the smelting and refining of metals tend to be located by the availability of hydroelectric energy. The Northwest has a large variety of metallic ores; many of them are, however, low grade but lend themselves to electroprocesses. Steel production in and near the major industrial centers is limited largely to the conversion of scrap metal into steel rather than the smelting of iron ore. The reduction of ores has been discussed in Chapter 9.

The Aluminum Industry

Cheap hydroelectric power was the main attraction in bringing the aluminum industry to the Northwest in the early 1940's. Bauxite, the common ore of aluminum, is not mined locally in commercial quantities; therefore, most of the aluminum has to be shipped into the region. The production of a finished aluminum article, be it a coffee pot or an airplane, involves at least five steps or operations. The first is the mining of the ore, bauxite, most of which comes from Arkansas, Jamaica, and South America. The next step is the heat treatment of the ore, which drives off the excess moisture and converts the bauxite to alumina (aluminum oxide). The alumina is shipped to the Pacific Northwest by rail for the third phase of the process, which is the reduction of the oxide to aluminum metal, usually in the form of ingots or pigs; this step requires large amounts of cheap electric energy. The shaping of ingots into sheets, wire, rods, bars, angles, and other semifinished forms constitutes the fourth step, followed by the fabrication of a great variety of finished aluminum products.

The growth of the aluminum industry in the Northwest has been spectacular. In 1939 not a single pound of new aluminum was produced in the region. In 1940 a reduction plant, with an original capacity of 85,000 tons, was established on the Columbia River just downstream from Vancouver, Washington (Plate 22B), and during that year 5000 tons of metal were produced. In 1941 the production of aluminum metal began at Longview, Washington, and soon a third plant was set up at Troutdale, Oregon. These tidewater plants on the lower Columbia are producing about 30 per cent of the nation's new aluminum and in 1950 represented about one-fourth of the nation's capacity. Another aluminum plant was built in 1941 at Mead, near Spokane; other plants are at Tacoma, Kitimat, British Columbia, Kalispell, Montana, and near Wenatchee, Washington. Military needs played a significant role in the rapid development of the industry, and Northwest plants are now producing over half of the total aluminum in the United States.

The Northwest has two fabrication plants, a rolling mill at Trentwood in the Spokane Valley and a wire, rod, and cable mill at Vancouver, Washington. In addition, there are estimated to be about 200 fabricating industries using aluminum in all forms, but they consume only a small fraction of the total output of pig and sheet aluminum. Because of the limited local market, a large part of the production moves out of the region, especially to California and the Midwest.

The Atomic Industries

Two great atomic plants, each using large quantities of electric energy and employing thousands of workers, are located at Hanford near Richland, Washington, and at Arco, Idaho. The basic raw material for these plants is uranium ore, most of which is obtained from the Belgian Congo, northern Canada, and the Rocky Mountains. The ore is smelted and refined outside the Northwest, and metallic uranium is shipped to the Hanford and Arco plants for conversion to plutonium, which is used in the manufacture of atom bombs and for many scientific and experimental purposes. By-products of these plants include a variety of isotopes, some of which have proved valuable to medicine and science. If atomic energy becomes a source of commercial power in the future, it could revolutionize the type and distribution of industry.

Other Mineral Industries

Cheap electric energy makes it economically feasible to process many other minerals in addition to aluminum. Large deposits of lead and zinc ores in northern Idaho are available, and about 80 per cent of the electrolytic capacity is in this region. Similar processes are used in the refining of lead and copper. Electroprocesses are employed in the manufacture of chlorine used in the paper industry, in water purification, and in the manufacture of insecticides. Electroprocessed potassium chlorate is used in the manufacture of matches, and caustic soda is consumed in the paper and plywood mills. Artificial abrasives are produced at Vancouver, Washington, by the electrolytic process, but the final fabrication of sandpaper, sanding belts, and grinding tools takes place outside the region. Other mineral industries include ferroalloys, phosphorus, and ammonia.

TRANSPORTATION

The Airplane Industry

The manufacture of airplanes is concentrated in Seattle and Renton (Plate 23A). This industry has had a spectacular growth, being stimulated by the great demands for airplanes during World War I, by the expansion of commercial airlines, and again by the demands of World War II. Heavy bombers and transport planes are specialties that require large quantities of aluminum sheets, castings, etc., only a part of which come from the Northwest. Magnesium, copper, and several varieties of steel are also needed. Although the factories are not dependent upon the Northwest for these metals, it is an advantage to have them produced in the region.

Ship and Boat Building

Because of its major activities—lumber carrying, fishing, the Alaska trade, and pleasure boating—the coastal margin of the Pacific Northwest has long been a steady market for vessels of every description. As a result, there are many shipbuilding and boatbuilding yards along the coast, for example at Bellingham, Washington, where skilled craftsmen turn out fishing boats, scows and barges, tugs and towboats, and hundreds of sail- and power-driven pleasure craft, especially. Merchant vessels are also launched at Seattle, Tacoma, and Portland. During both world wars, Columbia River and Puget Sound yards employed thousands of men. The Puget Sound Navy Yard at Bremerton, one of the great shipbuilding or repair and naval-supply centers of the United States, is employed only in naval construction. The supplying and repair of oceangoing and coastwise vessels is an important phase of the shipbuilding industry.

Carshops and Automotive Equipment

Among cities with railroad repair shops are Spokane, Tacoma, Everett, Renton, Portland, and Pocatello. Truck bodies and other automotive equipment are made in Spokane, and various coast cities and an automobile assembly plant is located in Portland.

LIGHT INDUSTRIES

Woolen Textiles

Commercial woolen manufacture dates back to 1857, when the first textile mill west of the Mississippi was built at Salem. Wool from local flocks was plentiful in the Willamette Valley, and home spinning and weaving were common on farms. Influenced by cheap and abundant raw material, local water for power and for washing fleeces, and the high price of imported woolen cloth, Oregon pioneers were encouraged to establish mills to supply the Northwest settlers and California gold miners with coarse but durable clothing material. By 1866 five more mills were in operation. The anticipated markets developed, the quality of local woolens improved steadily, and the industry prospered for a time.

The Willamette Valley and Portland, including Washougal, Washington, is the principal area of concentration. Valley mills are located as far south as Salem and there is also one at Pendleton in eastern Oregon. The woolen industry is controlled by local capitalists.

Most of the raw wool is obtained from the western and Rocky Mountain states through Portland, which is the nation's largest primary wool market. Although the larger share of the wool sold at the annual auction in Portland is purchased for intercoastal shipment to Boston, Oregon mills buy a considerable portion of the clip. Northwest mills produce good-quality fabrics. The principal output is in knit goods, suitings, and blankets, which have both a national and a local distribution.

Clothing

Portland and Seattle lead in the manufacture of clothing. Included in this broad category are: sportswear (ski togs, outing shirts, and jackets), knit goods (swimming suits and sweaters), work clothing (overalls and jackets), and women's dresses. Favorable factors for clothing manufacture in the two cities include their growing importance as retail market centers, favorable location for wholesale distribution, the advantage of an early start, and good management. Some factories, locally financed, have expanded into concerns with national and international reputations. Consistent national advertising has made the buying public trademark-conscious, particularly in the sportswear and swimming-suit field. The nationwide tendency to use the summer recreational facilities of Northwest parks and beaches, together with the rapid development of winter sports in the area, has definitely stimulated the production of all types of outdoor wear. Workmen's clothing, such as overalls, lumber jackets, and "tin" pants for use in the woods and elsewhere, is sold locally. There are seven plants in Washington and two well-known manufacturers in Portland. Men's and boys' clothing is made in twenty establishments. The manufacture of women's wear has become increasingly important in the Northwest, centering in Portland and Seattle. There are no less than twenty such plants in Oregon, and thirty-nine in Washington. There are no clothing factories in Idaho.

Printing and Publishing

These industries have no distinctive geographic or economic elements to make them stand apart as typical of the Northwest. They are primarily service industries catering directly to consumer's needs, such as the publishing of fiction and general books, technical and medical books, textbooks, children's books, periodicals, and newspapers. There are several hundred newspaper plants, printing and publishing establishments, and book and job printers in the Pacific Northwest. This area has the reputation of being an excellent book market and there is a marked demand for the history, wildlife, and biography of the local region which has stimulated the establishment of presses specializing in such books. Portland and Seattle are leading publishing centers, with the modest-sized city of Caldwell, Idaho, an interesting addition to the list.

Miscellaneous

Among the many thousands of manufacturing establishments are scores of industries that help supply the local market and also ship to outside points an appreciable proportion of their output. Among these are baking, brewing, soft-drink, and confectionery industries. Seattle and Portland process tea, coffee, and spices. Oregon has a few linen-weaving establishments using flax grown locally. Medicines, chemical paints, and fertilizers are other light industries.

Steel for the manufacture of consumer durables is of increasing importance. Stoves and furnaces are made in Seattle and Portland, along with mining machinery, marine engines, and automotive equipment. Cheney, Washington, makes a rotary rod weeder widely used in the wheat country. Concrete and metal building materials are made in many centers. The fabrication of electrical equipment is of local importance. Sedro Woolley makes logging equipment.

REFERENCES

Bonneville Power Administration, *Columbia River Industrial Site Survey, Astoria to the Dalles,* September, 1940 (re-issued April, 1944).

Bonneville Power Administration, *Pacific Northwest Mineral Occurrences, Atlas,* April, 1940.

Bonneville Power Administration, *Western Oregon Industrial Surveys, Atlas,* October, 1945.

Department of the Interior, Bureau of Reclamation, *The Columbia River,* Vol. I, 398 pp., 1947.

Goldhammer, Bernard, "Power Development in Northwest Vital to Business Growth," *Oregon Business Review,* October, 1951.

Jensen, J. Granville, "The Aluminum Industry of the Northwest," *Engineering Experiment Station, Oregon State College, Circular* No. 12, November, 1950.

Northwest Regional Council, *Economic Atlas of the Pacific Northwest,* 2nd edition, 1942.

Highsmith, Richard M., *Atlas of the Pacific Northwest,* Oregon State College, 1953.

National Resources Committee, *Regional Planning, Part I, Pacific Northwest,* U. S. Government Printing Office, 1936.

Oregon State Board of Higher Education, *Physical and Economic Geography of Oregon,* 1940, 319 pp.

Stanbery, V. B., *Growth and Trends of Manufacturing in the Pacific Northwest 1939–47,* U. S. Department of Commerce, 1950, 28 pp.

U. S. Bureau of the Census, *General Statistics for Manufacturing for the States of Washington, Oregon, Idaho, and Montana,* 1949.

U. S. Bureau of the Census, *1951 Annual Survey of Manufactures,* 1953.

CHAPTER 26

Foreign Trade of the
Pacific Northwest

FRANCES M. EARLE

Throughout its entire settlement and development the Pacific Northwest has looked with favor upon foreign trade and a water-borne commerce. The rich furs reported by Captain Cook and later exploited by the warring fur companies were carried across the Pacific in sailing ships to be sold in China. The California gold miners, too, busy to grow their own food, paid boom prices for wheat harvested by Oregon farmers in the Willamette Valley. Fir and cedar, cut in any convenient cove, could be sold readily and delivered cheaply anywhere around the fringe of the Pacific. Goods came also by sea. Land routes were long and uncertain, and the region did the bulk of its business by water.

Other stimuli to a sea-borne commerce were soon set in motion. When Japan abandoned her policy of isolation in 1854 and opened her ports to the world, a new era of Pacific commerce was inaugurated. Transcontinental railroads, first to Portland and later to Puget Sound, shortly provided the necessary connecting link with eastern United States. In 1896 the Nippon Yusen Kaisya, in conjunction with the Great Northern Railway, established the first direct steamship line giving regular service between Seattle and the Orient. The great-circle route, the shortest way to the ports of eastern Asia, constituted another advantage to Northwest traders and shipping men.

Then with great rapidity occurred the opening up of Alaska and the American acquisition of Hawaii and the Philippines. An even greater stimulus to ocean trade was the completion of the Panama Canal in 1914. With its tremendous economies in heavy freight costs, the new canal gave the Northwest competitive access to the Atlantic Ocean and to the markets of the Caribbean and of Europe.

Foreign trade grew concurrently with all other economic activities and is today one of the major interests of the region.

The Northwest Timber Ports

The water-borne commerce of the Pacific Northwest is handled through more than a dozen officially listed ports in Washington and Oregon (see Table 1). Some of these may include two or more cities;

TABLE 1

TONNAGE HANDLED BY MAJOR NORTHWEST PORTS, 1950 AND 1951 *

Customs District and Ports	Exports, 1950		Imports, 1950		Exports, 1951		Imports, 1951	
	Million Pounds	Million Dollars	Million Pounds	Million Dollars	Million Pounds	Million Dollars	Million Pounds	Million Dollars
Oregon	1900.5	77.9	215.8	24.1	1850.9	76.1	208.2	23.8
Astoria	109.7	4.3	28.9	4.5	108.3	4.2	28.7	4.5
Coos Bay	313.2	6.6	0.8	0.1	308.8	6.5	0.8	0.1
Portland	975.1	51.5	154.6	19.0	951.1	50.6	147.2	18.7
Longview, Wash.	289.4	8.7	29.8	0.5	289.8	8.7	29.7	0.5
Vancouver, Wash.	.....	....	.....	....	112.4	4.3	.....	....
Washington	1401.4	70.5	3174.0	87.1	1370.7	69.7	3121.7	86.5
Seattle	707.1	39.4	666.5	40.6	681.7	38.6	644.4	40.0
Tacoma	488.6	24.1	998.1	38.5	487.2	24.1	990.6	38.4
Aberdeen-Hoquiam	73.8	2.7	0.5	....	73.6	2.6	0.5	....
Bellingham	31.1	1.4	548.1	1.2	31.1	1.4	536.6	1.2
Everett	27.3	1.3	219.9	2.2	27.8	1.3	218.6	2.2
Port Angeles	27.0	0.8	194.9	1.0	20.0	0.7	187.7	1.1
Port Townsend	3.6	0.2	429.9	1.6	3.6	0.2	422.4	1.6
Anacortes	.....	....	.....	....	0.9	....	88.9	1.3
Total	3301.9	148.4	3389.8	111.2	3221.6	145.8	3329.9	110.3

* U. S. Foreign Trade, January–December, 1950, *Summary Report*, FT 972, also January–December, 1951, *Summary Report*, FT 972, Department of Commerce, Washington, D. C.

for example, Aberdeen and Hoquiam are both in Grays Harbor, and Coos Bay includes Coos Bay and North Bend. One basic fact in the regional economy is apparent: timber and the great array of products made from it, lumber, plywood, siding, piling, shingles, woodenware, pulp, and paper, etc., are the prime materials providing most of the incoming and outgoing tonnage for nearly all the smaller ports on the Northwest seaboard. Many handle nothing else of real importance.

Regardless of size, there is a remarkable similarity in the port functions and cargo handling of these timber-economy towns. Incoming log trains, mills on the water front, and freighters loading directly at millside are the usual pattern. Timber and its products account for 100 per cent of Olympia's exports; 98 per cent of Port Angeles, Port Townsend, and Port Gamble on the Olympic Peninsula; and 95 per cent of the exports of Grays Harbor and Coos Bay, which are now the leading lumber-shipping ports of the United States. Even in cities such as Everett, Bellingham, and Astoria, which have a more diversified economy, timber derivatives provide 80 to 90 per cent of the exports. Likewise, the import tonnage listed by a number of mill cities on Puget Sound consists in the main of logs or partially manufactured wood brought in from Canada for further processing.

The apparent decline in the export of wood and its products has been offset in large part by greater local consumption, the shipment of paper by rail, and the large amounts on government account for which no details are available.

General Cargo Ports

The handling of general cargo, including the entire range of raw materials for industry, machinery of every type, foodstuffs from all over the world, and the thousands of manufactured items for human use, is concentrated mainly in three of the Northwest ports: Seattle, Portland, and Tacoma. It should not be inferred, however, that these major ports play no part in the timber economy, because wood and wood products handled through Seattle and Portland compare favorably with the tonnages shipped by most primary timber ports. Although timber, with its manufactures, is unquestionably a dominant trade commodity, it is only one of many. To distinguish them from the smaller single-function ports, these three cities might be called multiple-function ports.

The three major ports, all located inland from the ocean, have taken the lead in Northwest trade because of a number of interrelated factors. An early start, strategic location, favorable access to agricultural hinterlands and raw materials, good harbors (natural or dredged), railway access to the East, and capital for investment, have all contributed in varying degree.

Portland, at the outlet to the richest agricultural valley in the Northwest, had an early start and the advantage of Columbia River transportation. It had the first transcontinental railway connection with the East by way of the Columbia gap through the Cascades, and still has an advantage in trade of the Inland Empire. The problem of handling larger ocean freighters was solved by dredging a deep-water harbor in the Willamette River and cutting a 40-foot channel through the bar at the mouth of the Columbia. Tacoma had the first railway to Puget Sound and an excellent anchorage on Commencement Bay, which has since been expanded by dredging several basins in the flats at the head of the bay. The Port Industrial Waterway is being dredged to provide an additional 1.5 miles of tidewater sites in the industrial area. Seattle, with a later start than Portland and poorer access to the East, has capitalized on its fine natural harbor on Elliott Bay and its superior location for trade with Canada, Alaska, and the Orient. With the steady growth of water-borne traffic, Seattle became the headquarters for more steamship lines than any of the other ports and expanded its harbor facilities to include not only the lower Duwamish flats, Smith Cove,[1] and Salmon Bay, but also Lakes Union and Washington, providing both fresh- and salt-water harbors. In 1950 Seattle established a Foreign Trade Zone, where goods may be repacked, displayed, or manufactured, and this zone will undoubtedly attract an increasing volume of trade in the future. All three ports now have ample facilities for handling all types of ocean traffic, equal access to Northwest power and raw materials, and approximately similar rail connections with eastern United States.

Commodities in Foreign Trade

In an early report on Northwest trade, Hittell wrote:

During 1880 considerable shipments of flour were made from Walla Walla to Liverpool, and 160,000 cases of salmon were shipped to foreign countries from the Washington side of the Columbia River. About 170 million feet of lumber were shipped to San Francisco, the Sandwich Islands, and Australia; and 200,000 tons of coal were shipped to various destinations.[2]

This 70-year-old account of foreign trade still sounds familiar. Lumber and flour have continued to hold a dominant export position, salmon has been valuable throughout the years, but coal has declined greatly in significance.

The general picture of commodities handled through Seattle, Portland, and Tacoma in 1950 was somewhat similar, but a careful analysis shows a number of significant differences (Table 2). In total tonnage Portland was formerly the unquestioned leader, but in 1950 Seattle took the lead, with Tacoma in second place and Portland third.

[1] Now used by the U. S. Navy.

[2] Hittell, *The Commerce and Industries of the Pacific Coast of North America*, 1882, p. 215.

TABLE 2

FOREIGN TRADE.   SEATTLE, PORTLAND, TACOMA, 1950 *

(short tons)

Commodity	Seattle, Washington		Portland, Oregon		Tacoma, Washington	
	Imports	Exports	Imports	Exports	Imports	Exports
Animals and animal products, edible	11,983	14,163	4,697	22,115	659	137
Inedible	3,552	10,012	2,176	7,504	576	2,605
Vegetable food products and beverages	79,894	219,487	14,326	293,620	4,848	138,015
Vegetable products, inedible	2,321	4,235	6,051	2,631	22,038	285
Textiles, fibers and manufactures	10,989	1,566	10,848	842	476	21
Wood and paper	82,729	36,347	4,259	138,631	150,590	30,481
Nonmetallic minerals	80,172	52,316	1,254	4,984	29,533	17,398
Metals and manufactures (except machinery and vehicles)	50,745	10,471	25,497	4,308	285,745	27,087
Machinery and vehicles	1,718	4,536	424	4,104	61	609
Chemicals and related products	25,720	3,705	7,026	7,805	2,991	27,404
Miscellaneous	2,539	131,248	851	235,201	1,736	65,269
Total foreign trade	352,362	488,076	77,589	721,744	499,243	309,311
Coastwise traffic, 1950	5,295,162	732,743	6,078,220	521,247	822,097	325,074

* *Water-Borne Commerce of the United States for the Calendar Year 1950*, Annual Report of the Chief of Engineers, Department of the Army, 1951, Part 2.

Portland has the greater export tonnage, shipping four times as much wood and paper as either Seattle or Tacoma, as well as larger amounts of farm produce. Wheat and flour for foreign markets are two of the big items in Portland's freight. With heavy imports of copper, chrome, manganese, and other ores, Tacoma ranked first in 1950. Seattle handled over four times the tonnage reaching Portland harbor from abroad. This import preponderance over Portland is greatest in wood and its products, agricultural produce, metallic and nonmetallic minerals, chemicals, as well as jute and manila hemp fibers and burlap and jute bagging from the Orient. One historic and valuable item, which accounted for much of Seattle's phenomenal increase in imports during the decade 1919–29, was the large amount of raw silk from Japan, transshipped by fast freight to eastern industrial centers. The Washington Customs District reported total imports valued at $216,000,000 in 1929, of which raw silk accounted for $151,000,000, or 69 per cent of the total. The economic depression and, later, rival silk routes via California ports or the Panama Canal cut silk imports through Seattle to $4,500,000 in 1939, a mere fraction of the trade's former value. With the resumption of trade with Japan, raw silk and silk manufactures have again begun to flow through Seattle.

In 1940 two-thirds of Tacoma's exports originated in Northwest forests, but by 1950 this category had been reduced to 10 per cent, while wheat and wheat flour ranked first among exports, accounting for 44 per cent of the total tonnage. Refined copper from the huge local smelter and industrial chemicals are widely marketed, and there is also a growing export of local manufactures. Copper ores and concentrates account for 40 per cent of the import tonnage; other ores, including chrome, lead, zinc, manganese, and aluminum, total another 16 per cent of imports.

It should be added that the domestic and intercoastal trade of all these ports not only is larger in volume but also includes a greater variety of commodities. Seattle's intercoastal, Gulf, and Hawaiian tonnages for 1950 and 1951 are shown in Table 3.

TABLE 3

SEATTLE TONNAGES: INTERCOASTAL, GULF, AND HAWAIIAN TRADES *

	Intercoastal		Gulf		Hawaii	
	Westbound	Eastbound	Westbound	Eastbound	Inbound	Outbound
1950	150,607.3	91,706.9	16,751.5	5,028.0	39,108.9	31,038.0
1951	179,901.8	50,159.5	8,468.7	2,246.0	58,286.2	33,698.2

* Source: Marine Exchange, Seattle Chamber of Commerce.

The intercoastal tonnages include Alaska; no separate statistics concerning this lucrative trade have been released since 1948.

Tables 1–3 show volume of trade in tonnage. It is difficult to compare a ton of copper ore, a ton of salmon, and a ton of evaporated milk; dollar value is probably a more desirable measure, despite fluctuations in prices. Table 4 gives dollar values of selected leading commodities imported into and exported from the Washington Customs District for the years 1938–40 and 1948–50.

Considerable export trade also moves via the Columbia River, which is a natural outlet for the productive Inland Empire (Table 5).

Department of Defense controlled cargo and special category commodities accounted for 54 per cent of the export tonnage while wheat, the only significant commercial export, was 39 per cent of the total.

TABLE 4

WASHINGTON CUSTOMS DISTRICT: VALUE OF LEADING EXPORTS AND IMPORTS *

($1000)

Exports	1938	1939	1940	1948	1949	1950
Wood and products	11,761	12,689	11,163	11,287	13,578	7,682
Wheat and wheat flour	5,750	7,469	7,373	31,839	17,082	20,695
Refined copper	14,641	18,834	3,902	12,844	20,031	9,986
Canned salmon	5,919	5,325	6,668	466	8,132	575
Fruits and vegetables	8,804	8,130	3,001	1,703	1,642	4,534
Evaporated milk	428	521	1,431	4,241	1,442	1,956
Machinery	4,764	4,173	7,694	3,708	11,187	7,062
Steel products	989	2,221	4,987	4,403	2,802	275
Aluminum and products	....	....	....	3,162	2,149	....
Zinc	....	....	....	1,365	1,191	1,020

Imports	1938	1939	1940	1948	1949	1950
Wood and wood products	7,451	11,517	13,286	54,696	39,856	68,715
Copper ores and concentrates	864	575	1,695	1,876	15,931	8,204
Fish and fish products	1,379	1,627	1,910	12,602	11,241	14,392
Green coffee	1,465	1,156	1,142	6,318	6,969	8,420
Animals and products	424	1,159	1,362	6,795	7,106	13,325
Fertilizer materials	595	926	1,054	4,354	5,815	7,134
Jute, burlaps, and fabrics	215	....	....	1,827	1,825	1,102
Automobiles	....	....	....	1,140	1,079	1,075
Undressed mink fur	490	549	756	720	1,073	1,105
Bananas	....	....	....	560	841	1,213
Silk	3,765	4,566	8,315	....	....	....
Sugar	2,172	2,126	1,242	....	....	....

* U. S. Department of Commerce, Bureau of the Census, *IM Report* 154 (Imports) and *EM Report* 562 (Exports).

Direction of Foreign Trade

Both the volume and direction of foreign trade reflect world conditions. Trade of the Pacific Northwest was affected by World War I of 1914–18, by the boom of the late 1920's ending in the market crash of 1929, by the world-wide economic depression of the early 1930's, by World War II, and by the Korean War. There has been a complete loss of markets in some countries, as well as new or increased trade with others.

Political uncertainties in the international situation are largely responsible for the current partial war economy. The resulting import and export licensing, quotas and allocations, and foreign exchange controls all introduce trade complications. For example, Department

TABLE 5

COLUMBIA RIVER: FOREIGN TRADE, 1950 *

(short tons)

Commodity	Imports	Exports
Animals and animal products	14,358	126
Vegetable food products and beverages (includes wheat 206,067)	11	232,336
Vegetable products, inedible	45	13
Textile fibers and manufactures	1	13
Wood and paper	364	43,972
Nonmetallic minerals	. . . . . .	180
Metals and manufactures, machinery and vehicles	26	126
Chemicals and related products	15,347	51
Miscellaneous (includes Department of Defense controlled cargo, 323,055)	. . . . . .	323,059
Total	30,162	599,877

* "Commercial Statistics: Waterborne Commerce of the United States for the Calendar Year 1950," *Annual Report of the Chief of Engineers,* Department of the Army, 1951, Part 2.

of Defense controlled cargo and special category commodities have increased to such an extent that in 1950 they constituted 21 per cent of the foreign exports of Tacoma, 25 per cent of Seattle's, and 33 per cent of Portland's. (The percentage was even higher in Longview, 44 per cent, and Astoria, 58 per cent.) Controlled cargo includes supplies and equipment for technical assistance programs in various foreign countries.

Ocean shipments of military supplies from ports under the jurisdiction of the Seattle Port of Embarkation averaged over 2 million tons annually during the decade 1942–51, with a war peak of 3.2 million tons in 1945. This was followed by a slump in 1946 which was of short duration because demands created by the rehabilitation of Japan caused exports to increase to a second peak of 3 million tons in 1949; included were the important items wheat and fertilizers. In 1950 exports amounted to 1.4 million tons, which in 1951 increased to 2.5 million, clearly reflecting the influence of the Korean War.

The U. S. Navy also exported a large volume of commodities from Seattle during World War II. The total volume of foreign trade is being further increased by the more general use of air freight.

Over 40 per cent of Seattle's commercial water-borne imports came from Canada in 1950, lesser amounts coming from Costa Rica, the

Philippine Islands, Netherlands, and Germany, in that order. About 18 per cent of all exports went to Canada, 13 per cent to the Philippine Islands, and lesser amounts to Peru, Belgium, and Norway.

Major commodities, on tonnage basis, imported from ten leading countries [3] through Seattle in 1950 were:

Canada: Newsprint; lumber; logs; limestone; coal.

Costa Rica: Bananas; coffee.

Philippine Islands: Logs and pilings; manila hemp and rope; copra meal and cake; veneer and plywood; concentrates of copper, gold, and silver.

Netherlands: Metals and machinery; creosote; fertilizers.

Germany: Metals and manufactures, including locomotives and engines.

United Kingdom: Creosote; coal-tar products; automobiles and trucks; alcoholic beverages.

Japan: Fresh and canned tuna; hardwood lumber; plywood and veneer; bamboo; paper manufactures; earthenware; toys.

Panama: Bananas.

Belgium: Metals and manufactures; hardware; glass.

France: Metals and manufactures.

Commercial exports, on tonnage basis, to ten leading countries were: [3]

Canada: Oil (fuel, diesel, kerosene, petroleum products); cement; lumber, logs, and piling; boats; crushed rock.

Philippine Islands: Grains (barley, oats, wheat, and wheat flour); condensed, evaporated, and dried milk; metal manufactures and machinery; paper; tallow; starch and glucose.

Peru: Wheat; boats and parts; lumber; woodpulp; prefabricated buildings; metal manufactures and machinery.

Belgium: Barley and wheat; fresh apples and pears; canned fruit; dried peas; lumber.

Norway: Wheat and wheat flour; lumber; canned fish; machinery.

Italy: Wheat; tallow; wood burls; canned salmon; fresh and dried apples; copper bars and ingots; lumber.

United Kingdom: Wheat; fresh apples; lumber; zinc bar and slab.

Japan: Corn, oats, wheat and wheat flour; condensed, evaporated, and dried milk; sugar; tallow; lumber; pulp; paper; starch and glucose.

Greece: Condensed and evaporated milk; wheat, metal manufactures and machinery.

Puerto Rico: Lumber, logs and piling; dried and canned peas and beans; canned salmon; salt cod; paper; soap; grains.

---

[3] Data compiled from *Port of Seattle Statistics, 1950 Summary,* The Marine Exchange of the Seattle Chamber of Commerce. Both countries and commodities are listed in order of importance.

Conclusion

Although it is true that foreign trade is far less valuable to the Northwest than its huge commerce with the rest of the United States, including Alaska and Hawaii, the import and export business has long been an integral part of the regional economy. It is a matter of some concern that both foreign and domestic commerce have been based so heavily upon one local resource, the softwood forests. Wood and wood products are still the very heart of trade. The more recent trend, fortunately, has been away from the export of the raw material and toward the sale of more highly processed and valuable wood manufactures. There has also been a welcome increase in the sale abroad of more agricultural, industrial, and chemical products, and, in the future, the region may be able to widen still further the range of its exportable goods. However, the position of the Northwest is highly competitive in many of these lines.

Although foreign trade has steadily increased in volume, significant changes are apparent in commodities and in the direction of trade. As a region, the Pacific Northwest is primarily an exporter of raw materials. Over a period of years the leading exports have been wheat and flour, wood and wood products, copper, fish, and fruits. With the rapid increase in population and the general economic development of the area, larger amounts of foodstuffs and raw materials are consumed locally, and industrial growth has stimulated the export of manufactures, especially such items as paper, plywood, furniture, refined copper, and aluminum. Incoming trade is relatively small in proportion, because both the population and the effective market of the Northwest are small in comparison to that of the United States and because of the great distance from consuming centers with the resultant high transportation costs. The improvement of port facilities, the establishment of a foreign trade zone, and the creation of industrial sites have been part of a constructive long-term plan to attract more water-borne commerce.

Rail competition and strikes have caused certain commodities formerly shipped by water, such as fresh apples, to move mainly by overland freight.[4] For example, the Inland Empire shipped 43,500 cars of fruit in 1951 and the Wenatchee-Okanogan valleys alone shipped

[4] When California ports were tied up, oranges were exported through Seattle.

an estimated 12,000 cars of apples.[5]   Several facts have contributed to the obvious decline in the export of canned salmon, including strikes which tied up shipping and caused a great decrease in the Alaska pack, expansion of the frozen fish business, and the competition of tuna.

Statistics for the 1940's do not present an accurate foreign trade picture because of restrictions, controls, and government participation, as well as the shortage of shipping space.

Concerning the future, there are reasons for both pessimism and optimism. Water-borne trade has been greatly handicapped by labor problems which create uncertainty and lack of confidence on the part of shippers. The probability of port tie-ups not only discourages trade but also indirectly affects the economic activity of thousands of persons in various related services.[6]

Seattle is faced with the problem of inadequate deep-water frontage to attract additional industry, but both Tacoma and Portland are in the process of reclaiming land for this purpose. Further improvements in terminal facilities are contemplated for the handling of bulk cargo and for the anticipated trade of the Inland Empire. Some 80,000 acres in the Columbia Basin project received its first water from Grand Coulee Dam early in 1952, and the irrigated area will be increased annually until the first development phase is completed. Another asset is the resumption of regularly scheduled Japanese shipping; it is possible that trade between Japan and the Pacific Northwest may in the future regain its prewar importance.

[5] Since 1936, freight-car loadings of the Northwest (Washington, Oregon, and northern Idaho) have exceeded 1 million annually; in 1951, 1,178,000 cars were shipped. *Pacific Northwest Industry*, April, 1952.

[6] In summarizing its strike losses, "The Alaska Steamship Co. estimated yesterday that the recent sailors' strike caused the company to lose $3,308,500 in revenue and caused laboring men to lose $1,087,102 in wages. The strike tied up the ships for 53 days. . . . Over 2550 northbound passengers and tourists were denied transportation. On the basis of all passenger reservations, it is estimated that the loss of revenue from the interruption of passenger service was $528,000. On a projection of last year's freight-traffic movement during the period from May 22 through July 14, it can be shown that the revenue loss due to the interruption of freight service was $2,780,500. The strike caused 28 voyages to be canceled by the Alaska Line, including 13 by passenger ships and 15 by freighters. The company estimated that wages lost by crews which would have sailed the ships amounted to $628,038. Longshoremen in Seattle lost $263,372 in wages, while longshoremen in Alaska ports lost $175,692. It was estimated that companies which sell supplies for Alaska Line ships lost sales amounting to $343,000." *The Seattle Times*, July 20, 1952.

REFERENCES

Hittell, J. S., *The Commerce and Industries of the Pacific Coast of North America*, A. L. Bancroft & Co., San Francisco, 1882.

Mears, E. G., *Maritime Trade of Western United States*, Stanford University Press, 1935.

Miller, Charles J., *A Foreign-Trade Zone for Puget Sound: Its Economic Desirability and Feasibility*, Port of Seattle and the Division of Progress and Industry Development of the State of Washington, January, 1947.

Winther, O. O., *The Old Oregon Country: A History of Frontier Trade, Transportation, and Travel*, Stanford University Press, 1950.

"Commercial Statistics, Waterborne Commerce of the United States for the Calendar Year 1950," *Annual Report of Chief of Engineers*, Department of the Army, Washington, D. C., 1951, Part 2.

"U. S. Exports of Domestic and Foreign Merchandise for the Calendar Year 1951," *Department of Commerce Report* FT410, Washington, D. C., April, 1952.

Waterborne Foreign Trade, Port of Seattle, compiled by The Marine Exchange of the Seattle Chamber of Commerce, Summaries for 1950 and 1951.

The Port of Portland and Its Facilities, prepared by Foreign Trade and Shipping Department, Portland Chamber of Commerce, 1951.

The Port of Seattle, *Annual Report*, 1951.

The Port of Portland Commission, *Biennial Report*, 1945–1946, 1947–1948, and 1949–1950.

Pacific Northwest Industry (monthly), Bureau of Business Research, University of Washington.

Port Series, U. S. Army, Corps of Engineers. Numbers 7, Seattle; 11, Portland; 23, Olympia and Port Angeles; 27, Tacoma; 28, Everett, Bellingham and Grays Harbor; 32, Astoria, Longview, and Vancouver.

Urban Development
in the Northwest

HOWARD H. MARTIN and ASSOCIATES [1]

Northwest settlements are of four major types: those with timber products as the principal source of income; the mining towns; those serving agricultural areas; and the transportation centers. A few agglomerations are the result of military activity, governmental organization, recreation and health, or the presence of state institutions. With the exception of five multifunctional cities (all above 100,000 in population) it is generally possible to classify the Northwest towns and cities according to predominant function.

TYPES OF TOWNS AND CITIES

A mining center seldom changes character throughout its existence, and it either progresses or declines. Some of the towns obviously have multiple interests: Pocatello is both a railroad town and a market and supply center for surrounding ranches; Bend, Oregon, specializes in lumber; Mt. Vernon, Washington, in dairying; and Puyallup in bulbs and horticulture. Many Northwest towns were planned before settlement. Anacortes (a transportation center) was planned in 1876; Kelso (agriculture and lumber) in 1884; Longview (lumbering and shipping) in 1922; and Holden (mining) in 1936. Everett was platted as both a lumber-sawing and iron-working city, although the iron works failed.

Lumber Settlements and Towns

Most of the settlements concerned with logging are relatively small, some of them no more than temporary camps which disappear with

[1] Sections of this chapter were contributed by Otis W. Freeman, Hallock F. Raup, John O. Dart, J. Lewis Robinson, Willis B. Merriam, and Marion E. Marts.

hardly a trace when their timber stand is exhausted. Other sawmill sites are more permanent and support a larger population during their periods of activity. Some sawmill towns are "company towns," nearly all their residents being employed by a single mill.

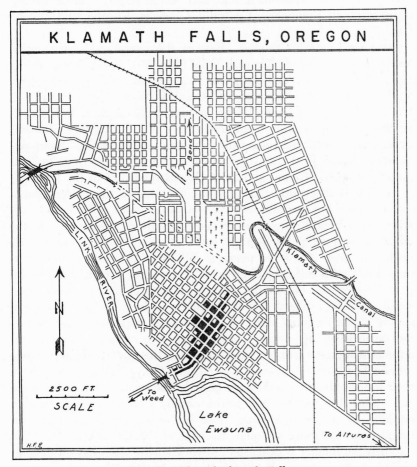

FIG. 50. Plan of Klamath Falls.

WESTERN LUMBER CITIES. A preferred location for the lumber mill is at tidewater, where ships can be loaded directly. Nearly all the coastal cities and towns of Oregon, Washington, and British Columbia owe their existence to lumber-export activities. Among such centers are Port Orford, Bandon, Coos Bay, Astoria, South Bend, Hoquiam, Aberdeen, Port Angeles, Everett and Bellingham. The three large cities on Puget Sound—Seattle, Vancouver, British Columbia, and Tacoma—are lumber exporters, as are the capital cities of Victoria and Olympia to a lesser extent. On the Columbia River, Portland, Vancouver (Washington), Saint Helens, Longview, and Kelso are other examples. Some sawmills are located where railroads alone furnish transportation; Enumclaw, Centralia, Chehalis, Eugene, and Oregon City.

INTERIOR LUMBER CENTERS. East of the Cascades, intermountain lumber centers include Klamath Falls (Fig. 50), Bend, Burns, Prineville, The Dalles, Pendleton, La Grande, and Baker in Oregon; Spokane, Newport, Okanogan, and Omak in Washington; and Lewiston, Potlatch, and Coeur d'Alene in Idaho. Saint Maries, Idaho, is headquarters for logging operations rather than for milling. Bonner, Polson, and Libby are among the Montana lumber towns. Some settlements have allied industries connected with lumbering, such as pulp and paper. Camas and Saint Helens specialize in the latter.

In most timber ports the dominant features of the cultural landscape are the big sawmills and storage yards. Alongside the big mill with its stacks and refuse burner (now rapidly disappearing) are the wharves with adjoining storage yards at which lumber carriers tie up for loading. Clustered near the mill are the houses of the workmen, built with different degrees of permanence. Sometimes "company houses," all cut in the same architectural pattern, have been supplied. The business section is seldom as large as that of a farm-supply center of equal size because the rural population near a sawmill town is usually small; a sawmill center is often a community in a forest wilderness with no industries other than woodworking. Some mill centers such as Spokane, Everett, and Grays Harbor now receive their log supply from a distance because the nearby timber has been cut. Since the interior mill towns usually have other industries in addition to simple lumbering, their business sections are larger in proportion than those of equal size west of the Cascades.

When the lumber is exhausted, sawmill towns often have a difficult period of readjustment, but if the location is attractive, as in Bandon, Oregon, or Coeur d'Alene, Idaho, tourist trade may become a partial substitute for the mills.

GHOST LUMBER TOWNS. Many mill sites have been entirely abandoned, and such "ghost towns" have depressing cultural landscapes, dominated by the big mill with its cold and rusty beehive-shaped sawdust burner slowly crumbling to ruin. When the timber was cut off, the mill closed, the burners no longer exhaled black smoke, and the residents left. Some buildings were torn down; others were destroyed by fire. Unless new resources were found, the town might be entirely gone and its very site forgotten. Carlisle on the Olympic peninsula, Hope on Pend Oreille Lake, as well as the towns of Elk and Loon Lake, near Spokane, and McInnis Mills in Pend Oreille County, are examples of the many ghost towns. Former lumber towns which no longer appear on the map of Washington include Branham, Pluvius, Buckeye, Cedarville, and Clipper.

The Mining Settlements

The Northwest has a wide variety of mineral deposits, and many communities have benefited from mining. Most of the settlements that depend upon mining are small in population and located in mountain areas; some of the larger centers are so situated that they command the easiest routes to the mines. They fall roughly into two groups: those concerned with the extraction of minerals or ores and those dependent upon processing and shipment of ores. Some towns engage in both mining and processing. Others rely solely upon the furnishing of supplies to miners and mine operators.

THE NORTHERN ROCKIES. Butte, in the Montana Rockies, is the largest city in the Americas with the extraction of metallic ores as its principal industry. Many mining towns of the Coeur d'Alene district have been active for years. Other metal-mining towns include Phillipsburg in southwestern Montana, Neihart in the Little Belt Mountains of central Montana, Canyon City in the Blue Mountains, and Kimberley, British Columbia. Closely allied to mining are ore reduction centers such as Anaconda, Montana, Kellogg, Idaho, and Trail, British Columbia (Plate 11A). Holden, near Lake Chelan, is a modern town planned by a copper-mining company for its many employees.

THE CASCADE MOUNTAINS. Coal towns tend to be in the Cascades rather than in the northern Rockies, for example, Roslyn and Cle Elum, Washington. A few towns have been built near plants that process cement rock, including Concrete and Grotto in western Washington and Lime in eastern Oregon.

GHOST MINING TOWNS. Mining towns are notoriously short-lived, especially those dependent on placer workings. Only the piles of washing gravel and the foundations of a few buildings remain after the minerals are exhausted. A few old placer towns like Helena, Montana, and Canyon City, Oregon, may have other industries to support them after the placers are exhausted, but usually such centers function for only a few years. Carbonado and Black Diamond, once prosperous coal towns, suffered sharp declines when the mines closed down. Ghost towns are found where good showings of ore did not persist in depth or where once-productive mines were worked out, as in Monte Cristo in western Washington, Altyn, in what is now Glacier Park, and Silver City and dozens of other examples in the Idaho mountains. Sometimes the old mines are reopened when new ore discoveries are made or a new process permits the recovery of paying quantities of minerals. Cornucopia, in the Wallowa Mountains, now the site of the largest gold mine in Oregon, had such a rejuvenation.

The Agricultural Settlements

Eastern Washington and Oregon and southern Idaho, because of weather conditions and lack of forest cover, are devoted to agricultural pursuits and grazing on a fairly extensive scale, although the Willamette Valley and the Puget Sound Lowland on the west side specialize in dairying and fruit growing. Dairy centers are distinguished by their numerous creameries, milk condenseries, and cheese factories. In contrast to those west of the Cascades, the agricultural towns of the interior are usually less complex in development and function, serving as market or supply centers for the surrounding farms or as a combination of the two.

The trade centers vary from a general store or a few simple services for farmers, such as a grain elevator or warehouse, grocery, gas station, hardware, and implements, up to larger and more complex urban communities with a variety of stores, businesses, and complete professional services. Banking, theaters, hotels, newspapers, hospitals, furniture, fashionable clothing, automobiles, and expensive machinery are usually found only in the larger centers. In this day of automobile travel a shopping trip of 50 or 100 miles is practicable.

WHEAT CENTERS. In an area such as the Palouse, where most of the land is tillable, both farms and supply towns are evenly distributed; in irrigated sections there is a tendency toward concentration. Dryland wheat farming requires rail facilities for marketing the crop. Shipping and supply towns are strung along the railroads at intervals of 10 to 30 miles. Both towns and rail lines occupy the valleys because of ease of construction; often the towns, lying as they do below the horizon of the hilltops, are invisible until approached closely. The shift from handling wheat in sacks to shipping in bulk has changed the skyline of the wheat centers because the low warehouses, once sufficient for sacked grain, have now been replaced by high elevators.

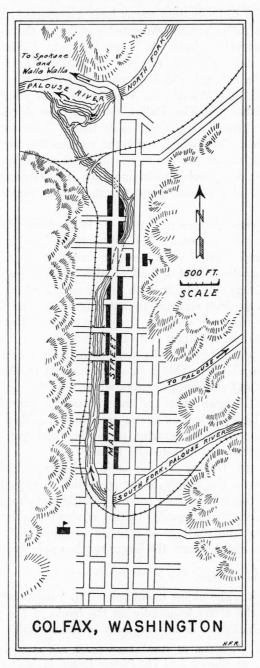

COLFAX, WASHINGTON

Fɪɢ. 51. Plan of Colfax, Washington, a "shoestring" town in a narrow valley.

Many of the valley-bottom towns have a restricted site, and their pattern tends to be greatly elongated parallel to the rail line, with the short transverse streets on steep hillsides. Colfax (Fig. 51), Washington, and Arlington, Oregon, are typical "shoestring" towns. Some towns on railroads also have an elongated business street fronting the tracks, like Wenatchee, Washington, and Shoshone, Idaho. Lewiston, Idaho, and The Dalles, Oregon, have developed similar characteristics from facing a navigable river. There are few industries other than those which serve the surrounding farmers. Flour mills are common, as are creameries and pea canneries.

If climate or soil prove unsatisfactory for grain farming, abandoned supply centers may become ghost towns, such as Stauffer and Lake, Oregon.[2]

FRUIT CENTERS. Towns supported by horticulture offer sharp contrasts to the wheat towns. The cultivation of apple orchards or patches of small fruits is more intensive than that of grain, and landholdings are smaller. East of the Cascades, farms range from 10 to 40 acres in the irrigated districts, with supply centers at intervals of 5 to 10 miles. In the fruit sections, the packing houses and fruit-shipping sheds stretch for some distance along the railroad line. The towns merge with the surrounding cultivated land, so that it is difficult to distinguish a town house with its home orchard from a fruit farm with its modern farmhouse. This is in sharp contrast to the farm-supply town in the wheat and ranch districts, where there is a line of demarcation between the town limits and the surrounding grain fields or pastures. The larger irrigation towns are usually marked by such industries as box factories, canning, preserving, and fruit-drying; flour mills and sawmills are occasionally found.

RANCH-SUPPLY TOWNS. In the cattle and sheep ranching sections of the Northwest the supply towns are widely scattered, in contrast to the wheat centers and fruit centers. Cattle and sheep ranches are large, some covering thousands of acres, compared to the hundreds of acres in wheat and the tens of acres in irrigated fruit. A hundred miles or more may separate the larger ranch-supply towns.

Transportation Centers

RIVER PORTS. The oldest towns related to transportation are those found along the rivers, especially on the banks of the Columbia at points of embarkation or interruptions in stream traffic. Before the

[2] For further description of farm abandonment and town abandonment in eastern Oregon, see Chapter 8 of *The Pioneer Fringe,* by Isiah Bowman.

railroad period, bulky commodities were brought upstream from Portland and distributed from riverside. The Dalles, Lewiston, Wallula, Almota, and other landings on the Columbia and Snake rivers were used. Where these streams flow in incised channels or gorges, the principal requirement for a steamboat landing is accessibility, usually by way of transverse valleys leading back to the hinterland. After the construction of the rail lines, river ports declined except as they became useful in other ways, as The Dalles and Lewiston. The building of locks and canals, mentioned in Chapter 24, resulted in great increase in the use of waterways, to the advantage of the towns of Umatilla, Wallula, Pasco, The Dalles, and Lewiston.

A typical town on the Columbia had its business section facing the river, but after the arrival of the railroads the river-front stores and warehouses deteriorated, the business district moving away from the river; warehouses and factories were placed along the railroad. This tendency can be observed at The Dalles and Lewiston.

RAILROAD TOWNS. Railroad construction brought in new towns and diversified the functions of old ones. At convenient intervals the railroads established division points, junctions of branch lines, and repair shops. Car shops were located at greater distances, usually at some main combined division and junction point or terminal. In some Northwest towns, the principal income has always been derived from the rail lines, as at Pasco, Washington, Huntington, Oregon, Whitefish, Montana, and Pocatello (Fig. 57), Idaho, although Pocatello and Pasco have other industries. Rail towns have extensive yards where freight cars are handled and trains made up; round houses, car shops, and supply depots are characteristic adjuncts. Close by the yards are rooming houses and eating places for the train crews and other employees. In many smaller places the business section faces the railroad in one long street with all the stores on one side of the highway, in contrast to the type of town developed at the intersection of two major highways.

TABLE 1

POPULATION OF PACIFIC NORTHWEST CITIES (1950 Census)

Idaho		Oregon (Continued)	
Boise	34,393	The Dalles	7,676
Pocatello	26,131	McMinnville	6,635
Idaho Falls	19,218	Coos Bay	6,223
Twin Falls	17,600	North Bend	6,099
Nampa	16,185	Lebanon	5,873
Lewiston	12,985	Milwaukie	5,253
Coeur d'Alene	12,198	Hillsboro	5,142
Moscow	10,593	Forest Grove	4,343
Caldwell	10,487	Hood River	3,701
Burley	5,924	Cottage Grove	3,536
Blackfoot	5,180	Burns	3,093
Kellogg	4,913	*Washington*	
Alameda	4,694	Seattle	467,591
Jerome	4,523	Spokane	161,721
Sandpoint	4,265	Tacoma	143,673
Rexburg	4,253	Vancouver	41,664
Preston	4,045	Yakima	38,486
Payette	4,032	Bellingham	34,112
Weiser	3,961	Everett	33,849
Wallace	3,140	Bremerton	27,678
Gooding	3,099	Walla Walla	24,102
Rupert	3,098	Richland	21,809
Emmett	3,067	Longview	20,339
Montana		Aberdeen	19,653
Great Falls	39,214	Renton	16,039
Butte	33,251	Olympia	15,819
Billings	31,834	Wenatchee	13,072
Missoula	22,834	Pullman	12,022
Helena	17,581	Port Angeles	11,233
Bozeman	11,325	Hoquiam	11,123
Anaconda	11,254	Pasco	10,228
Kalispell	9,737	Kennewick	10,106
Whitefish	3,268	Puyallup	10,010
Oregon		Centralia	8,657
Portland	373,628	Ellensburg	8,430
Salem	43,140	Kelso	7,345
Eugene	35,879	Anacortes	6,919
Medford	17,305	Port Townsend	6,888
Corvallis	16,207	Auburn	6,497
Klamath Falls	15,875	Chehalis	5,639
Astoria	12,331	Clarkston	5,617
Pendleton	11,774	Toppenish	5,265
Bend	11,409	Mt. Vernon	5,230
Springfield	10,807	Shelton	5,045
Albany	10,115	Camas	4,725
Baker	9,471	Kirkland	4,713
LaGrande	8,635	Ephrata	4,589
Roseburg	8,390	Medical Lake	4,488
Grants Pass	8,116	Sunnyside	4,194
Ashland	7,739	Raymond	4,110
Oregon City	7,682		

URBAN PATTERN OF WESTERN OREGON

JOHN O. DART

Early Town Location

The Willamette Valley was the earliest region of settlement in the Pacific Northwest, the Oregon pioneers being primarily attracted by the level expanse of fertile cropland. Covered with coniferous timber, the surrounding uplands also provided an easily saleable resource. The location and function of the lowland communities are largely a result of physical, historical, and economic factors. Towns developed as agricultural, trade, and wood-processing centers, located mainly along the Willamette River, since it offered the most convenient means of communication. Later, as the roads and railways were constructed, other towns developed along the routes of overland travel.

Because of the generally uniform physical factors, the distribution of population is quite even throughout most of the valley, although the major urban centers show a distinct pattern. Cities over 15,000 exhibit a similarity of both function and location. All are situated on the Willamette River; all have had an early start, an advantage that other centers have not been able to overcome. They function as educational and political centers, each with a college or university; each has become a county seat; and all are primarily engaged in the processing of agricultural and forest products, while serving as supply centers for the farms and logging camps.

Cities on the Willamette River

Portland dominates the valley as well as the state because of its superior location close to the junction of the Willamette and Columbia rivers. The other major cities are almost evenly spaced along the Willamette River and the main highway and rail lines. Salem (43,140), 40 miles south of Portland, is the state capital, the home of Willamette University, and an important berry, fruit, and vegetable processing and woodworking center. On the west bank of the Willamette, 35 miles to the south, is Corvallis (16,207), with Oregon State College as its leading business. Across the river, Albany (10,115), also a county seat and situated on major intersecting highways, competes for the farm and forest trade of the surrounding area.

Eugene-Springfield

Eugene, situated in the southern end of the valley, was at the head of Willamette navigation in steamboat days. Serving a large tributary radius of fertile farm lands, Eugene (35,879) is the site of the University of Oregon, and also one of the largest sawmilling, plywood, and pulp centers in the Northwest. Together with nearby Springfield (10,807), a rapidly growing mill town with many wood-processing plants, it has become the recognized hub of west-central Oregon.

The smaller urban centers are widely scattered over the valley, usually along the river or at junctions of valley highways with others leading to passes through the Coast Range or Cascades. Oregon City in the Portland suburban area has large pulp and paper mills; it is one of the oldest cities in the state, and early settlers were attracted by the water power available where the Willamette flows over a basalt ledge.

The interest in culture and learning which has been evident in the valley since pioneer days is indicated by the large number of colleges and universities. In addition to those already mentioned, Monmouth, McMinnville, Newberg, and Forest Grove have institutions of higher learning.

Rogue River Cities

Linked to the Willamette Valley by major lines of communication between California and Puget Sound, the Rogue River Valley is served by three cities. Medford (17,305) is in the center of a rich orchard district; in addition to fruit packing and lumbering, it is a summer resort and tourist center, with easy access to Crater Lake, Rogue River Gorge, and the southern Oregon coast. Grants Pass (8116), 30 miles to the west, is the commercial center for a district engaged in fruit raising, dairying, and bulb culture, and the surrounding uplands furnish the raw materials for a wood-products industry. Ashland (7739), with similar activities, has a state college of education.

KLAMATH FALLS. Across the Cascade divide, but closely allied with western Oregon, Klamath Falls is a lumber mill city (Fig. 50) with "boom town" characteristics. Population increased from 4800 in 1920 to 16,093 in 1930, declining to 15,875 in 1950. Rapid growth was the direct outcome of the Klamath Falls-Eugene link of the Southern Pacific Railroad which made this part of southern Oregon economically accessible. Crossing the Cascade range at Odell Lake, this route superseded the Rogue Valley line as the main connection between Oregon and California. In 1929, a rail connection with Alturas, California, tapped the eastern hinterland of Klamath Falls for its lumber, potatoes, livestock, and grain.

The lumber industry draws pine logs from higher elevations bordering Upper Klamath Basin, keeping Klamath Falls in first rank among Oregon pine-milling towns. A related but unique item in the city's prosperity is the inclusion of the timber-rich population of the Klamath Indian Reservation within its trading area. The city also profits from its position on a favored motor highway between the Northwest and California.

ASTORIA. The oldest white settlement in the Northwest, Astoria is a port with industries and functions that have changed greatly. Located on the southern shore and near the mouth of the Columbia River estuary, it began as a Hudson Bay fur-trading post in 1811. Later the post was moved to Vancouver and the townsite nearly abandoned until revived as a sawmill center. At present Astoria is an important fishing center, canning salmon and tuna and shipping fresh fish. The city, unfortunately, has a forested and relatively unproductive hinterland to the south, and to the north the broad estuary can be crossed only by ferry, thus isolating Astoria from main travel routes. In 1890, it had a population of 8000, increasing to 14,000 in 1920 and declining to 12,331 in 1950. Located too close to the mouth of the river, Astoria has not been able to compete with Portland, which is better located to serve the Northwest.

Portland

Portland, second largest city of the Pacific Northwest, gained its present prominence through its activities as a trade center, as a port, and, more recently, through the expansion of manufacturing. Its location on the banks of the navigable Willamette River near its confluence with the Columbia has been of major significance for urban development. Through Portland has passed the rich and varied products from the fertile Willamette Valley, the heavily forested slopes of the Cascades, and the semiarid farm- and rangelands to the east. Its natural crossroads position at the junction of the main north-south route from California to Puget Sound and the only water-level passage from the Columbia Basin to the coast has been a valuable asset throughout Portland's history. Down the gorge carved by the turbulent Columbia came the pioneers to claim the rich farmlands of Oregon. Train, truck, and barge, heavily freight-laden, all take advantage of this economical corridor through the Cascades.

Now in its second century, Portland is the oldest and most mature city in the region, with an interest in books, national problems, art, music, and learning that is more like the eastern seaboard than the Northwest. The original site on the west bank of the Willamette was

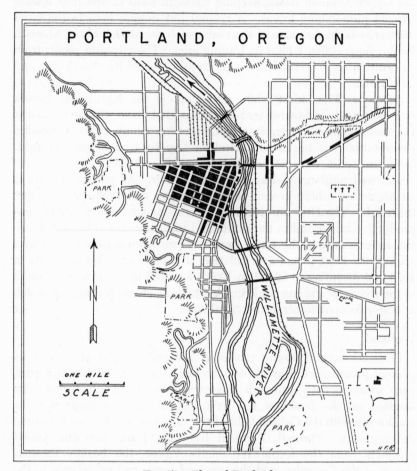

FIG. 52. Plan of Portland.

platted in 1844, and the city was incorporated 7 years later. It expanded to the north, east, and south but was restricted on the west by a wooded bluff rising sharply from the valley floor. Today the somewhat congested commercial core wedged between the bluff and the river occupies the site of the original settlement; it is flanked on each side by railways and thoroughfares and by the major industrial and port area. Along both banks, east and north of the business center, are the docks, elevators, storage warehouses, lumber wharves, and oil tank farms. The river divides the city into two sections, which are connected by nine bridges (Fig. 52). Some businesses have crossed to the east side, invading former residential neighborhoods. The narrow downtown streets, which duplicate almost exactly the village pattern of a hundred years ago, cause many traffic difficulties. A one-way street system in the main business district provides a partial solution.

There has been an increase in residential building, some of it in the luxury class, on the view property in the west and southwest. Below the hill lies the city and the green fields of the valley, and in the background rise the Cascades, surmounted by the snow-capped Mt. Hood. Unlike its urban rivals, San Francisco and Seattle, Portland has a maximum of level terrain for expansion.

Early growth was based primarily upon forest resources; the transporting, manufacturing, and shipping of lumber, plywood, furniture, paper, and other forest products are still the major activities. The crops of the Willamette Valley have also been extremely significant in Portland's development. The packing, canning, and freezing of fruits and vegetables, flour milling and the preparation of animal feeds, meat packing, and the manufacture of woolen and linen yarns, textiles, and clothing are based on materials supplied from the valley or the intermontane regions to the east. Portland has the largest wool market west of Boston and the leading meat-packing center of the Pacific Coast. Locally manufactured knit goods and sportswear have a nationwide reputation for style and quality.

Because of its central location Portland has become the headquarters for numerous governmental agencies and bureaus; many eastern corporations have branch distributing plants and northwestern headquarters here.

Shipbuilding, chemical, and electrometallurgical industries, aided by cheap hydroelectric power generated at Bonneville and other northwest dams, were greatly expanded during World War II. The Willamette provided space for rapid expansion of shipbuilding, the yards completing 1200 ocean-going vessels during the war years. However, the industry has almost ceased operations and is restricted to ship repair, conversion, and scrapping. Three aluminum plants (Vancouver and Longview, Washington; Troutdale, Oregon) have been operating in or adjacent to the Portland metropolitan area since 1940. A rod and bar mill and aluminum transmission plant has been constructed at Vancouver, indicating more fabrication of this metal in the future.

Metalworking, including machinery production, is a leading industry. Although a wide variety of products are made, the most significant are automotive trucks and trailers for the logging and timber industry, sawmill and lumber manufacturing machinery, and other types of specialized agricultural and industrial equipment.

Portland has the only large fresh-water harbor on the Pacific Coast, and since 1878 the 100-mile stretch of lower Columbia has been greatly improved for navigation. Breakwaters have been constructed at the river entrance and the channel deepened to 35 feet. The major port facilities are along the Willamette, although a secondary harbor is located on the south bank of the Columbia. Before World War II the exporting of lumber and grain was the main activity. Disrupted by the war, this traditional trade was more than replaced by the great lend-lease shipments which dominated the water-borne traffic of the West Coast, and facilities were expanded to handle heavy machinery and general cargo. Shipping rates to Alaska, which have been made identical with those from Seattle, have now placed Portland technically on a par with its Puget Sound rival.

Despite improvements in stream and harbor facilities, Portland is handicapped in foreign and intercoastal trade. The upstream trip is more hazardous than entering Puget Sound and during stormy weather vessels are delayed at the bar across the river mouth. On the credit side is the traffic which a well-integrated inland waterway system has brought to the Portland harbor. The combined internal commerce up and down the Columbia annually amounts to approximately 25 per cent of the total water-borne traffic. Downstream tonnage is usually greater, consisting mainly of wheat, paper, lumber, and crushed stone; the major products moving upstream are petroleum and gasoline. Barge traffic on the middle Columbia between Portland and Pasco has grown tremendously since stream improvement and dam construction was begun.

Portland enjoyed a steady but unspectacular growth until World War II, which, with its rapid increase in industry and shipping, caused an influx of 100,000 persons. The 1950 population was 373,628, but the metropolitan area, which includes Multnomah, Clackamas, and Washington counties in Oregon and Clark county in Washington, has over 700,000.

Alert to business opportunities but with a somewhat conservative attitude toward expensive innovations, such as towering skyscrapers,

Portland gets along without undue straining after either size, commerce, or industry. The Portlander follows a solid way of life, transplanted in the beginning from New England and the Middle West, but completely modified to fit the more colorful western environment.

URBAN PATTERN OF WESTERN WASHINGTON

HOWARD H. MARTIN

Puget Sound: Focus of Urban Development

Since the beginning of settlement, deep-water frontage on Puget Sound has been a prime objective and has determined the basic pattern of urban location in Western Washington. Nine cities, ranging in size from Port Townsend and Anacortes, each with about 7000 population, to Seattle with just under a half million, are scattered around the perimeter of Puget Sound. From Port Angeles (11,233) on the Strait of Juan de Fuca, with its timber, fisheries, and ferry services, a swing southward around the Sound will encounter a port every 30 or 40 miles.[1] Port Townsend and Bremerton are on the west side of the Sound. Two far-south arms have the busy pulp town of Shelton and the port of Olympia (15,819), with its state capitol, wood products, canning, and brewing.

On the east side of the Sound, accessible to the great transcontinental railway lines, with freight terminals, deep-water dock facilities, and better farming and forest hinterlands, Tacoma, Seattle, Everett, and Bellingham have grown to city size. All of them have tidewater frontage suitable for industrial sites, and their growth has been affected by various economic and historical considerations.

Everett

Platted in 1892 on a wooded promontory between Puget Sound and the delta of the Snohomish River, Everett is a planned city. The flattish 4-mile peninsula was laid out in a regular grid pattern, with main streets 100 feet wide and a business district in the center evenly surrounded by 80-foot residential streets. A 300-foot bluff to the

[1] The irregular eastern shore of the Olympic Peninsula was once rimmed with aspiring small ports, each hoping to become a great railway and shipping terminus. Their names, Port Discovery, Port Ludlow, Port Gamble, Keyport, and Gig Harbor, indicate the aspiration; their present status is that of quiet villages or near-ghost towns. The once-active iron smelter town of Irondale is now a ghost.

southwest provides another residential area where narrower streets follow contours. Below steep cliffs to the west there is a narrow coastal plain, and on the east the peninsula slopes gradually to the broader floodplain.

The Sound provides deep-water frontage suitable for factory and dock sites, and the city is now ringed with a semicircle of lumber, pulp and paper, plywood, shingle, and door plants. A local iron works makes sawmill and pulpmill machinery; there is also a stove works, and a flourishing fisheries industry. The Great Northern Railroad via Stevens Pass reaches tidewater here, en route to Seattle. Everett is also well located on both railway and highway between Seattle and Vancouver, Canada. Stopped by peninsularity from further expansion on three sides, residential growth is now in the direction of Seattle.[2]

Bellingham

A sawmill at the mouth of Whatcom Creek in 1853 marked the first settlement of Bellingham on a deep, well-sheltered bay of the same name. Coal had been discovered, and in 1855 a thick seam was opened and export begun. Coal mining flourished intermittently during the following century.

Four rival communities were platted around the curve of the bay, competing for mineral rights, timber, fisheries, new settlers, and coastal shipping. Speculative fever ran high. By 1890 the rivalry had narrowed to Whatcom and Fairhaven, each with 4000 inhabitants. Following consolidation under the name of Bellingham in 1903, population increased rapidly to 24,300 in 1910.

Before 1890 the bayhead towns were engaged in coal mining, logging, and sawmilling, and also had the richest salmon fishing in the Northwest. After 1900, shingle mills were added. As the rich lowland was cleared, prime dairy herds, poultry, and fruit and vegetables increased, Bellingham becoming the recognized canning, quick-freezing, market supply, and wholesale center for a highly productive hinterland. Western Washington College of Education is both an economic and a cultural asset.

Timber still comes from the Cascades, but closer utilization means less lumber and more plywood, pulp, and paper. Coal and fish play lesser roles in the city's economy. Heavy manufactures, concentrated

---

[2] For a detailed study of Everett see Francis W. Anderson, *The Urban Geography of Everett, Washington*, M.A. Thesis, University of Washington, 1951.

around the waterfront, include wood products, ship- and boatbuilding, and cement.

Less compactly planned than Everett, Bellingham is still reworking its uncoordinated city pattern, which dates back to the four rival towns. The incorporated area is too large for the present population of 34,112, as attested by farms and numerous vacant lots inside the city limits. As an urban center, however, Bellingham reached maturity in 1910 and has been highly successful in adjusting to the resources and limitations of its hinterland.[3]

Bremerton

Across the Sound from Seattle, Bremerton has long been the site of the Puget Sound Navy Yard, where United States vessels are built and repaired. Here the government is the only big-scale employer, and the size of the city fluctuates in proportion to the needs of national defense. The population of Bremerton, 15,133 in 1940, more than doubled during World War II, dropping again to 27,678 in 1950. In time of war thousands work in the Navy Yard, living outside the city and crowding roads and ferries daily.

Grays Harbor

Reached by an easy corridor extending from the Puget Lowland to the coast, Grays Harbor developed as a great sawmill center. Here two rival seaports, Aberdeen (19,653) at the mouth of the Chehalis River and Hoquiam (11,123) 3 miles to the west, are well located to mill the timber of the Coast Range. With the decline of local Douglas fir, the Grays Harbor cities have turned to closer wood utilization, including rayon pulp, paper, plywood, and other products using cedar and the more plentiful hemlock. Salmon, tuna, and crab fisheries are also part of the local economy.

The Interior Towns

The lowland between Puget Sound and the Columbia River does not equal the Willamette Valley in agricultural excellence, but there are local areas of rich soil and intensive farming, market gardening, and horticulture. Settled in 1877, Puyallup in the fertile valley of the same name, famous for its annual daffodil festival, has increased to 10,000. Sumner, Auburn, and Kent in the White River Valley are smaller service towns. Midway between Portland and Puget Sound,

[3] Dale E. Courtney, *Bellingham: An Urban Analysis*, M.A. Thesis, University of Washington, 1950.

Centralia and Chehalis, sawmill and farm-supply centers, are situated at major rail and highway junctions; they have a combined population of 14,000.

Longview

In contrast to the haphazard establishment of most timber towns, Longview was well planned in advance of settlement. Laid out on a large scale as a company town in 1922, it grew to 10,000 by 1926 and 20,339 in 1950. It has excellent rail connections with the interior; its Columbia River wharves are reached by ocean vessels; and plants for pulp, plywood, and bark products have been added to the original mills. Diversification including aluminum has increased the local pay roll.

Vancouver

Across the Interstate bridge from Portland, and highly valued as part of its metropolitan area, Vancouver functions as an industrial center on the Columbia, with many dockside plants. Rapid expansion in aluminum manufacture and in shipbuilding during the war raised the Vancouver population to 41,664 in 1950, first among the smaller cities in Washington.

MAJOR PORTS OF PUGET SOUND

Seattle

Environmentally speaking, Seattle is one of the most highly water-conditioned and water-conscious cities in America. Like its larger sister ports, New York and San Francisco, metropolitan Seattle is almost entirely surrounded by water. At its commercial front door is an arm of Puget Sound, Elliott Bay, with ample anchorage and miles of wharf and dock frontage. In its urban midsection is Lake Union, now completely ringed with industrial plants using or making water-borne materials. Lake Washington, 26 miles long and rimmed with homes, bounds it on the east. To unite the three, Lakes Union and Washington were joined by a short navigable channel to give their waters a common level, and a canal with locks was cut from Lake Union to Salmon Bay on the Sound. The great Ballard Locks with a lift of 26 feet provide easy marine access to Lake Union, which ocean vessels can use as a fresh-water anchorage. Fishing craft, pleasure boats, and tugs with barges move freely between Puget waters and the lakes. In south Seattle, part of the lower Duwamish River has also been dredged to ocean-going depth. Lakes, canals, bays, and the Sound form one vast interlinked system which gives Seattle optimum flexibility in water haulage.

Loosely sprawled between Lake Washington and the Sound (Fig. 53), the city is built on a series of hills or roughly parallel north-south ridges composed of glacial debris. Like classical Rome, Seattle is said to be built on seven hills. The number is actually indeterminate, and the hills are irregular, jumbled masses, including many steep ridges of unconsolidated gravels. At best they provide a difficult base on which to work out any major urban adjustment. So, in addition to being water-conscious, Seattle is also hill-conditioned and hill-conscious.

The first settlement inside the present urban area was made at Alki Point in 1851, but this proved to be a poor location. The following year settlers moved across Elliott Bay, clustering near the sawmill at the foot of what is now Yesler Way, the center around which the new town took shape. The bay plain at this point was narrow, Yesler Hill ascending steeply to the east. As the village logged off its fir and cedar, there were two possible directions for expansion: first, the flat and swampy plain which widened southward to the Duwamish flats; and, second, a moderately steep slope northwestward along the shore of Elliott Bay. The immediate waterfront offered level land for little more than one or two streets. The growing town turned its back on the swamps and took the steeper path; first residences and then business blocks ascended northward until, decades later, they were to be stopped by Denny Hill.

Today the central business core begins at Yesler Way near the waterfront, rising gradually northward some twenty blocks in a fairly compact oblong. About five blocks wide at the southern end, it broadens to eight or ten after the flatter summit is attained.

Residential Seattle early sought the high ridges and hilltops. Discriminating citizens selected pleasing sites with vistas of mountain, lake, or Sound. Construction of homes proceeded up Yesler Hill, went over the top, moved unevenly across the logged-off ridges, and in time reached the escarpment overlooking Lake Washington. The less desirable tracts between view ridges were left as gaps in the settlement pattern. Some additions were made by absorption. Ballard, a busy fishing and sawmill town fronting on Salmon Bay, was added in 1907; West Seattle, with its Alki Point pioneer marker, came

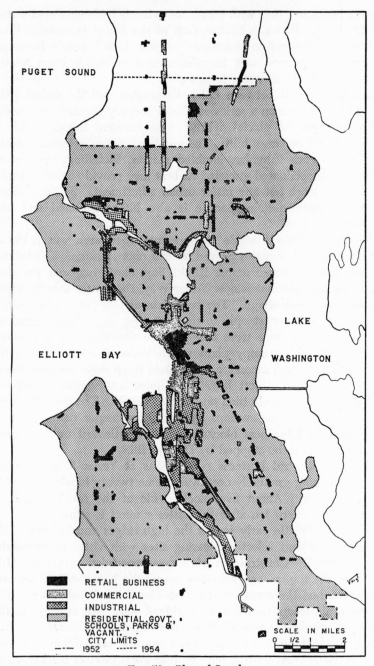

PUGET SOUND

LAKE

ELLIOTT   BAY

WASHINGTON

RETAIL BUSINESS
COMMERCIAL
INDUSTRIAL
RESIDENTIAL, GOVT.,
SCHOOLS, PARKS &
VACANT.
CITY LIMITS
—·— 1952   ------ 1954

SCALE   IN   MILES
0   1/2   1   2

FIG. 53. Plan of Seattle.

in the same year. Industrial Georgetown and blue-stocking Laurel-hurst were admitted in 1910. Thereafter, Seattle became conservative about annexing adjoining suburbs, and few additions were made between 1910 and the end of World War II. Since then suburban absorption has elongated the city pattern along a north-south axis (Fig. 53). In time the city proper will cover the entire western end of King County, forming an almost continuous residential agglomeration on both sides of the Everett-Seattle-Tacoma highway and filling most of the available area between Lake Washington and Puget Sound.

It was fortunate that the early town chose the highland for its business district and ignored the lowlands. The railroads, arriving in the 1880's, followed the narrow valleys and spread out their terminals and yards on the almost unused tide flats. By skirting Elliott Bay and following other flats between glacial ridges, later lines from the north found equally advantageous routes. All the railroads use the narrow water front. Railroad Avenue is hemmed in tightly between the hills and the Bay, but it offers the maximum of efficiency in linking rail and ocean routes. Spur tracks to each wharf bring freight cars directly alongside cargo carriers.

During nearly half a century of moderate growth, Seattle was one of three or even four towns of relative mediocrity on Puget Sound. Then on July 17, 1897, a steamer from Alaska arrived with the discovery shipment of gold. The following year the Klondike rush began, Seattle becoming the recognized gateway and securing the cream of the outfitting business. The exact value of Alaska to the striving port on Elliott Bay remains a question, but the stimulus was undeniable. Seattle and Alaska were linked together in the public mind, a fact of no small advertising value. Between 1898 and 1910 Seattle had its greatest growth, changing from a muddy sawmill and lumber-shipping town to a recognized urban center in the short space of 12 years (Table 2). Many years later the city was to acknowledge its debt. Dressed up with a new seawall and with its hodgepodge of frayed piling-and-plank roadway replaced by concrete paving, old Railroad Avenue, busiest freight thoroughfare in the Northwest, became officially Alaskan Way.

Just as New York is forever tearing down buildings and erecting new ones, Seattle is forever regrading its hills. In the early 1900's, certain glacial ridges blocked the extension of streets, and so the city washed them down with hydraulic mining equipment, sluicing the mud and gravel out into the Sound. Later, the Jackson Street project leveled the side of another large hill. Denny Hill stood squarely in

TABLE 2

GROWTH OF MAJOR CITIES IN THE PACIFIC NORTHWEST

Year	Seattle	Portland	Vancouver, B. C.	Spokane	Tacoma
1870	1,107	8,293			
1880	3,533	17,577	297 (1883)	350	1,098
1890	42,837	46,385	13,432 (1891)	19,922	36,006
1900	80,671	90,426	29,432 (1901)	36,848	37,714
1910	237,194	207,214	120,847 (1911)	104,402	83,743
1920	317,312	258,288	163,220 (1921)	104,437	96,975
1930	365,583	301,815	246,593 (1931)	115,514	106,817
1940	368,302	307,572	275,353 (1941)	122,001	109,408
1950	467,591	373,628	385,500 (est.)	161,721	143,673

the way of the expanding business district, and in 1929 it was attacked with electric shovels and a conveyor belt, scows dumping the dirt in the Bay. Completed in 1931, the Denny regrade added thirty-seven blocks of level building sites. Seattle has completed more than sixty regrade projects in the past 50 years, and over 50 million tons of earth have been sluiced into Elliott Bay or used to fill low mud flats. It is doubtful whether any other American city has moved so much dirt.

The terrain has affected the city pattern in many ways. For years scattered settlement was the practice, and streets were surveyed without any coherent plan, some areas being platted in one direction, some in another. These residential islands are being brought together; the resulting angular unconformities have created some transportation difficulties but give a not unpleasing variety to the city pattern. Even today much of Seattle is uncoordinated, with many unbuilt gaps. Haphazard expansion of this type has made city services, including light, water mains, sewers, and bus transportation, more expensive than in compactly built urban centers.

Access to the area across Puget Sound early made Seattle, like New York and San Francisco, a city of ferry communication. Numerous services carry commuters to Bainbridge and Vashon islands and to towns along the Olympic Peninsula. Bremerton shipyard workers who live in Seattle jam the ferries night and morning. Until 1939 ferries also crossed Lake Washington to suburban centers on the east side. A floating bridge of concrete pontoons now spans the lake, giving motor traffic rapid access to downtown Seattle. Kirkland (4713) and other east-side suburbs are growing steadily; Renton (16,039), at the south end of Lake Washington and contiguous to the Duwamish Valley, is an expanding industrial suburb in the metropolitan area.

The industrial character of Seattle is not well defined, but three main types of manufacturing give it a certain industrial personality. The woodworking group lists, among others, lumber, sash and door plants, shingles, and a furniture industry. The mechanical group includes marine engineering and its allied crafts such as woodworking machinery, shipbuilding and repairing, and extensive airplane plants. The processing of foodstuffs includes the canning and quick-freezing of fish, fruits, and vegetables, the milling of flour, preparation of coffee, tea, and spices, and numerous bakeries. Hinterland raw materials, particularly softwoods, have been the dominant bases for manufacture. Entrepôt manufacturing (the processing of commercial materials passing through Seattle) is far less than might be expected. For the future, available and potential hydroelectric power is ample for any foreseeable expansion.

Factories are generally located in the south part of the city, along the lower Duwamish flats, on Terminal Island, around Lake Union, and around Salmon Bay in the Ballard district. Any location fronting on tidewater or the lakes may be a factory site now or later.

Seattle's largest industrial pay roll is airplane manufacture, a home-grown industry which began in a modest way in a small shop on Lake Union, expanding with the national growth of air transportation. Now located on the Duwamish flats in south Seattle, where modern shops and huge assembly plants cover a wide acreage, it has become one of the major industries of the Pacific Northwest.

The shipyards, dry-dock companies, and machine works on Elliott Bay and Lake Union build new vessels and recondition old ones. In 1941, as part of the national defense program, this industry expanded rapidly with additional shipyards and ways, largely abandoned after the war.

In spite of Seattle's talk of new plants and industrial pay rolls, the water front rather than the factory dominates its urban personality. It is primarily a handler of cargoes. Not satisfied with the miles of dock space along the margin of Elliott Bay proper, the city reached to the north, dredged new berthing space at Smith Cove, and built Piers 90 and 91, among the world's largest ocean terminals. Taken over and enlarged by the U. S. Navy, this facility is now the headquarters of the 13th Naval District. Including Smith Cove, the deepened Duwamish, and Harbor Island, Seattle now has over 50 miles of ocean-depth frontage.

The water front might well have as its theme song the whirring of winches stowing sling loads of freight. In normal times over 5000 workers are employed along the water front and many more in allied occupations. Ships of all nations load and unload, and it is not uncommon to find a dozen to twenty-five vessels on berth simultaneously. A glance at the shipping page any week will reveal that the *Denali,* the *Dongedyk,* the *Java Mail,* the *Heian Maru,* or the *Santa Eliana,* as the case may be, is to load a full cargo of lumber for Hawaii; loading general cargo for Alaska; discharging sulfur lifted at the Gulf; in from South America with coffee and River Plate items to let down; at Pier 48 loading canned salmon, dried apples, and lumber; loading 300 tons of magnesite at Ames Terminal; taking a full load of wheat for Japan; or a coastwise carrier is stowing piling in East Waterway, or a reefer is loading boxed apples for South America.

When the world is at peace as many as twenty or thirty refrigerator ships, known in maritime circles as "reefers," may lift boxed fruit in the course of a single month. Timber products make up the great bulk of outbound shipments, but imports include a wide list of general cargo items from the East Coast and Europe by way of the Panama Canal. Seattle still has an almost proprietary interest in Alaska, and several lines are concerned only with Alaska freight and passengers. A vigorous attempt is also being made to channel the reviving trade of Japan through this port. In steaming distance, Puget Sound ports are nearly 2 days closer to the Orient than either of their rivals, San Francisco or Los Angeles.

The Seattle-Tacoma International Airport is the starting point for a trans-Pacific air route curving up across Alaska and down to the Orient, following roughly the same great-circle route that shortens the sailing distance across the North Pacific.

Seattle seems likely to remain a city with a salt-water flavor, where the water front and its railway and shipping services are paramount, where the urge is for speed, efficiency, and cost-cutting in the handling of cargo. After a 40-year struggle to remake its physical setting, cut down its hills, drain its remaining swamps, coordinate its waterways, and remove as many transportation bottlenecks as possible, the city on Elliott Bay is still striving to improve its access. After obtaining faster rail service to Chicago and the East, Seattle turned its attention to faster traffic arteries. A double-deck viaduct above Alaskan Way provides a motor highway by-passing much of the business district, and plans have been drawn for a freeway to connect Highway 99 both north and south of the city limits.

Tacoma

Tacoma is located on tidewater near the northern end of the Puget
Lowland, where the Puyallup River empties into Commencement Bay
(Fig. 54). This southern end of Puget Sound is 142 miles from the

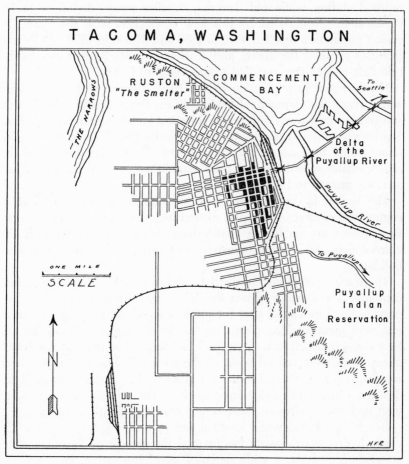

Fig. 54. Plan of Tacoma.

Pacific Ocean. The entrance to Commencement Bay is 4½ miles
wide, and the water alongshore is so deep that early settlers boasted
that any ship could be moored to the trees along the bank.

In 1852 a small sawmill was built on the south shore of Commencement Bay. The settlement which grew up around it, now called "Old

Tacoma," was at a point where the coastal plain was only 300 feet wide. Early in the 1870's Tacoma was selected as the Puget Sound terminus of the Northern Pacific Railway. The terminal was located on the broad lowland at the head of the bay, where there was ample room for station and yards. A new town soon grew up around the railroad station while old Tacoma, 3 miles away, dwindled to insignificance. Stimulated by this new connection with the East, Tacoma's population reached 4400 in 1884 and 36,000 in 1890. Mills and factories rimmed the shore, and scattered plants pushed out to the tide flats and to the so-called prairies south of town.

Nearly equal in population before 1900, Tacoma and Seattle were active rivals for commercial leadership on Puget Sound until Seattle secured better railway and ocean shipping facilities than its neighbor. Seattle also profited greatly from the Alaska gold rush, which was of minor value to Tacoma. By the end of World War I most of the characteristic industries had been established, and Tacoma has had a steady growth to 143,673 in 1950.

The harbor is commodious, with a minimum depth of 25 feet at commercial wharves. The port district includes all of Commencement Bay, where six navigable basins have been dredged through the alluvial flats and a large industrial area created by filling in behind bulkheads.

There are three industrial districts, almost entirely below the 50-foot contour. The Puyallup River floodplain and the reclaimed tide flats provide level industrial sites for lumber, wood products, pulp, chemical, and metalworking plants; access to the major railroad lines is by a municipal belt line. A second industrial zone running northwest along the narrow coastal plain of the peninsula has a thin ribbon of woodworking plants and flour and other mills. A third group of industries without tidewater frontage is in the narrow valley running west and south between the business core and South Tacoma.

In addition to tidewater location and favorable access to materials, cheap hydroelectric power has favored the growth of Tacoma's characteristic industries: a wide range of wood processing, flour milling, electrometallurgy, electrochemicals with their related industries, and boat- and shipbuilding.

Few industries have had a more significant role than wood processing. Since the building of the first sawmill in 1852, wood and its derivatives have ranked first, employing one-half of the wage earners. Although in the early years lumber and cooperage stock were the sole exports, the list now includes nearly every type of wood product. Specialty shops make such diverse things as berry crates, egg cases, wood flour, cabinets, matches, broom handles, step ladders, beehives, and fish kits. With fourteen factories, some of which specialize in high-quality upholstered pieces, Tacoma is one of the principal centers of Northwest furniture manufacturing. It is also a major plywood center and outstanding in the manufacture of paper and pulp. Electrochemical companies have western branches in Tacoma to manufacture chlorine and caustic soda for the pulp and paper industry.

Copper refining, known locally as "The Smelter," is a city within a city. Located in Ruston, a company town, it is completely surrounded by Tacoma and is an integral part of the urban area. Refining about one-tenth of the nation's output, this is the largest combined copper smelter and refinery in the United States. Its enormous brick stack which carries away smoke and fumes is a feature of the industrial landscape.

Vigorous competition from the larger cities of Seattle, 30 miles to the north, and Portland, 150 miles to the south, together with the Cascade barrier to the east, has set sharp restrictions upon the commercial hinterland of Tacoma. It serves as the shopping center and wholesale distributing point for much of the farming and timber-working territory 60 miles to the south and as far west as the Pacific Ocean; but even in this area Seattle is a trade rival. The Narrows Bridge, opened in 1950, provides a direct highway link with the Olympic Peninsula, where Tacoma now has an advantage.

The street pattern accommodates itself to various coastal contours, as well as to numerous deep ravines that penetrate the hills. The business and shopping district occupies the first easy slope which rises gradually from the tide flats; residential Tacoma, including the College of Puget Sound, is on rolling hills and uplands south and west of the harbor, and along picturesque bluffs overlooking Commencement Bay. The residential level is isolated from the main transport arteries so that travelers by rail or highway seldom see this attractive section.[1]

[1] "Tacoma, Lumber Metropolis," Gertrude L. McKean, *Economic Geography*, Vol. 17, July, 1941.

THE CANADIAN PORTS

J. LEWIS ROBINSON

Vancouver

Vancouver is Canada's third largest city and its second port after Montreal. The city is situated on the south side of scenic, sheltered Burrard Inlet, frequently listed among the world's best and most beautiful harbors (Fig. 55). Settlement started with a sawmill in 1862, and lumber and allied products still provide the industrial bases of the modern city. The few scattered settlements along the south side of the inner harbor came into prominence when this excellent site was chosen as the western terminus of the Canadian Pacific Railway. The first train arrived in 1887. Since that time Vancouver has grown to a population of 385,500 in 1951. Settlement spread southward from the harbor over the uplands of an ancient glacial delta, and soon merged with the smaller towns such as New Westminster, along the North Arm of Fraser River. Urban settlement has since spread eastward into the adjoining municipality of Burnaby and along the base of picturesque mountains north of Burrard Inlet in North and West Vancouver. The Greater Vancouver urban area now occupies most of the land between the Fraser River and the Coastal Mountains to the north and has a population of more than 550,000.

Throughout its history Vancouver has performed certain functions for the province of British Columbia. Known as the chief West-Coast port of Canada, it serves a more important function in the busy coastal traffic of the province. It is the supply and service center for the many coastal settlements northward on Vancouver Island and the mainland coast. In turn, the products of the coastal region, chiefly logs, paper, and fish, are brought to Greater Vancouver for processing. About 50 per cent of the forest and fish products manufactured in British Columbia are exported to foreign markets, and most of them are transshipped through Vancouver. Large grain elevators dominate the skyline of the eastern end of the inner harbor and the city exports much of the wheat grown in Alberta. The construction of oil pipelines from Alberta will increase the importance of oil refineries which already serve the province. Other industries, such as sugar refineries, utilize imported products.

The downtown commercial core occupies the upland between Burrard Inlet and a former glacial channel southward, known as False Creek. From this core, suburban commercial zones are now spreading eastward and southward along the main streets. West of the com-

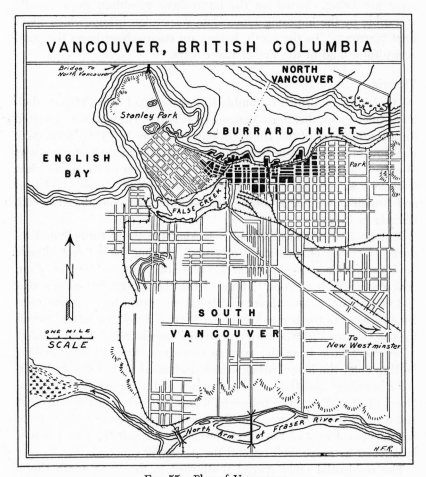

FIG. 55. Plan of Vancouver.

mercial core, the stately, well-kept forest of Stanley Park (Plate 23B) dominates the narrow entrance to the inner harbor and provides a thousand-acre refuge for the nearby city dwellers. Industries are located along the harbor, with the lumber mills concentrated in False Creek and the North Arm of Fraser River. Since most of the industrial sites are now occupied, new industry is forced to move eastward along the railway lines in adjoining Burnaby. The remainder of Vancouver's area is now almost fully covered with residences. The University of British Columbia has a generous campus with an imposing sweep of the Gulf of Georgia. As population increases, residential areas are being cleared on the north-shore mountain slopes, easily accessible by the imposing Lions Gate suspension bridge which spans First Narrows. To the south, homes are encroaching upon the good agricultural land of the Fraser River delta.

Victoria

The capital of British Columbia lies at the head of a twisting, sheltered inlet in southeastern Vancouver Island. The site was selected for a trading post of the Hudson's Bay Company in 1842. Settlement was slow until the Fraser River gold rush of 1858 made Victoria a port of entry into British Columbia. Its future function was assured when it became the capital of the combined colonies of Vancouver Island and British Columbia, retaining this position after confederation with Canada in 1871.

Victoria is a quiet, stately city, lacking the usual turmoil and industrial activity characteristic of ports. Having the mildest climate in Canada, it has proved popular as a place of retirement for Canadians and other British citizens. Many of the shops attempt to keep that "bit of England" atmosphere, which has an appeal to American tourists, and some of the homes are similar to small English estates. Nevertheless, Greater Victoria, with a dispersed population of about 100,000, differs very little from the average Canadian city. Visitors arriving by ship enter the inner harbor, which is rimmed by the stately Parliament buildings and the parklike grounds of the ivy-covered Empress Hotel (Plate 23B). The commercial core is located in the northeast, and a small industrial area, chiefly sawmills and woodworking plants, has developed west of the Inner Harbor; as a result the port has now broadened its scope well beyond the passenger function.

The residential areas spread southward to the steep south shores which face the Strait of Juan de Fuca. Residences noted for their beautiful gardens have filled in most of the southeastern tip of Vancouver Island. The finest homes lie to the east and northeast of the older city, and new residential building is gradually extending northward into the fertile agricultural lands of Saanich Peninsula. West of Victoria, on another inlet, is the adjoining municipality of Esquimalt, an important naval base and a shipbuilding and repair center.

Although the tourist trade is well publicized, Victoria has a sounder basis for growth than its "old English" charm; its main function in British Columbia is administrative. To southern Vancouver Island, however, it is the chief supply and wholesale center, and is a cultural attraction to the part-time farming areas along the east coast of the island.

CITIES OF EASTERN WASHINGTON
HOWARD H. MARTIN

Irrigation Communities of the Cascade Flanks.

Based upon a plentiful water supply from the mountains, an irregular belt of irrigation settlements has developed along the east flank of the Cascades from Penticton in the Okanagan Valley of British Columbia southward across Washington to the Columbia River. Included are the Okanogan Valley with Omak and Okanogan, Chelan at the foot of Lake Chelan, the Wenatchee Valley with Cashmere and Wenatchee (13,072), and the extensive Yakima Valley, which in addition to Yakima itself has numerous smaller centers including Wapato, Sunnyside, Toppenish, and Prosser. These towns, ranging from 2000 to 5000 in size, together with many smaller ones, all handle fruit in season. Only Yakima and Wenatchee function as large urban centers.

In addition to Kittitas Valley farming and ranching, Ellensburg (8430) is well known for its Central Washington College of Education. Below the junction of the Yakima River with the Columbia, Kennewick and Pasco are partly based on irrigation, partly on transportation and other functions. The Dalles (7676) packs fruits and does a large grain-handling, livestock, and flour-milling business; here barge haulage on the Columbia is a major asset.

Yakima

Yakima, with a population of 38,486 in 1950, is three times the size of its next largest valley rival, Wenatchee (13,072). This smartly modern fruit capital functions as the metropolis and wholesaler for an area estimated to have an additional 40,000 persons within a 10-mile radius. Here vegetables, apricots, peaches, and other soft fruits are canned or quick-frozen; thousands of carloads of boxed apples are shipped annually. Busy Produce Row (Plate 24A), separated from the retail district by many railroad tracks, has a mile and a half of packing houses, numerous canneries, dehydrators, refrigerated warehouses, and box factories.

POTENTIAL IRRIGATION TOWNS. East of the river in Grant County, where the Columbia Basin Project is under way, new irrigation will eventually bring closer settlement. Here a few small and widely separated supply centers serve the present needs of ranching and dry farming. With more intensive land use as Grand Coulee water is made available, the older centers may begin to take on the characteristics of the fruit towns in the Wenatchee and Yakima valleys. Ephrata (4589), present headquarters for reclamation work, and Moses Lake (2679) are the forerunners of this trend, which will see the founding and growth of many towns.

Richland

Immediately south of the Hanford atomic works is the new government-constructed city of Richland. This community is the direct outgrowth of a new type of manufacture, the transmuting of uranium into plutonium. The Hanford Operations Office of the U. S. Atomic Energy Commission is probably the most concentrated and expensive single manufacturing establishment in the Northwest, located here because of available power, abundant water supply, and protective isolation.

Before World War II, the Big Bend of the Columbia in Benton County was a scantly populated area. Hanford, Richland, and White Bluffs were sleepy little farm villages, a few truck farmers raising asparagus, grapes, soft fruits, and mint. In 1943 the government acquired a tract of 620 square miles between the Columbia and the Yakima Ridge and Rattlesnake Hills. The local population was moved out, and an army of construction men moved in to build the mysterious Hanford Works. At its peak some 50,000 men were employed.

At the war's end the temporary mushroom city of Hanford was abandoned, the employees of the A.E.C. moving to newly built Richland, 8 miles south of the security area. With a population of 246 in 1942 and 21,809 in 1950, Richland is now the administrative and residential center for the Hanford operation.[1]

[1] The peacetime operator of the Hanford project is the General Electric Co., now one of the largest employers in the state.

The Tri-Cities

Together with Richland, Pasco (10,228) and Kennewick (10,106), a short distance downriver, expanded rapidly as residential areas for the Hanford operation. Both are located at a major crossroads where the Snake enters the Columbia from the east, and the Yakima Valley provides a corridor westward. Pasco is a railroad town and a natural market center.

The Dry-Land Supply Centers

GRAIN FARMING AND RANCH COMMUNITIES. West and south of Spokane most of the cities and scattered small towns are local supply centers for wheat farming and ranching areas. Colfax (3057), a shoe-string pattern town, serves a cash-grain hinterland, as do Davenport (1417), Waterville (1017), Ritzville (2145), and Dayton (2979). Cheney (2797) also has flour milling and is the site of Eastern Washington College of Education. In addition to their farm-supply functions, Pullman (12,022) and Moscow (10,593) are educational centers, with Washington State College and the University of Idaho, respectively.

Lewiston, Idaho (12,985), and Clarkston, Washington (5617), are at the junction where the Clearwater flows into the Snake River, and these twin cities have a combination of wheat, orchard, and white-pine enterprises. Pendleton, La Grande, and Baker, along the old Oregon Trail, all have sawmills but are basically ranch-supply towns for large tributary areas.

WALLA WALLA. One of the oldest settlements in the Northwest, Walla Walla (24,102) shows the influence of an early start, a favorable agricultural hinterland, and no urban rivals in the extensive area between the Snake River and the Blue Mountains. After many decades of grain marketing and farm supply, intensive truck farming and fruit growing expanded. Vegetables, especially peas and asparagus for canning and quick-freezing, augmented the local income. Walla Walla serves as the regional capital and trading center for southeast Washington; Whitman and Walla Walla colleges attract students from many states.

INLAND EMPIRE CENTER

WILLIS B. MERRIAM

Spokane

As the economic capital of the Inland Empire, Spokane is the largest interior city in the Northwest. Occupying both banks of the Spokane River, and spreading out on highland rims and gravel prairies north and south of the river valley, it is located at a strategic site for the convergence of transportation routes from four main directions. It is in line with the only passes for 200 miles north or south where railroads and highways can cross the Northern Rockies and reach the Inland Empire at a reasonable grade.

Hydroelectric power also accounts in large measure for Spokane's growth. Six commercial generating stations have been developed on the river, two within the city limits. Pioneered by the Washington Water Power Company, these plants, now augmented from the Northwest Power Pool, provide an abundance of low-cost electricity that has proved an incentive to numerous large-scale industrial plants.

The city is located at the northeast corner of the Columbia Basin, adjacent to the timbered and mineralized highlands of the Rocky Mountains, the productive agriculture in the Palouse, Big Bend, Spokane Valley, and the various valleys of the highlands in Washington, Idaho, and western Montana. It receives an impressive flow of agricultural products and livestock for processing or shipment. The mineral-rich Coeur d'Alene and Okanogan Highlands also contribute to Spokane's economy. Several office buildings and business blocks are monuments to the profits from the mines. Accessible stands of commercial timber have also placed their stamp on the industrial complex through numerous lumber mills and a Spokane valley pulpmill.

The city, originally known as Spokane Falls, was settled in 1873 and incorporated in 1881, the "Falls" being dropped from the name in 1891. In 1880, it was a village of 350. The railroad boom brought it to 20,000 in 1890, and a fivefold increase to 100,000 occurred by 1910. In 1950, the population reached 161,721, the gain coming mainly from light-metal industries, a major military air base, and a naval-supply depot.

Functional zonation has followed rather strict geographical controls. The retail and business centers of downtown Spokane are situated on the south side of the river and include only ten blocks on three or four avenues (Fig. 56). Constriction of the river canyon below the falls and encroachment of a highland rim of basaltic rock marking the south-hill residential districts have limited the space for commercial development. The center of highest rental values has not moved more

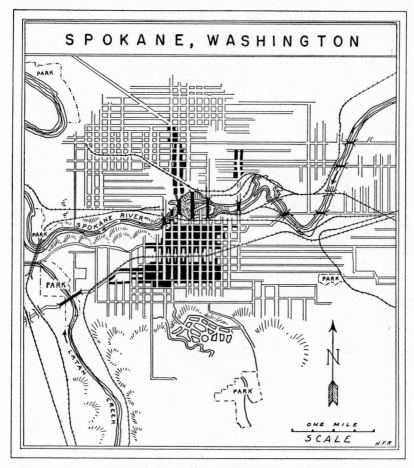

Fig. 56. Plan of Spokane.

than a block or two in 50 years. The commercial center has evolved mainly through replacement of obsolete structures and a modest tendency toward skyscrapers, largely eliminating any blighted areas of architectural obsolescence.

Overflowing these barriers, the commercial districts have expanded along the principal streets leading to the extremities of the city, resulting in numerous decentralized neighborhood units.

Dominant wholesale districts owe their location to the transportation lines which traverse the northern and southern margins of the central retail and commercial districts. Along these rail lines wholesale establishments have developed, frequently replacing earlier business uses. A second wholesale district is found in the scabland area north of the river, where the irregular surface was unsuitable for the extension of the street pattern. Many railroad spurs penetrate this section, which is coming into use as topographic barriers are removed.

Manufacturing districts are found on the valley plain or on the gravel prairie lands east of the commercial district and north beyond the city limits. They have developed along the rail lines where land is level but too gravelly for agricultural use. Here are found the lumber mills, reworking mills for sashes and doors, meat-packing plants, gas plants, aluminum rolling mill, refineries, iron works, and car shops. Such industries are likely to be either noisy or odoriferous; hence the tendency is for them to be located on the leeward side of the city.

The most desirable residential areas are on the south-hill rimlands, where basalt knobs interrupt a rectangular street pattern, but where there are a variety of natural features suitable for landscaping. Homes here overlook the city, making this district a show spot. Residential suburbs rim the city on the extreme southern and northern margins, providing dwellings for an additional 29,000.

Spokane is a city of bridges; ten spans carry traffic across the river. Railroads enter and leave from the east by way of the Spokane valley or from the west or southwest over high bridges across the gorge below the falls or by way of the tributary Latah Creek Valley. Three transcontinental lines and several branches serve the city, making Spokane the largest interior rail center between the Twin Cities and the North Pacific Coast.

Transportation convenience has favored the concentration of jobbing and wholesale establishments. Improved highways as well as the railroads bring retail buyers from a wide radius, embracing the entire Inland Empire, from the Cascades to the continental divide of the Rockies and from across the Canadian border to northeastern Oregon.

Spokane is more important in distribution than in manufacturing. Industrial plants include woodworking, meat packing, flour, light metals, ironworking, and an ever-widening group of industries with national outlets and the usual list of local consumer goods and service industries.

URBAN PATTERN OF IDAHO AND WESTERN MONTANA

MARION E. MARTS

The towns of southern Idaho and the Rocky Mountain valleys possess some sectional individuality, stemming from their markedly monocultural nature, the density of urban centers in irrigated areas, the convergence of transportation routes at mountain or desert crossings, and the isolation of many communities.

The individual communities fall logically into four groups: southwestern Idaho and adjacent towns in eastern Oregon, south-central Idaho, southeastern Idaho, and the mountain towns of northern Idaho and Montana.

Southwestern Idaho

One of the densest populations in the interior Northwest is in parts of southwestern Idaho and eastern Oregon. This density results from the intensive agriculture made possible by the irrigation of 350,000 acres along the Snake River and in the tributary valleys from Weiser to Boise, Idaho. Three cities have populations in excess of 10,000: Boise (34,393 with an additional 10,000 in the suburbs), Nampa (16,185), and Caldwell (10,487). The others, all less than 5000, include Payette and Emmett, Idaho, and Ontario, Nyssa, and Vale, Oregon.

BOISE. Boise dominates not only this area but the entire intermountain section of the Pacific Northwest south of the Blue Mountains (Plate 24A). Its regional importance is enhanced by the distance to major western cities: 371 miles to Salt Lake City by highway, 397 miles to Spokane, 467 miles to Portland, and 430 miles to Reno. Rail distances are even greater. As a result, Boise has a wholesale and retail distribution function far out of proportion to its population. The state capital adds prestige as well as an administrative pay roll.

Boise is attractively situated at the foot of the Rocky Mountains, which provide recreation, water for irrigation and power, timber, and minerals.[1] Hunting and fishing are favorite outdoor sports, and many

---

[1] The discovery of gold in the nearby mountains was responsible for the initial settlement at Boise in 1862.

visitors are surprised to find that grocery stores regularly carry stocks of ammunition.[2]

The central business district and the adjacent, older residential area are oriented to the Boise River. Expansion of the commercial and industrial districts onto the floodplain was retarded by flood hazard before the construction of Anderson Ranch and Lucky Peak dams. The latter, primarily a flood-control structure, is only a few miles from the city and will provide a reservoir for water sports. It is impossible to cross southern Idaho by paved highway without passing through Boise. All routes from the west and north converge here, with only one highway crossing the desert to the east.

South-Central Idaho

Even more than the southwestern Idaho communities, the towns of south-central Idaho are oriented to irrigation. Almost all the development, both urban and rural, has occurred during the present century. In view of this rapid transition from sagebrush desert to prosperous agriculture, local residents refer to the area as the "Magic Valley." Here 675,000 acres have been brought under irrigation, supporting a population of more than 90,000.[3] The major city is Twin Falls (17,600), a planned community. Smaller irrigation centers include Burley (5924), Jerome, Gooding, and Rupert.

All the towns are almost wholly dependent on agriculture. Only Gooding is on the main line of the Union Pacific Railroad, the other towns being served by branch lines.

Southeastern Idaho

The towns of southeastern Idaho are older and more diversified in function. Many were founded in the nineteenth century as settlements of the Mormon Church.

Pocatello (26,131, with another 4694 in adjacent Alameda) is one of the most important railroad centers between Omaha and the Pacific Coast (Fig. 57). Located at the point where the Portneuf River debouches onto the Snake River Plain and at the crossing of the Union Pacific main line and the Salt Lake City-Butte rail line, the city is both a rail and highway entrant to the Pacific Northwest. The Union

---

[2] Boise is the cultural capital of a large Basque colony, attracted to southwestern Idaho by the range-sheep industry. The Mormon Church, strong here as in most of southern Idaho, also provides a closely knit cultural group.

[3] See *The Columbia River Basin Report*, U. S. Department of the Interior, Washington, D. C., 1947, pp. 77–81.

Pacific Railroad shops dominate both the economy and the configuration of the city. The agricultural supply and service are less significant. During and after World War II Pocatello manufactured elemental phosphorus and phosphate fertilizer from rock quarried nearby. Pocatello is also the site of Idaho State College.

Fig. 57. Plan of Pocatello.

A thin ribbon of irrigated land and dependent towns extends northeastward along the Snake River for 100 miles. The major centers are Idaho Falls (19,218), Blackfoot (5180), and Rexburg (4253). Idaho Falls is an agricultural service center; since highways converge on the western approaches to Yellowstone and Grand Teton National Parks, it serves many tourists in season.

Far out in the middle of the Snake River Plain, northwest of Black-foot, is the reactor plant of the Atomic Energy Commission, located here partly because of the desolate nature of the desert. This development has caused a population boom in the nearby communities of Blackfoot and Arco.

The Rocky Mountain Valleys

The urban centers of the Rocky Mountain section are directly related to the valley pattern, the controlling influences being natural resources and transportation. The major centers have good railway and highway connections, but some of the smaller communities, many of them mining camps, are isolated during the winter months.

BUTTE. Butte, Montana (33,251), the largest city in this section, is situated in a high, broad-floored valley west of the continental divide. Much of the site is on the lower slopes of a mountain underlain with veins of copper, zinc, silver, and manganese. With its satellite towns it is an urban agglomeration of approximately 50,000 (Fig. 58).

Although famed for copper mining since the first discoveries of ore in 1875, Butte is also a commercial distribution and transportation center served by four major railroads as well as an ore-carrying rail line to the smelters of nearby Anaconda. Although the best and most accessible ores have been removed, advances in mechanized and large-scale mining methods have extended the life of the mines and hence of the town. The ground is honeycombed with shafts and tunnels; headframes and mine dumps dot the landscape. Butte has long had a reputation as a rough and ready western mining camp but, with age, has subsided into mature, unexciting respectability.

Coeur d'Alene District

Other mountain towns primarily oriented toward mining include Kellogg (4913), Wallace (3140), Mullan (2036), and Burke (less than 1000), all in the famous Coeur d'Alene mining district of northern Idaho. Kellogg is the smelting and refining center for the lead, zinc, and cadmium ores. Burke is located in a canyon so narrow that automobiles and railroad trains share the main street and snow slides are a serious menace.

Midway between the Butte and Coeur d'Alene mining districts is Missoula in a broad mountain valley near the junction of three streams, the Bitterroot, Blackfoot, and Clark Fork. Converging transportation routes enable the city to tap a large hinterland having ranching,

FIG. 58. Plan of Butte.

farming, and lumbering, and it vies with Butte for commercial supremacy in western Montana. Montana State University is located here.

Kalispell (9737) in the Flathead Valley, 125 miles north of Missoula, is the leading town of northwestern Montana. In this area the major activities are lumbering and agriculture, but the completion of Hungry Horse Dam, 20 miles east of Kalispell, adds to the industrial potential.[4]

Recreation Centers

Of the many smaller communities, three are of special interest because they are supported mainly by tourist and recreational activities. McCall, on Payette Lake in central Idaho, is a summer resort, and Ketchum, in the mountains of southern Idaho, is an old mining town that has experienced a renascence since construction of the Sun Valley resort a mile to the north. Formerly ranching headquarters, Jackson, Wyoming, is now a major tourist center catering to the throngs visiting Grand Teton and Yellowstone national parks. West Yellowstone, Idaho, and Gardner, Montana, are at other entrances to Yellowstone National Park. Minor health resorts include Warm Springs, Montana, and Soda Springs, Idaho.

[4] Selection of Columbia Falls, 15 miles northeast of Kalispell, as the site of an aluminum reduction plant, was announced in 1952.

PLATE 1A. *Top.* Indians fishing at Celilo Falls. These falls will disappear on the completion of the Dalles Dam, construction of which began in 1952. (*Courtesy of Seattle Times.*)

Bottom. Gates of the mountains near Helena, where the Missouri River flows through the Rockies. The Lewis and Clark Expedition discovered and named this place in 1805. (*Courtesy Northern Pacific Railway.*)

481

PLATE 1B. *Top.* Old Fort Walla Walla in 1818. *Middle.* Fort Okanogan. Built in 1811 by the John Jacob Astor Company at the junction of the Okanogan and Columbia rivers. *Bottom.* The oldest standing house in Washington, built in 1843 at Fort Nisqually.

PLATE 2A. *Top.* Mount Olympus from the east. (*Photograph by Glover.*) *Bottom.* Willapa Hills, a part of the Coast Range in southwestern Washington. The photograph shows staggered logging. (*Photograph by 41st Div. Aviation, Washington National Guard.*)

483

PLATE 2B. *Top.* Looking southward from the vicinity of Coos Bay, Oregon. In the foreground, Isthmus Slough and the Coos Bay Lumber Mill. In the upper right is Coalbank Slough, with tidal flats, and in the upper part of the view are the low ridges of the Coast Range. Two freighters are loading lumber at the dock. (*Photograph Delano Aerial Surveys.*)

Bottom. A view from the southwest, across the Rogue River Valley, immediately to the south of Medford. Pear orchards occupy a large part of the valley floor. In the distance are the peaks and ridges of the Klamath Mountains (Siskiyou section). (*Photograph Jackson County Chamber of Commerce.*)

Plate 3A. *Top.* The Willamette Valley near Newberg. Note the intensive land use of this fertile region. The orchards are walnuts, prunes, and filberts. Nearly all kinds of farm systems are practiced here. (*Photograph by Soil Conservation Service.*)

Bottom. Head of Lake Chelan. (*Photograph by Lindsley.*)

485

PLATE 3B. *Top.* Aerial view of Cascades looking north with the Three Sisters in the foreground. Taken with infra-red light. The peaks in the distance are nearly 300 miles distant. (*U. S. Army Air Corps.*)

Bottom. Palouse Hills from the west. Note greater steepness and snow banks on the northeast slopes.

PLATE 4A. *Top.* Scabland tract near Cheney, showing isolated hill of Palouse soil and topography surrounded by "scabrock" from which the soil was removed by glacial meltwater. (*Soil Conservation Service.*)

Bottom. The "Potholes" in the Columbia Basin southwest of Moses Lake. The view is taken from the south and shows peculiar shape of sand dunes developed on a rocky floor. (*Photograph by 41st Div. Aviation, Washington National Guard.*)

487

PLATE 4B. *Top.* Columbia Plains near Umatilla. (*Soil Conservation Service.*) *Bottom.* Slopes of the Tri-state Uplands north of the Blue Mountains in Washington. Note contour cultivation of land, only partly successful in preventing erosion. (*Soil Conservation Service.*)

Plate 5A. *Top.* The Snake River Canyon, the deepest in North America. The view is near the site of the proposed Hell's Canyon dams.

Bottom. Air view of the irrigated and intensively cultivated Snake River Valley in western Idaho. (*Soil Conservation Service.*)

489

PLATE 5B. *Top.* Aerial view from northeast of the high fault scarp of Steens Mountain. An example of the "Basin Range" structure in southeastern Oregon. (*Photograph by Richard E. Fuller.*)

Bottom. Two Medicine Lake, Glacier National Park. The mountains are mainly carved from metamorphosed sediments, called argillite, by the action of stream and glacier erosions. (*Photograph by Great Northern Railway.*)

490

PLATE 6A. *Top.* Chief Mountain, Glacier National Park, a peak resulting from erosion along the Lewis Overthrust.

Bottom. The Purcell trench, looking north to the Canadian boundary, 30 miles away, along the Kootenai River, which flows in this part of the trench. The picture was taken from a point 2 miles east of Bonners Ferry, Idaho. (*Photograph by Ross Hall.*)

491

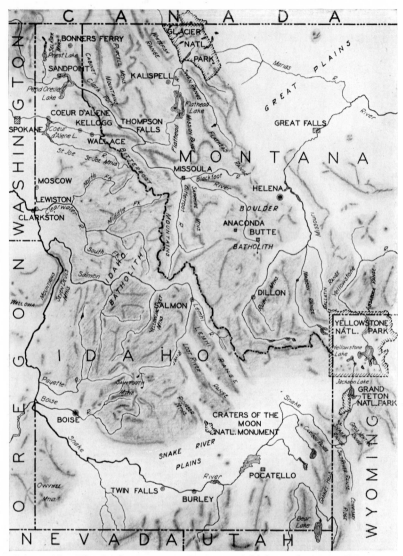

PLATE 6B.   The Rocky Mountain Province of Idaho and western Montana.

492

PLATE 7A. *Top.* Grand Teton mountains from the Jackson Hole, Wyoming. (*U. S. Department of Interior.*)
 Bottom. Trident Peak and Columbia River, British Columbia.

493

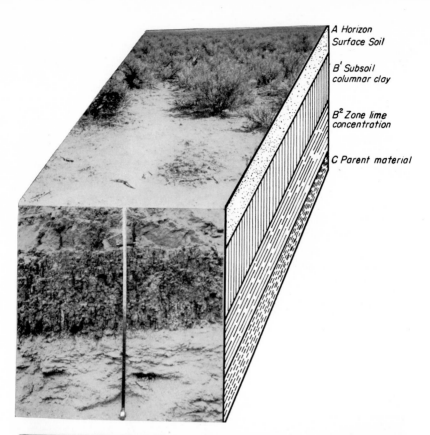

A Horizon
Surface Soil

B' Subsoil
columnar clay

B² Zone lime
concentration

C Parent material

PLATE 7B. *Top.* Soil profile.
Bottom. Gully erosion threatens to engulf farm buildings along Tatman Creek.
Garfield County, Washington. (*Soil Conservation Service.*)

PLATE 8A. *Top.* Soil slips and earth flows are found by the thousands in the Northwest every spring. In this instance, the entire plow layer slid off from this 50-foot-wide area, piling up at the foot of the steep slope. Near Dusty, Washington. *Bottom.* Sheet erosion and the deposition that results. Near Touchet, Washington. (*Photographs by Soil Conservation Service.*)

495

PLATE 8B. *Top.* Severe gully erosion in winter wheat near Athena, Oregon, in the foothills of the Blue Mountains. (*Soil Conservation Service.*)

Bottom. Wind erosion is severe in many range and dry-farming localities. Photograph taken 15 miles south of Boardman in eastern Oregon. (*Soil Conservation Service.*)

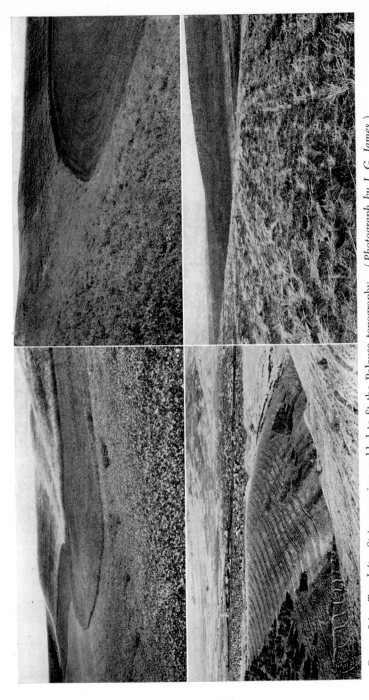

PLATE 9A. *Top left.* Strip cropping molded to fit the Palouse topography. (*Photograph by J. G. James.*) *Bottom left.* Contour furrows constructed on steep, overgrazed mountain sides adjoining Pocatello, Idaho. (*Photograph by J. G. James.*) *Top right.* Cover crops now found on many thousands of acres of steeply sloping land in the Northwest. (*Photograph by A. L. Hafenrichter.*) *Bottom right.* Trashy fallow, an extremely important practice in the prevention of soil erosion; near Johnson, Washington. (*Photograph by J. G. James.*)

PLATE 9B. *Top.* Land capability classes. This shows graphically the application of the land capability classification to lands in the Palouse Region. This land near Latah, Washington. (*Photograph by Soil Conservation Service.*)

Bottom. The Pullman Soil Conservation Service Nursery has attained world-wide fame for its testing of grasses and legumes from all parts of the world. These tests included strain selection, breeding, and growing of better grasses and legumes for soil conservation. Some shrubs and trees were also similarly studied.

498

(A) A general view of rangeland in good condition.

(B) The density, ground cover, and feed produced by the perennial grasses of the climax vegetation.

(C) Typical overgrazed and improperly managed rangeland that is severely eroded and now contains only low-value cheatgrass (*Bromus tectorum*).

(D) Badly depleted, severely eroded and gullied rangeland with only a sagebrush cover interspersed with poor annual grass.

PLATE 10A. Typical views of the grasslands of the Pacific Northwest.

499

PLATE 10B. The more common grasses of the Palouse prairie climax: (A) Bluebunch wheatgrass (*Agropyron spicatum*); (B) beardless wheatgrass (*A. inerme*); (C) Idaho fescue (*Festuca idahoensis*); (D) Sandberg's bluegrass (*Poa secunda*); (E) big bluegrass (*P. ampla*); and (F) June grass (*Koeleria cristata*). All these grasses are valuable feeds and can be maintained under proper range management.

PLATE 11A.   *Top.*   Aerial view of reduction works at Anaconda.   (*Photo-graph by Anaconda Copper Mining Co.*)
Bottom.   Smelter at Trail, British Columbia.

PLATE 11B. *Top.* Purse seine fishermen overhauling nets at Salmon Bay Terminal, Seattle. (*Courtesy Pacific Fisherman.*)

Bottom. Brailing the last of a salmon catch from a purse seine. (*Courtesy J. Walter Thompson Co.*)

Plate 12A. *Top.* Sluicing 35,000 Bristol Bay Reds from scow to cannery
elevator, Naknek, Alaska. (*Courtesy Ruben L. Jensen.*)

Bottom. Salmon cannery on coast of British Columbia. The water supply
comes from the lake above, towards which the salmon migrate up the swift
stream. The cannery and living quarters are on tidewater.

Plate 12B. *Top.* Ketchikan, fishing and canning center of southeast Alaska, located on Tongass Narrows. Prince of Wales Island in the distance. (*Courtesy Shallerer's Photo Shop.*)

Bottom. This halibut is classed as a "whale." In the unloading bucket behind are several dozen mediums. (*Courtesy Pacific Fisherman.*)

504

PLATE 13A.   Grand Coulee Dam.   (*Photograph by U. S. Bureau of Reclamation.*)

505

Reservoir and
irrigation canal

Desert
sagebrush
land

Irrigation
in the
Columbia
Basin

PLATE 13B. Three views showing story of western irrigation. (*Photographs by U. S. Bureau of Reclamation.*)

506

PLATE 14A.   *Top.*   The Willamette Falls at Oregon City illustrates multiple use of water.

Bottom.   Tug and loaded gasoline barges.

507

PLATE 14B. *Top.* Seattle City Light's Ross Dam, 540 feet high, fifth highest dam in the world, illustrates the character of mountain canyon sites harnessed for power. (*Seattle City Light.*)

Bottom. Bonneville is a triple-purpose dam. It includes a large power plant, fishways for passage of salmon, and the largest lift lock north of Panama. (*Courtesy Bonneville Project.*)

PLATE 15A. *Top left:* mature western hemlock. *Top right:* mature Douglas fir. *Bottom left:* silver fir. *Bottom right:* larch-Douglas fir forest in Montana.

PLATE 15B. *Top left:* juniper. *Top right:* subalpine type. *Bottom left:* ponderosa pine. *Bottom right:* logs being dumped into log flume.

PLATE 16A. *Top left:* mature western white pine. *Top right:* lodgepole pine.
Bottom: a central Oregon lumber mill.

511

PLATE 16B. *Top.* A logging arch at the foot of a spar tree is loading logs on a truck for transportation to the sawmill. This staggered logging area with nearly complete cutting of all trees will be naturally seeded from the surrounding standing timber. (*Photograph by Forde and Carter.*) *Middle.* Loading big "peeler" logs, used for plywood. (*Photograph by Simpson Logging Company.*) *Bottom.* In the mill a log is placed on a moving carriage that carries it back and forth in order that the bandsaw with teeth on each side can make a cut on each journey. (*Photograph by K. S. Brown.*)

PLATE 17A. *Top.* Colony of Caspian terns and Farallon cormorants in lower Klamath Lake, one of the largest wild bird refuges, established by Theodore Roosevelt, 1908. (*Photograph taken in 1905.*) *Middle.* Lower Klamath Lake deprived of water and changed to an alkali desert, devoid of life. (*Photograph taken in 1935.*) *Bottom.* Angling in the Deschutes River. (*All photographs by William L. Finley.*)

513

PLATE 17B. Birds of the Northwest. *Top left:* California or valley quail. *Top right:* female white-tailed ptarmigan at nest. *Bottom left:* female Chinese pheasant. *Bottom right:* sooty or blue grouse. *(Photographs by William L. and Irene Finley.)* *Right.* Bull elk wintering in the snow. *(Photograph by U. S. Forest Service.)*

514

PLATE 18A. Big game animals of the Pacific Northwest. *Top left:* mule deer doe of a species abundant east of the Cascades. *Top right:* bull Shiras moose, horns still in the velvet. *Bottom left:* antelope or pronghorn. *Bottom right:* mountain sheep, or bighorn. (*Photographs by William L. and Irene Finley.*)

PLATE 18B. *Top.* The Many Glacier region in Glacier National Park. (*Photograph by T. J. Hileman.*)

Bottom. Valley of the Bow River at Banff. Golf course on the right. (*Courtesy Canadian Pacific Railway.*)

PLATE 19A. *Top.* Combines operating in central Washington. The wheat is trucked in bulk to the railway. (*Photograph by State College of Washington.*)

Bottom. Pear orchard in the Rogue River Valley, near Medford, Oregon. Cascade Mountains in the background. (*Photograph by Jackson County Chamber of Commerce, Medford, Oregon.*)

517

PLATE 19B. *Top.* Naches Heights in the Yakima Valley, where orchards average about 20 acres. Irregularities in outline of orchards are due largely to slope of land and direction in which water flows to best advantage. Bare spots scattered over the picture consist of rock outcroppings, slopes too steep to farm, gravel spots, and spots too high to be irrigated from present ditches.

Bottom. Emmett Valley, Idaho. Note contrast between irrigated valley and adjoining wasteland. (*Photograph by Jackson Studio.*)

Plate 20A. *Top.* Apple-picking time. (*Photograph by Asahel Curtis.*)
Bottom. Raspberries near Sumner in the Puyallup Valley, western Washington.
(*Courtesy Northern Pacific Railway.*)

519

PLATE 20B. *Left.* Picking hops with a portable machine in the Yakima Valley. (*Photograph by Yakima Chamber of Commerce.*)

Right. Apples just received from orchard being placed in cold storage, pending packing. (*Photograph by Cashmere Fruit Growers Union.*)

520

PLATE 21A. *Top.* Sheep on mountain pasture during the summer.
Middle. The sheep herder and his dog drive to the summer grazing grounds.
Bottom. Fall pasture in wheat stubble. (*All photographs by Mary Mac-Lennon.*)

PLATE 21B. *Top:* flock of young turkeys. *Middle:* modern poultry plant at Prosser, Washington. (*Photographs by Asahel Curtis.*)

Bottom. Poultry plant near Lynden, western Washington. (*Photograph by Corbett.*)

PLATE 22A. *Top.* Douglas fir saw mill at Aberdeen, Washington. The advantages of this site on the Chehalis River near Grays Harbor include water transport for log rafts and freighter shipment of lumber. (*Photograph by the "Timberman."*)

Bottom. The largest white pine sawmill in the Northwest at Lewiston, Idaho.

PLATE 22B. *Top.* The Cascades Plywood Mill on the Santiam River near Lebanon, Oregon. (*Photograph by the "Timberman."*)

Bottom. The Alcoa Aluminum Refinery near Vancouver, Washington, the first to be constructed in the Pacific Northwest. The Columbia River is in the foreground and Vancouver Lake in the background. (*Photograph by Delano Aerial Surveys.*)

524

PLATE 23A. *Top.* The Boeing Airplane Company Plant 2. The large saw-tooth building at right is the main assembly plant. To the left is the engineering center, and in the upper left is the wind tunnel. (*Photograph by Boeing Airplane Company.*)

Bottom. Packing and cold-storage plant of Cashmere Fruit Growers Union at Cashmere, Washington. (*Courtesy Cashmere Fruit Growers Union.*)

PLATE 23B. *Top.* Air view of Vancouver, Canada, showing city skyline and section of Stanley Park. (*Courtesy Royal Canadian Air Force.*)

Bottom. Inner Harbor, Victoria, with Parliament buildings in the center. (*Courtesy Victoria and Island Publicity Bureau.*)

PLATE 24A. *Top.* Fruit row at Yakima from the air. (*Photograph by Yakima Chamber of Commerce.*)

Bottom. Boise from the air, looking northeast. (*Photograph by 41st Div. Aviation, Washington National Guard.*)

527

PLATE 24B. *Top.* Old Faithful Geyser, Yellowstone National Park.
Bottom. Cattle in Montana.

Index

The Pacific Northwest